1.50
1.25

CLASSICAL DYNAMICS

Also by R. H. Atkin

MATHEMATICS AND WAVE MECHANICS

CLASSICAL DYNAMICS

by

R. H. ATKIN, M.A., M.Sc.

Principal of Unischol Tutorial College, London
Formerly Senior Lecturer in Mathematics,
Northampton College of Advanced Technology, London

HEINEMANN

LONDON MELBOURNE TORONTO

FIRST PUBLISHED 1959

uo

PUBLISHED BY
WILLIAM HEINEMANN LTD
15–16 QUEEN STREET LONDON W1
PRINTED IN GREAT BRITAIN BY
THE WHITEFRIARS PRESS LTD
LONDON & TONBRIDGE

CONTENTS

PREFACE

I HAVE written this book in the belief that it is possible to learn Dynamics and answer examination questions at the same time. Indeed, the number of such questions which have accumulated over the last century and which have circulated in the textbooks and examination papers is so great that the weak student may perhaps be forgiven for suspecting that the subject consists of a bewildering set of tricks especially devised for their solution.

In fact, the foundations of the subject consist only of a few simple experimental laws and physical observations, but they are applicable to a very wide selection of the natural phenomena of everyday experience. It therefore seems sensible to present the subject by first explaining the ideas which are involved, in a suitable algebraic framework, and then illustrating the scope of their applications by solving a large number of typical problems. By selecting most of these problems from university examination papers I have tried to take some of the sting out of these as well.

The theory of vectors has recently provided a novel approach to many dynamical problems, particularly those concerned with non-holonomic systems, and it is now desirable to weave the vector methods and the analytical methods into some sort of harmony. The final emphasis will really be a matter of individual taste, but the student would be ill-advised to condemn one or other of the techniques until he has thoroughly appreciated its possibilities. To acquire facility in using vector methods it is important to understand the concepts of " linearly independent vectors " and " rotating frames of reference " and also to be able to expand certain vector products. Because of this, and to ensure that all the relevant theory is available, I have included a chapter on Vector Algebra ; this, in spite of the fact that many textbooks now have chapters on " vectors," although the effect on our students is as yet far from decisive.

I have been greatly helped by the kindness of Professor H. Bondi and of Dr. L. Pincherle, both of whom read the manuscript, and I was glad to be able to take advantage of much of their advice.

My thanks are due both to the University of London for permission to reprint examination questions and to the Syndics of the Cambridge University Press for permission to reproduce questions set in the Tripos papers and also questions which are to be found in *Theoretical Mechanics*, by A. E. H. Love. These latter questions are denoted by the letter (C.) in the exercises at the ends of the chapters.

Finally, it does not seem inappropriate to commend the publishers once more for their persistence and daring in encouraging me to write the book.

R. H. ATKIN

London, 1959.

CHAPTER I

HISTORICAL FOUNDATIONS

1.1. Galileo Galilei *

It is truly said that the modern science of dynamics was founded by Galileo.

He was the first man to systematically investigate the motion of falling bodies. Prior to this men had generally felt reasonably satisfied with the vague Aristotelian view that every object must seek its " place " in the universe : thus heavy bodies must fall and light ones rise or, at least, fall less quickly. This was the *why* of falling bodies. Galileo set himself the task of discovering *how* bodies fall, and in succeeding admirably in this he was in fact laying the intellectual foundations of what we now call science.

By careful experiments with a ball rolling down an inclined plane Galileo discovered the formulæ $v = gt$ and $s = \frac{1}{2}gt^2$, where g is a constant, and here it is as well to remember that there were no clocks available which he could use for accurate measurements of small intervals of time. The constant g, being the ratio of velocity to time, is a measure of *acceleration*, and this idea too was contributed by Galileo. Thus he had solved the general problem of the motion of a body which moves in a straight line with a constant acceleration.

Now the fact that a heavy body falls to the ground had always been associated with the fact that a heavy body has a *weight*, i.e. is acted on by a *force*, but, before Galileo, it was not known in what sense force produces motion. It was Galileo who first perceived that force (or pressure) is not determinative of either position or velocity but of acceleration, or change of velocity. And here it is important for us to appreciate the concept of force in its historical context.

The word *force*, or forces, had arisen as an equivalence to the words *circumstances which determine motion*, and once the precise nature of this determination had been discovered (that is to say, " that which determines motion " is " that which determines acceleration ") it was immediately possible to deduce the Law of Inertia, viz. " when there are no forces acting on a body it moves in a straight line with constant (including zero) velocity."

In connection with his work on bodies falling under gravity (or under their weights) Galileo was also able to solve the problem of a projectile with oblique projection. His method was that found in our

* Italian mathematician-scientist. Born in Pisa 1564. Died 1642.

early school text-books, but we mention it here because it illustrates the idea that separate forces acting on a body produce their own accelerations which, in the proper circumstances, can be separately treated in finding velocities and distances. Thus, in the case of the projectile we have a constant acceleration in the direction of the downward vertical and a zero acceleration horizontally. The distances travelled in a time t in these two directions, assuming the velocity of projection is V inclined at an angle α to the horizontal and below the horizontal, will be simply

$$y = Vt \sin \alpha + \tfrac{1}{2}gt^2 \quad \text{(downwards)}$$

and

$$x = Vt \cos \alpha \quad \text{(horizontally)}$$

These immediately give the *parabolic arc*

$$y = x \tan \alpha + \frac{gx^2}{2V^2 \cos^2 \alpha}$$

The fact that these two motions take place simultaneously and independently illustrates the principle of the *parallelogram law* for accelerations. This parallelogram rule was already an accepted part of Statics, having been ably demonstrated by the Dutch mathematician Simon Stevinus.* Generally speaking we can say that it is the *independence* of the forces (accelerations) which results in a parallelogram law for their composition. This property of independence enables us to identify a one-to-one correspondence between the "vector" and a geometrical displacement, and two simultaneous displacements are equivalent to a third which lies along the relevant diagonal of a certain parallelogram. These ideas we shall analyse more fully when we come to consider vectors in Chapter II.

Finally we shall mention Galileo's examination of the oscillations of a simple pendulum, both the isochronism and the general form of the formula for the periodic time being known to him. Furthermore, motion on a curve (the circular arc described by the bob of the pendulum) meant for Galileo motion on a succession of infinitesimal inclined planes, and with the aid of the pendulum he was able to show that the velocity acquired by a heavy body in moving freely down an inclined plane was dependent only on the *height* through which it had effectively fallen. Thus the bob of a pendulum will rise on one side of the lowest position just as high as it has previously fallen on the other, and by suddenly shortening the length of string when the bob was in the lowest position (by placing stops at appropriate points) this property was shown to be independent of the radius of the arc described—and therefore independent of the particular "succession of inclined planes" described.

* 1548–1620. Stevinus investigated equilibrium on an inclined plane; demonstrated the resolution of forces as well as their composition, and distinguished between stable and unstable equilibrium.

It is clear that this result amounted to the principle of the *conservation of energy*, a principle which we now know to be of tremendous significance.

1.2 Christiaan Huygens *

In his contribution to dynamics Huygens proved, among other things, that a body which describes a circle of radius r with a constant velocity v must experience an acceleration towards the centre of $\frac{v^2}{r}$. This involved the idea that velocity possesses not only *magnitude* but also *direction*, and that acceleration can mean change of direction of velocity even when there is no change in the magnitude of the velocity.

Huygens also did a great deal of work on the pendulum and invented the first pendulum clock—inventing the escapement on the way. In this connection he went much further than did Galileo in that he solved the problem of the "centre of oscillation" of a compound pendulum. This, of course, involved the dynamics of several connected bodies (or particles of a rigid body) and his method involved such an original concept that it is worth discussing in more detail.

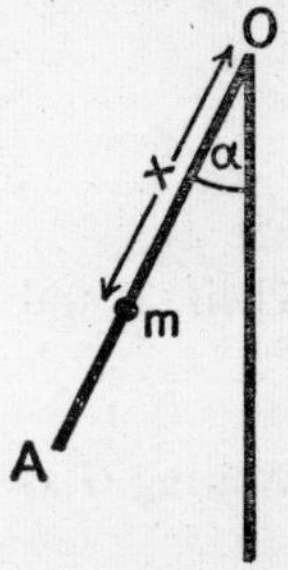

FIG. 1.

Consider a rigid body in the form of a heavy rod OA which is free to move in a vertical plane about a horizontal axis through one end O, as in Fig. 1. Now regard the rod as made up of a large number of small masses $m_1, m_2, \ldots$ at distances $x_1, x_2, \ldots$ from the end O, and let m in the diagram be a typical mass. Suppose now that we let the rod swing freely under gravity from its extreme position in which it is inclined at an angle α to the downward vertical. Then Huygens argued that *the centre of gravity of the rod must rise through the same distance as it falls.* This is an imaginative extension of Galileo's result obtained for the motion of a single mass, and again we can clearly see that it amounts to the modern principle of the conservation of energy.

Suppose the centre of gravity falls a distance z by the time the rod reaches the vertical position, then

$$z \sum m = m_1 x_1 \cos \alpha + m_2 x_2 \cos \alpha + \ldots$$
$$= \cos \alpha \sum mx$$

giving

$$z = \cos \alpha \frac{\sum mx}{\sum m} \quad . \quad . \quad . \quad . \quad . \quad (1)$$

* 1629–95. Dutch mathematician, famous also for his wave theory of light and Huygens' Principle.

Let the point P on OA, where $OP = 1$, acquire a velocity u during the downward swing, then the mass m acquires a velocity xu. But Galileo showed that a body with velocity v will rise a height $\frac{v^2}{2g}$ and so each particle of the rod will rise a height $\frac{u^2}{2g} \times x^2$. The centre of gravity will therefore rise a height z' given by

$$z' \sum m = \frac{u^2}{2g} \sum mx^2 \quad . \quad . \quad . \quad (2)$$

If we put $z' = z$, (1) and (2) give

$$\frac{u^2}{2g} \sum mx^2 = \cos a \sum mx \quad . \quad . \quad . \quad (3)$$

To find the length of the equivalent simple pendulum (say l) we can apply (3) to the single mass of the imagined bob whence

$$\frac{u^2}{2g} . l = \cos a \quad . \quad . \quad . \quad . \quad (4)$$

Then (3) and (4) give
$$l = \frac{\sum mx^2}{\sum mx}$$

Writing G as the centre of gravity and $OG = \bar{x}$, $\sum m = M$ we get

$$l = \frac{\sum mx^2}{M\bar{x}} \quad . \quad . \quad . \quad . \quad (5)$$

We thus see that Huygens had also discovered the quantity $\sum mx^2$, now known (after Euler) as the *moment of inertia* of the rod about the axis through O. Indeed he went on to obtain the " parallel axes " theorem and the complete analysis of what we now call the compound pendulum.

Other contributions by Huygens included an analysis of the cycloid and its isochronous property and furthermore, in 1669, he submitted to the Royal Society his work on the impact of elastic bodies. In this latter problem he obtained the correct solution, indicating therein the significance of the product mass $\times$ velocity (momentum). Here we must mention that both Wallis and Wren had submitted equally correct solutions at the end of 1668, the one dealing with collisions of inelastic bodies and the other with elastic collisions. The final form of the laws of impact was to be provided by Newton and published in his *Principia*.

1.3 Isaac Newton *

From the point of view of this study the two great achievements of Newton were (*a*) his theory of universal gravitation, and (*b*) his formulation of the principles of mechanics. It is very important for us to examine, in some detail, the concepts which he introduced and clarified in the course of his work.

Ever since Galileo had invented his telescope men had been studying the motions of the planets with ever increasing interest and accuracy. In particular, a great deal of observed data had been collected by Tycho Brahe,† and from this Kepler ‡ had deduced his famous three laws describing the motion of the planets about the sun. These amounted to :

(1) The planets describe ellipses with the sun situated at a focus.

(2) The radius vector joining the sun with a planet describes equal areas in equal times, i.e. the rate of description of sectorial area is constant.

(3) The cubes of the mean distances of the planets from the sun are proportional to the squares of their times of revolution, i.e. if $2a$ is the major axis of the elliptic orbit and t is the periodic time then $t^2 \propto a^3$.

Newton was able to show that these laws were compatible with the assumption that each planet possesses an acceleration towards the sun which is inversely proportional to the square of their distance from it. Furthermore he saw this acceleration as being of the same nature as that experienced by bodies falling near the earth's surface. This remarkable generalisation led him to the concept that all bodies, taken in pairs, induce in each other mutual accelerations. Translating this into terms of *force* requires a new principle and Newton supplied this in his law of "action and reaction"—and this in its turn provides us with a view of *mass* not possessed by any of Newton's predecessors, a concept which distinguishes between mass and heaviness (or weight).

The *laws of motion* which Newton published in his *Principia* amount to the following :

Law I Every body perseveres in its state of rest or of uniform motion in a straight line except in so far as it is compelled to change that state by impressed forces.

Law II Change of momentum is proportional to the impressed force and takes place along the line of action of that force.

* 1642–1727. English mathematician. His great work, *Philosophiae Naturalis Principia Mathematica*, was published in 1687.

† Danish astronomer, 1546–1601.

‡ German mathematician, 1571–1630.

Law III Action and reaction are always equal and opposite ; that is to say, the actions of two bodies upon each other are equal and directly opposite.

Newton perceived that a body possesses an invariable property known as its mass and that, when it possesses an acceleration f then the force acting on the body will be $P = kmf$, where k is a constant of proportionality. In modern notation Law II will be written Force $\propto \frac{d}{dt}(mv)$ or $m\frac{dv}{dt}$ when the mass m does not artificially change with time. Thus we see that the weight of a body, being the force mg, can vary if g varies, whereas the mass m will at the same time remain constant. Furthermore, the *masses* of two bodies can be accurately *compared* by weighing them in the two pans of a balance and the *weight* of any one body will be found by weighing it with a spring balance. If we suppose the units of measurement to be suitably chosen we can write $k = 1$ and Law II as

$$\text{Force} = \text{mass} \times \text{acceleration}$$

Then Law III, applied to two bodies A and B of masses m_1 and m_2 respectively (Fig. 2), says that the *mutual forces* P and Q are equal.

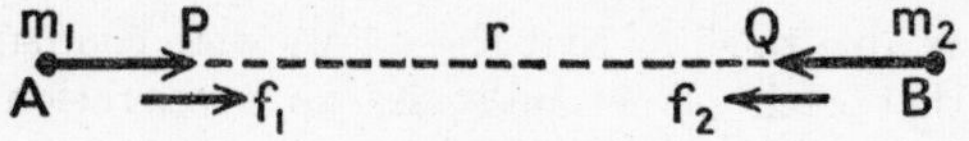

FIG. 2.

If A possesses acceleration f_1 and B f_2 we get

$$P = m_1 f_1 = m_2 f_2 = Q$$

and so

$$\frac{m_1}{m_2} = \frac{f_2}{f_1} \quad . \quad . \quad . \quad . \quad . \quad (1)$$

Unfortunately Newton defined mass as density × volume, and since density involves the idea of mass this " definition " is clearly inadequate. Since Law II attempts to relate mass to force it is necessary to have a logically independent view of the one before we can talk about the other. Law III also involves the idea of mass. Considering also the rather obvious fact that Law I is an immediate deduction from Law II it is clear that these laws are not the most economical possible.

A set of propositions designed to reduce Newton's laws to their simplest and most economical in thought was given by E. Mach at the beginning of this century. These emphasise the experimental nature of the foundations of mechanics and are as follows :

I. Experimental proposition. Two bodies set opposite each other induce in each other opposite accelerations in the direction of their line of junction.

Definition. The mass-ratio of any two bodies is the numerical value of the inverse ratio of their mutually induced accelerations.

Definition. Moving force is the product mass × acceleration for any body.

II. Experimental proposition. The accelerations which any number of bodies A_1, A_2, . . . induce in a body B, are independent of each other.

The two definitions of mass and force lead deductively to Newton's law of action–reaction and, of course, include Laws II and I. The second experimental proposition implies the *parallelogram of forces*, which was itself explicitly stated by Newton in a corollary to his three laws of motion.

Units of mass, force

The units of mass are the *pound* (lb.) and the *gramme* (gm.).

The units of force are the *poundal* (when mass is in pounds and acceleration in ft./sec./sec.), and the *dyne* (when mass is in grammes and acceleration in cm./sec./sec.). The two systems are referred to as the ft. lb. sec.-system and the c.g.s.-system.

When forces are measured in terms of weights, as they can be, this is indicated by calling them pounds-weight (lb. wt.) or grammes-weight (gm. wt.). The law of motion being now

$$\text{Force (dynes)} = \text{mass (gm.)} \times \text{acceleration (c.g.s.)}$$

we have

$$1 \text{ gm. wt.} = 1 \text{ gm.} \times g \text{ cm./sec./sec.} = g \text{ dynes}$$

Thus

$$x \text{ gm. wt.} = gx \text{ dynes}$$

and

$$x \text{ lb. wt.} = gx \text{ poundals}$$

The values of g in the two systems of units are 32·2 ft./sec./sec. and 981 cm./sec./sec. The basic (Newtonian) equation, viz. $F = \frac{d}{dt}(mv)$, holds only in terms of these *absolute units*.

1.4 Universal gravitation

As mentioned in 1.3, Newton solved the age-old problem of the motion of the planets about the sun by ascribing to each planet an acceleration towards the sun proportional to $\frac{1}{r^2}$, r being the distance between sun and planet. In terms of force we can now write :

> *every body attracts every other body with a force which is inversely proportional to the square of their distance apart and directly proportional to the product of their masses.*

Thus, in Fig. 2 of 1.3, we should write

$$P = Q = \gamma \frac{m_1 m_2}{r^2} \quad . \quad . \quad . \quad . \quad . \quad (1)$$

where γ is a universal constant.

If now, for example, A is the sun and B is a planet, the acceleration of B towards A will be

$$f_2 = \frac{Q}{m^2} = \gamma \frac{m_1}{r^2} = \frac{\mu}{r^2} \cdot \quad . \quad . \quad . \quad . \quad (2)$$

where μ will be the same for all planets of the sun. The value of γ has been determined to be $6{\cdot}66 \times 10^{-8}$ c.g.s. units.

It is also clear from (1) that ideally the distance r can only be known precisely when the masses at A and B are identified as very small *particles* of matter, occupying negligible volumes. In dealing with finite distributions of matter we are therefore obliged to use the methods of the integral calculus involving, as they do, limiting processes in which the objects of calculation are divided into infinitesimal elements. There are one or two simple cases which, by way of illustration, we can very well examine at this stage.

Example 1. To find the gravitational attraction on a particle of unit mass due to a uniform rod AB of density ρ per unit length.

Let the point P be a distance p from the line of the rod, which we

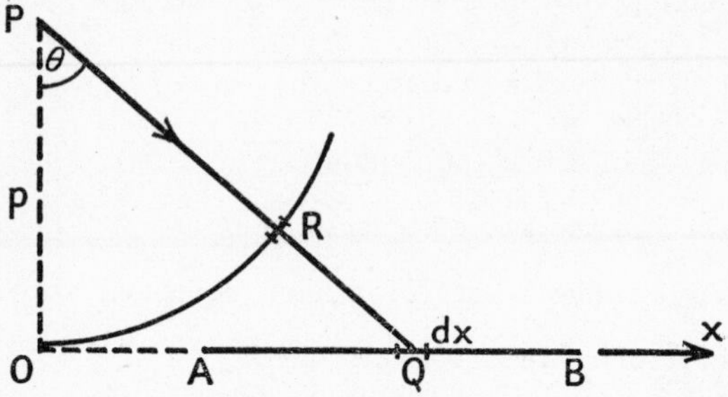

FIG. 3.

take to be the x-axis in Fig. 3. Let $\rho\, dx$ be an element of mass at any point Q of AB, then the attraction at P of this will be $\gamma . \frac{\rho\, dx}{PQ^2}$. Writing $OQ = x = p \tan \theta$ this becomes

$$\gamma\rho . \frac{p^2 \sec^2 \theta}{p \sec^2 \theta} d\theta = \gamma \frac{\rho p\, d\theta}{p^2}$$

which equals the attraction at P of the corresponding arc at R of the circle, centre P, radius p. Thus the resultant attraction of the rod AB at P bisects the angle APB (see Fig. 4) and is of magnitude

$$F = 2\int_0^{\alpha} \frac{\gamma\rho}{p}.\cos\phi\, d\phi = \frac{2\gamma\rho}{p}\sin\alpha = \frac{2\gamma\rho}{p}\sin\left(\tfrac{1}{2}\angle APB\right)$$

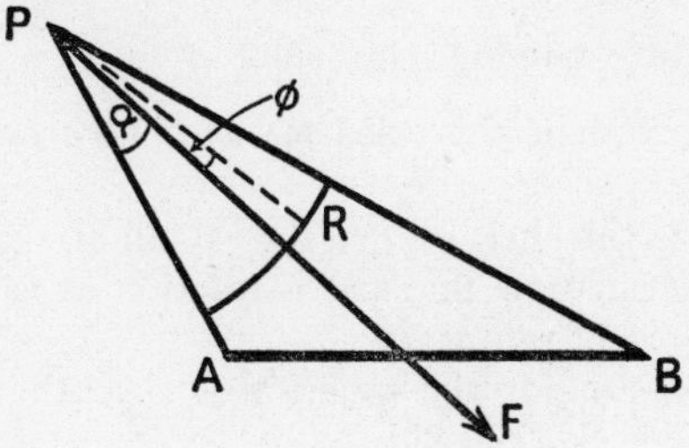

FIG. 4.

Example 2. To find the attraction per unit mass at a point P which is either outside or inside a uniform spherical shell of density ρ and radius a.

Let P be outside the shell as shown in Fig. 5 with $OP = c > a$.

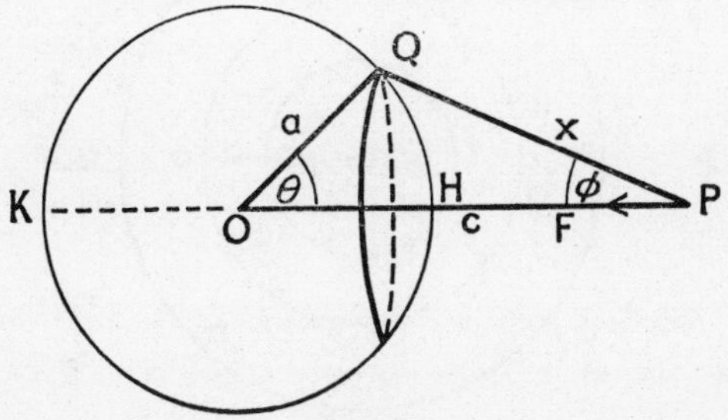

FIG. 5.

Divide the surface into small circles around OP as axis as shown. Then each point on such a small circle is the same distance x from P and by symmetry the resultant attraction F at P is along PO. The attraction at P due to any one small circle will be

$$\gamma\frac{(\text{mass})}{x^2}\cos\phi = \gamma\frac{\rho\,.\,2\pi a^2\sin\theta\cos\phi}{x^2}.d\theta$$

Since $x^2 = a^2 + c^2 - 2ac\cos\theta$ it follows that $x\,dx = ac\sin\theta\, d\theta$ and we get

$$F = 2\pi\rho\gamma\int_{PH}^{PK}\frac{ax\cos\phi}{cx^2}\,dx$$

Since $a^2 = x^2 + c^2 - 2xc \cos \phi$ this becomes

$$F = \frac{\pi\rho\gamma . a}{c^2} \int_{PH}^{PK} \left\{1 + \frac{c^2 - a^2}{x^2}\right\} dx$$

When P is outside the shell $PH = c - a$, $PK = c + a$.
When P is inside the shell $PH = a - c$, $PK = a + c$.

Thus when P lies outside the shell $F = \gamma . \frac{4\pi a^2 \rho}{c^2} = \gamma \frac{M}{c^2}$, where M = total mass, and in this case *the shell behaves like a particle of mass M at the centre O.*
When P lies inside the shell we get $F = 0$ (all c).

Corollary. We can now find the attraction at a point P due to a uniform solid sphere of radius a.

(i) When P lies outside the sphere it is clear that the attraction is

$$\gamma \frac{\text{(Mass)}}{c^2} = \tfrac{4}{3} . \gamma\pi\rho a^3/c^2$$

(ii) When P lies inside we get, from Fig. 6,

$$\text{Attraction} = \gamma(\tfrac{4}{3}\pi\rho c^3)/c^2 = \tfrac{4}{3}\pi\gamma\rho c$$

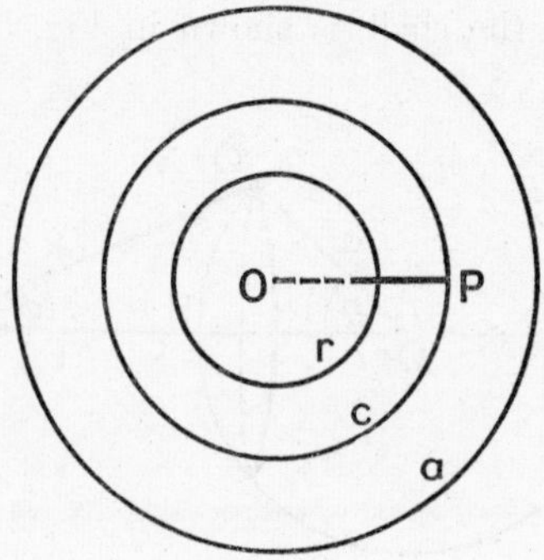

FIG. 6.

1.5 Laws of impact

We have already noticed that the problems of the collisions between perfectly elastic bodies (those which completely recover their former shapes after deformation) and between inelastic bodies (those which suffer permanent deformation) had been studied and solved by Wren, Huygens and Wallis. All three had found that the separate *momenta* of the colliding bodies suffered sudden changes, i.e. suffered *finite discontinuities*.

Newton also conducted elaborate experiments on the problem of impact and published his laws relating to it in *Principia*. If two rolling smooth spheres (e.g.) meet in collision on a horizontal table the momentum of each changes suddenly through a finite amount. We say that each sphere has received an *impulsive blow* or *impulse*, and that this impulse equals the change in the momentum. Thus (v. Fig. 7) if the velocities of A and B are u_1, v_1 just before impact and u_2, v_2 just after impact, if the the mass of A is M and of B is M' we shall have

$$Mu_2 - Mu_1 = -I \quad . \quad . \quad . \quad . \quad (1)$$

$$M'v_2 - M'v_1 = I \quad . \quad . \quad . \quad . \quad (2)$$

Notice that here again the law of action–reaction is invoked to say that the impulses on A and B are equal and opposite. This can be

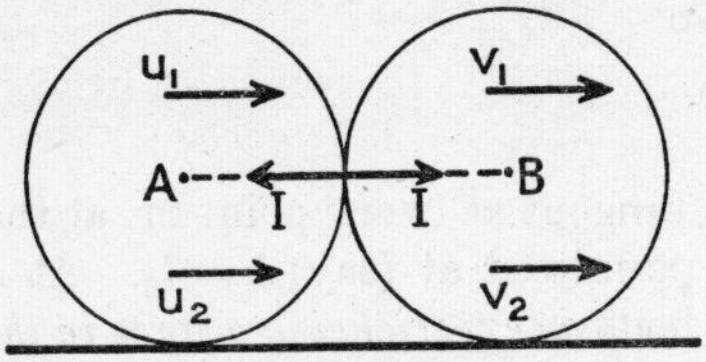

FIG. 7.

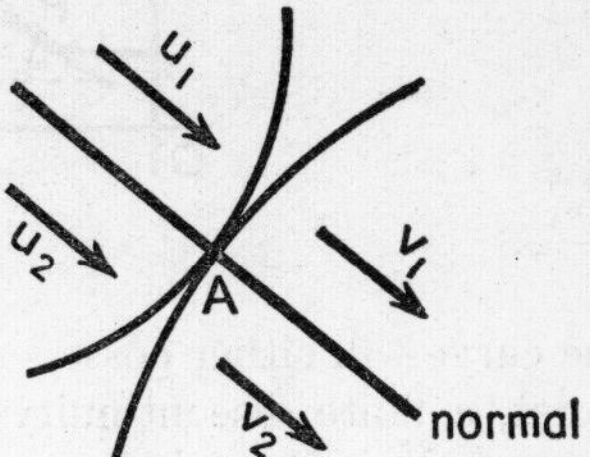

FIG. 8.

directly confirmed experimentally since, by adding (1) and (2), we get

$$Mu_1 + M'v_1 = Mu_2 + M'v_2 \quad . \quad . \quad . \quad (3)$$

The total momentum remains unchanged.

The question to be settled is now, " in what proportion is the initial momentum shared between the two bodies immediately after impact ? " *Newton's experimental law* provides the answer in saying

$$\textit{Velocity of separation} = e \times \textit{Velocity of approach} \quad . \quad (4)$$

where e is a constant, known as the *coefficient of restitution*, and which depends on the elastic properties of the two bodies. Thus (4) means we can write

$$v_2 - u_2 = e(u_1 - v_1) \quad . \quad . \quad . \quad (5)$$

whence (3) and (5) solve the problem.

We shall now take a generalisation of (4) as a basis for solving more diverse problems of collision. We shall say that (v. Fig. 8) *whenever two smooth surfaces collide the velocities of the respective bodies along the line of the common normal* (at A) *are related before and after impact by equation* (4).

1.6 Conclusion

In considering the dynamics of a single body the principles of Galileo-Newton lead us to the following point of view.

We may suppose that the body possesses a mass, m, and a velocity (say) v, and that the momentum mv is a function of the time t. For simplicity let us suppose that the body is moving in a straight line, the x-axis. Now in a perfectly general motion along the x-axis the function of t, viz. mv, need only remain finite and so its general curve, plotted against t, will be of the form shown in Fig. 9 ; that is to say

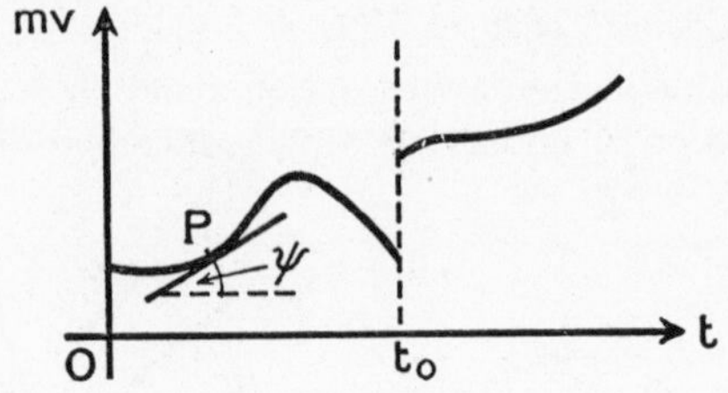

FIG. 9.

the curve will either possess a unique tangent at every point or, at the worst, a finite discontinuity will be permitted at (say) $t = t_0$. At a point such as P we shall say that the body *is experiencing a force in the direction of the positive x-axis whose magnitude equals* $\frac{d}{dt}(mv)$ *or* $\tan \psi$. At a point such as $t = t_0$ we shall say that the body *is experiencing an impulse in the positive x-direction whose magnitude equals* $\Delta(mv) = \lim_{t \to t_0 + 0} (mv) - \lim_{t \to t_0 - 0} (mv)$.

It is as well to remember also that at a finite discontinuity in mv there is no change in the instantaneous value of x, of position.

We must also point out that the words " single body " may commonly be replaced by the word " particle." In dynamics the word particle does not cause the same sort of embarrassment as it frequently can in other branches of modern theoretical physics. Here, by particle, we mean only a convenient single body possessing mass whose position can be conveniently and adequately defined by a geometrical point. In one instance the particle might be as large as the earth and in another as small as the calculus requires.

The work of Huygens is not in the direct line of Galileo and Newton but in effect deals with ideas of velocity (squared) and work done. These we shall return to later when they will appear important in added refinements to the mathematical formulation of dynamics.

Other historical developments, such as the principle of D'Alembert and the method of Lagrange, will find their proper place in the text.

The foundations laid by Galileo and Newton are sufficient to account for nearly three centuries of dynamical theory and application.

Exercise I.

1. Three perfectly elastic particles (coefficient of restitution $e = 1$) of masses m_1, m_2, m_3 lie, in that order and not in contact, in a smooth horizontal groove. If m_1 is projected towards m_2 with velocity U, find the velocities of each particle after two impacts have occurred and show that there will not be a third if

$$m_2(m_1 + m_2 + m_3) > 3m_1m_3 \qquad \text{(L.U.)}$$

2. Two smooth spheres of masses m, nm impinge obliquely, at an acute angle α with their line of centres, with equal and opposite momenta of magnitude mnv. Show that immediately after the impact the spheres possess equal and opposite momenta of amount

$$mnv\sqrt{\sin^2 \alpha + e^2 \cos^2 \alpha}$$

e being the coefficient of restitution. If the direction of travel of each ball has turned through a right angle, prove $\tan^2 \alpha = e$. (L.U.)

3. Use Galileo's theory of the path of a projectile to solve the following problem.

A projectile has a range R on the horizontal plane through the point projection O when the angle of projection is α ($< 45°$). If this angle is increased to β, the speed of projection remaining constant, find at what height the projectile crosses the vertical plane at a distance R from O. If this height is a maximum prove that

$$\tan \beta = \operatorname{cosec} 2\alpha$$

and that the maximum height is then

$$\tfrac{1}{2}R\,(\operatorname{cosec} 2\alpha - \sin 2\alpha) \qquad \text{(L.U.)}$$

4. Four equal uniform rods, each of length $2a$ and line density λ, are joined at their ends to form a square $ABCD$. A fifth uniform rod EF, of length $a(\sqrt{7} - \sqrt{2})$ and line density λ', is perpendicular to $ABCD$, and EF produced passes through the centre of the square. If E is at a distance $a\sqrt{7}$ from the square, show that the gravitational attraction of the square on the rod is $4\gamma\lambda\lambda' \log (\frac{3}{2})$. (L.U.)

5. Prove that the attraction of a thin uniform circular plate of radius a and mass M at a point on the axis distant r from centre is

$$\frac{2\gamma M}{a^2}\left\{1 - \frac{r}{\sqrt{r^2 + a^2}}\right\}$$

γ being the constant of gravitation.

The centre of such a plate is C and A and B are the corners of an equilateral triangle of sides $4a$ with vertex at C. The triangle lies in a plane normal to that of the plate with AB parallel to the plate. Attracting particles, each of mass m, are placed at A, B respectively. If a particle of unit mass is in equilibrium at the circumcentre of the triangle ABC, prove that

$$\frac{m}{M} = \frac{32}{3}\left\{1 - \frac{4}{\sqrt{19}}\right\} \qquad \text{(L.U.)}$$

6. A uniform circular lamina is divided into two segments by a chord which subtends an angle 2α at the centre. Prove that the attraction of the minor segment at the end of the diameter perpendicular to the chord, remote from the minor segment, is

$$4\gamma\sigma\left\{\log\tan\left(\frac{\pi}{4}+\frac{\alpha}{4}\right)-\sin\frac{\alpha}{2}\right\}$$

where σ is the surface density of the lamina. (L.U.)

CHAPTER II

THE THEORY OF VECTORS

2.1 Dynamical requirements

Our aim is to develop the theory of dynamics and to apply it to a wide variety of problems, but before we can do this it is necessary to decide on the concepts which are involved and to construct a mathematical formalism to handle these concepts. Such a formalism is provided in the theory of Vector Algebra.

We have seen in Chapter I that dynamics involves quantities like mass and time which possess magnitude, and also quantities like velocity, acceleration, force and impulse which involve the additional idea of direction in space. Furthermore, we know that these directed quantities are combined in addition by the parallelogram law.

It follows that the first quantities are basically *algebraic* (that is to say, can be represented by symbols of elementary algebra) whilst the second set are basically *geometrical*. A quantity like mass, which possesses a magnitude which is independent of the position of the body, we shall call a *scalar*. Other examples of scalar quantities are temperature and energy (v. " kinetic energy " and " work done by a force "). The directed quantities already mentioned we shall regard as examples of a *vector*, a word which must be precisely defined before we can represent such quantities by mathematical symbols.

Firstly we notice that (e.g.) a force possesses not only magnitude and direction but also a *line of action* and a *point of application*. Are these latter properties to form part of the general definition of a vector? Plainly no, since such a restriction would exclude a quantity like a *couple* which otherwise possesses both magnitude and direction, as the following argument shows.

Consider a very large lamina which is acted upon by a couple of moment Γ and let the forces F acting in the plane of the lamina at points A and B be a possible representation of this couple (v. Fig. 10). Then $\Gamma = pF$ which also equals the resultant moment of the forces F about every point in the plane. Hence the choice of the forces F and the points A and B becomes arbitrary so long as the value of p is so chosen as to make $pF = \Gamma$.

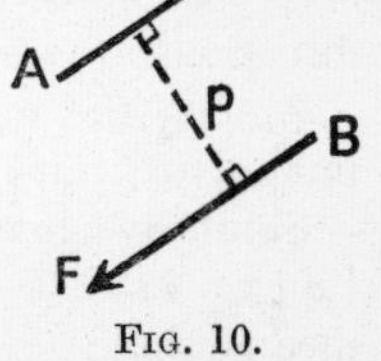

FIG. 10.

Also the effect of the couple on the lamina is a turning effect with an imaginary axis perpendicular to the plane. This axis, which is not fixed in position, may be called the direction of the couple whilst Γ is its magnitude. Thus the couple has magnitude and direction but no line of action or point of application ; it is merely a " couple in the plane." Since a couple can clearly induce motion in a lamina it is dynamically significant and must therefore be included in any theory of vectors.

We must therefore define a vector entirely in terms of the words " magnitude " and " direction," plus the idea of the parallelogram of forces. The definition must also exclude any dependence upon a choice of geometrical axes in space ; the properties of a vector must not depend upon the description of the vector.

2.2 Definition of a free vector

Suppose we are given two points A_0, B_0 in space. Then consider any other point-pair A_r, B_r which is such that

(i) the length A_rB_r = the length A_0B_0
(ii) the line A_rB_r is parallel to the line A_0B_0
(iii) the directional sense $A_r \to B_r$ is the same as $A_0 \to B_0$.

We may now say that the whole class of such point-pairs $\{A_r, B_r\}$ $(r = 0, 1, 2, \ldots)$ defines the *free vector* $\overline{AB}$, where (A, B) is any point-pair of the class. The class, of course, must not be confused with its members, there being a subtle but definite distinction between the two. Thus the " class of chess-players " is a concept which is the extension of the idea of " people who play chess." Any person who plays chess is a member of the class but the class itself is not the same thing as the totality of its members, for clearly in a hundred years from now all the present members (let us say) will have died, although there will still remain the class of chess-players.

If now we use a bold type to denote a vector and write (say) $\boldsymbol{F} = \overline{AB}$, then we shall say that every point-pair (A_r, B_r) is a *representation* of a free vector $\boldsymbol{F}$. The length AB is called the *modulus* (or magnitude) of $\boldsymbol{F}$ and this will be written as $|\boldsymbol{F}|$ or, when there is no ambiguity, as F.

Two vectors $\boldsymbol{F}_1$ and $\boldsymbol{F}_2$ are equal when they are defined by the same class of representations, that is to say, when $F_1 = F_2$ and their directions are the same.

Among the set of vectors $\{\boldsymbol{F}\}$ there will be infinitely many whose moduli are unity, $|\boldsymbol{F}| = AB = 1$. Such vectors are called *unit vectors*.

Similarly there will be those vectors $\boldsymbol{F}$ which have zero modulus, $|\boldsymbol{F}| = AB = 0$. This means that A_r coincides with B_r, which also means that we cannot speak of the direction of the vector. Such vectors are therefore indistinguishable and so we speak of *the nul vector* defined by the class $\{A_r, B_r\}$ with $A_r \equiv B_r$ (all r). We write it as $\mathbf{0}$.

2.3 Line vector and position vector

These are defined by sub-classes of the class of 2.2.

(*a*) Suppose the point-pairs (A_r, B_r) of 2.2 must now satisfy a fourth requirement, viz.

(iv) A_r, B_r must lie in the line defined by A_0, B_0.

Then we say that the class $\{A_r, B_r\}$ defines a *line vector* $\overline{AB}$ associated with (or lying in) the line λ (defined by A_0, B_0). These vectors will allow for the notion of " line of action."

(*b*) Suppose the point-pairs (A_r, B_r) of 2.2 must now satisfy a different fourth requirement, viz.

(iv) A_r must coincide with A_0 (all r).

Then also it is clear that $B_r \equiv B_0$ (all r) and, in effect, the class $\{A_r, B_r\}$ only contains *one member*, i.e. the vector possesses a unique representation. This is called *the position vector* $\overline{A_0B_0}$, defining the position of B_0 w.r.t. A_0. This idea will be useful in discussing geometry; starting with an origin O in space we shall be able to define the position of every point P by the position vector (say) $\boldsymbol{r} = \overline{OP}$. It is usual to use small letters to denote position vectors, but not exclusively.

2.4 The triangle law of addition

Let $\overline{OA}$ and $\overline{AB}$ be representations of the free vector $\boldsymbol{a}$, $\boldsymbol{b}$ respectively (v. Fig. 11). Then we define their sum by the Δ-*law of addition*, viz.

$$\boldsymbol{a} + \boldsymbol{b} = \overline{OA} + \overline{AB} = \overline{OB} = \boldsymbol{c}$$

This law is also equivalent to that known as the " parallelogram law."

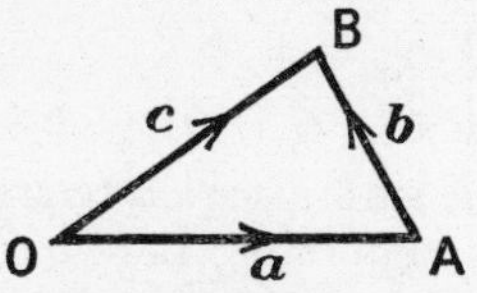

FIG. 11.

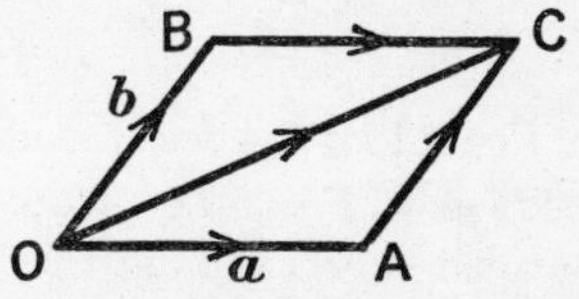

FIG. 12.

Thus, in Fig. 12, if $\overline{OA}$ and $\overline{OB}$ are representations of $\boldsymbol{a}$ and $\boldsymbol{b}$ respectively then, by the properties of the parallelogram, $\overline{AC}$ is also a representation of $\boldsymbol{b}$ and so $\boldsymbol{a} + \boldsymbol{b} = \overline{OA} + \overline{OB} = \overline{OA} + \overline{AC} = \overline{OC}$.

It is important to remember that the algebra of vectors is really the algebra of free vectors. The line and position vectors, having a restricted class of representations, will naturally obey the same laws but only when this is possible without doing violence to their representations.

The above parallelogram of Fig. 12 shows that the *addition of vectors is commutative.* Thus we can write

$$\boldsymbol{a} + \boldsymbol{b} = \boldsymbol{b} + \boldsymbol{a} \quad \text{since } \overline{OA} + \overline{AC} = \overline{OC} = \overline{OB} + \overline{BC}$$

That *addition is also associative* follows by applying the Δ-law to Fig. 13, whence

$$\boldsymbol{a} + (\boldsymbol{b} + \boldsymbol{c}) = \boldsymbol{a} + \overline{AC} = \overline{OC}$$

and
$$(\boldsymbol{a} + \boldsymbol{b}) + \boldsymbol{c} = \overline{OB} + \boldsymbol{c} = \overline{OC}$$

We therefore write simply $\boldsymbol{a} + \boldsymbol{b} + \boldsymbol{c}$ for the sum of three vectors.

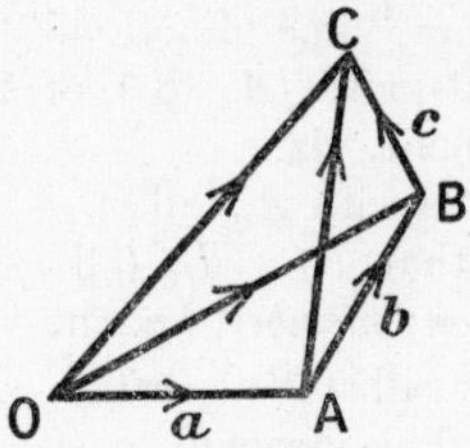

FIG. 13.

2.5 Positive and negative vectors

The vectors discussed so far may now be thought of as positive, and multiplication of a vector $\boldsymbol{F}$ by a real number $x(>0)$ giving $x\boldsymbol{F}$ will be interpreted as a new vector differing from $\boldsymbol{F}$ only by the fact that its modulus is $x\,|\,\boldsymbol{F}\,|$. The possibility of x being negative means that we must be able to interpret $-\boldsymbol{F}$. This is the common problem, found in all algebraic rings, of the *additive inverse*. Thus we define the vector $-\boldsymbol{F}$ by the equation

$$\boldsymbol{F} + (-\boldsymbol{F}) = \boldsymbol{0}$$

From Fig. 11 of 2.4 we deduce that, with $\boldsymbol{F} = \overline{OA}$, $\overline{OB} = \boldsymbol{0}$ implies that $\overline{AB} = -\boldsymbol{F} = \overline{AO}$. Thus $-\boldsymbol{F}$ is $+\boldsymbol{F}$ with *direction reversed.*

We must now examine the possibilities of forming the product of two vectors. From the point of view of building an algebra we naturally seek a product which is itself a vector, but with an eye on the applications of the algebra we find it very convenient to consider other ways of combining two vectors, ways which we also bless with the name of "product." At this stage we shall examine two kinds of product, according as the result is a scalar or a vector (v. 2.13).

2.6 The scalar product

The scalar product of two vectors $\boldsymbol{a}$ and $\boldsymbol{b}$ is written $\boldsymbol{a}.\boldsymbol{b}$ (read "$\boldsymbol{a}$ dot $\boldsymbol{b}$") and is defined by

$$\boldsymbol{a}.\boldsymbol{b} = ab \cos\theta \quad . \quad . \quad . \quad . \quad (1)$$

where θ is the angle between $\boldsymbol{a}$ and $\boldsymbol{b}$ (v. Fig. 14) and $a = |\,\boldsymbol{a}\,|$, $b = |\,\boldsymbol{b}\,|$.

Since (e.g.) $b \cos \theta$ is the orthogonal projection of $\overline{OB}$ on $\overline{OA}$ we can also write

$$\boldsymbol{a}.\boldsymbol{b} = (\text{modulus of one vector}) \times (\text{projection of the other on it})$$

The sense in which θ is measured is irrelevant since $\cos -\theta = \cos \theta$ and since $ab = ba$ we can write $\boldsymbol{a}.\boldsymbol{b} = \boldsymbol{b}.\boldsymbol{a}$: the *scalar product is commutative.*

The *associative law* of multiplication is irrelevant since $(\boldsymbol{a}.\boldsymbol{b}).\boldsymbol{c}$ cannot be formed, $(\boldsymbol{a}.\boldsymbol{b})$ not being a vector.

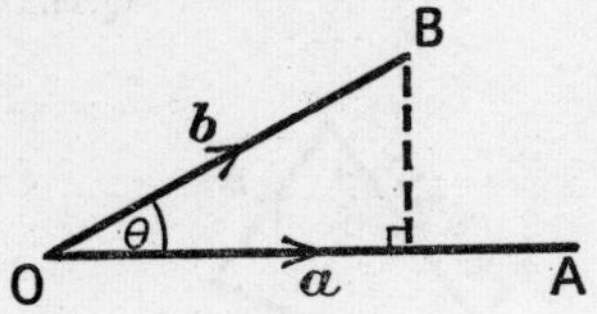

Fig. 14.

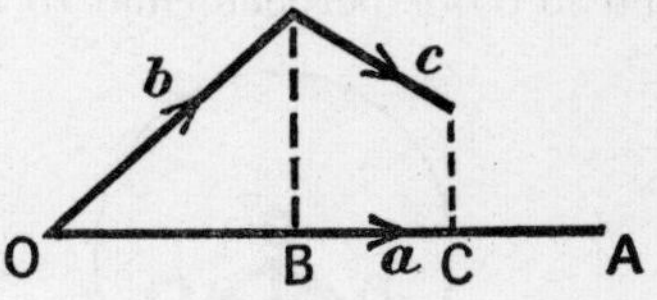

Fig. 15.

The *distributive law* can be shown to hold by appealing to the properties of projections. Thus, in Fig. 15, we can write

$$\boldsymbol{a}.(\boldsymbol{b} + \boldsymbol{c}) = \boldsymbol{a}.\boldsymbol{b} + \boldsymbol{a}.\boldsymbol{c}$$

since $OC = OB + BC$ for all $\boldsymbol{b}, \boldsymbol{c}$. This does not depend upon Fig. 15 being plane.

Now equation (1) contains some important properties.

(i) $\boldsymbol{a}.\boldsymbol{a} = a^2$ (all $\boldsymbol{a}$) since $\cos 0 = 1$: we usually write $\boldsymbol{a}^2$ for $\boldsymbol{a}.\boldsymbol{a}$ and then $\boldsymbol{a}^2 = a^2 = |\boldsymbol{a}|^2$.

(ii) If $\boldsymbol{e}$ is a unit vector $\boldsymbol{e}^2 = 1$.

(iii) $(\boldsymbol{a} + \boldsymbol{b}).(\boldsymbol{c} + \boldsymbol{d}) = \boldsymbol{a}.\boldsymbol{c} + \boldsymbol{a}.\boldsymbol{d} + \boldsymbol{b}.\boldsymbol{c} + \boldsymbol{b}.\boldsymbol{d}$ by the distributive law, and in particular $(\boldsymbol{a} + \boldsymbol{b})^2 = \boldsymbol{a}^2 + 2(\boldsymbol{a}.\boldsymbol{b}) + \boldsymbol{b}^2$.

(iv) If $\boldsymbol{a}.\boldsymbol{b} = 0$ then we can deduce that $\boldsymbol{a} = \boldsymbol{0}$, $\boldsymbol{b} = \boldsymbol{0}$ or $\theta = \pi/_2$. When $\theta = \pi/_2$ we say the vectors are *orthogonal*; their representations are then perpendicular.

Example 1. Given two points A_1, A_2 in space, defined by position vectors $\boldsymbol{r}_1$ and $\boldsymbol{r}_2$, to find the point B which divides A_1A_2 internally in the ratio of $\kappa_1 : \kappa_2$ (v. Fig. 16).

By the Δ-law of 2.4 we can write $\overline{A_2B} = \dfrac{\kappa_2}{\kappa_1 + \kappa_2}.\overline{A_2A_1}$, where $\overline{A_2A_1} = (\boldsymbol{r}_1 - \boldsymbol{r}_2)$. But $\overline{A_2B} = \boldsymbol{r} - \boldsymbol{r}_2$ and so

$$\boldsymbol{r} - \boldsymbol{r}_2 = \left(\frac{\kappa_2}{\kappa_1 + \kappa_2}\right)(\boldsymbol{r}_1 - \boldsymbol{r}_2)$$

giving
$$\boldsymbol{r} = \frac{\kappa_1\boldsymbol{r}_2 + \kappa_2\boldsymbol{r}_1}{\kappa_1 + \kappa_2}$$

In particular the mid-point of A_1A_2 will be $\frac{1}{2}(\boldsymbol{r}_1 + \boldsymbol{r}_2)$.

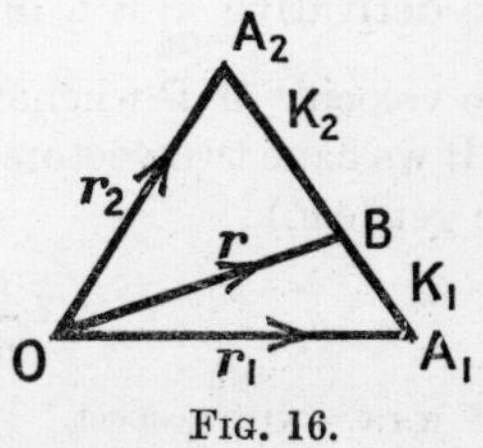

Fig. 16.

Example 2. To prove that the line joining the centre of a circle to the mid-point of a chord is perpendicular to the chord.

Let the circle, centre O, have radius a and let $A_2(\boldsymbol{r}_1)$ and $A_2(\boldsymbol{r}_2)$ be the ends of a chord as shown in Fig. 17. The mid-point B has position vector $\frac{1}{2}(\boldsymbol{r}_1 + \boldsymbol{r}_2)$ by Ex. 1, and the line $\overline{A_2A_1}$ is the vector $(\boldsymbol{r}_1 - \boldsymbol{r}_2)$, by 2.4. Since $OA_1 = OA_2 = a$ we also have $\boldsymbol{r}_1{}^2 = \boldsymbol{r}_2{}^2 = a^2$. Now it follows that

$$\overline{OB}.\overline{A_2A_1} = \tfrac{1}{2}(\boldsymbol{r}_1 + \boldsymbol{r}_2).(\boldsymbol{r}_1 - \boldsymbol{r}_2) = \tfrac{1}{2}(\boldsymbol{r}_1{}^2 - \boldsymbol{r}_2{}^2) = 0$$

and so $\overline{OB}$ is perpendicular to $\overline{A_2A_1}$. Q.E.D.

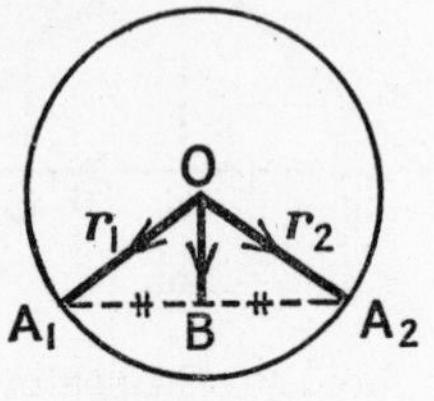

FIG. 17.

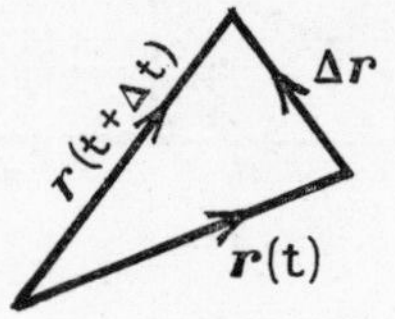

FIG. 18.

2.7 Differentiation of a vector w.r.t.* a parameter

Suppose we have a vector $\boldsymbol{r}$ whose representation is a function of some parameter t, e.g. $\boldsymbol{r}$ might be the position vector of a point P which moves w.r.t. the time t. Then we define the derivative $\frac{d\boldsymbol{r}}{dt}$ by

$$\frac{d\boldsymbol{r}}{dt} = \lim_{\Delta t \to 0} \frac{\boldsymbol{r}(t + \Delta t) - \boldsymbol{r}(t)}{\Delta t}$$

assuming the limit to exist.

Now the vector $\boldsymbol{r}(t + \Delta t)$ will differ from $\boldsymbol{r}(t)$ in both magnitude and direction so that if we write

$$\boldsymbol{r}(t + \Delta t) = \boldsymbol{r}(t) + \Delta\boldsymbol{r}$$

we get the triangle of Fig. 18. In the limit $|\Delta\boldsymbol{r}| \to 0$ as $\Delta t \to 0$ and the direction of $\Delta\boldsymbol{r}$ tends to a definite limit.

If we let $\boldsymbol{r}(t)$ be the position vector of a point P it now follows that the derivative $\frac{d\boldsymbol{r}}{dt}$ is a line vector passing through P and representing the velocity of P whenever t is the time.

If we have two vectors $\boldsymbol{a}(t)$ and $\boldsymbol{b}(t)$ which are separately differentiable we get (e.g.)

$$\frac{d}{dt}(\boldsymbol{a}.\boldsymbol{b}) = \frac{d\boldsymbol{a}}{dt}.\boldsymbol{b} + \boldsymbol{a}.\frac{d\boldsymbol{b}}{dt} \quad . \quad . \quad . \quad (1)$$

* w.r.t.=with respect.

In particular, if $\boldsymbol{e}(t)$ is a *unit vector* we have $\boldsymbol{e}.\boldsymbol{e} = 1$ which implies, from (1),

$$\boldsymbol{e}.\frac{d\boldsymbol{e}}{dt} = 0 \quad . \quad . \quad . \quad . \quad . \qquad (2)$$

Hence $\boldsymbol{e}$ and $\dfrac{d\boldsymbol{e}}{dt}$ are *perpendicular vectors*, a result which clearly holds for every vector of constant modulus.

2.8 The vector product

Consider two vectors $\boldsymbol{a}$ and $\boldsymbol{b}$ and let $\boldsymbol{n}$ be a unit vector which is perpendicular to both $\boldsymbol{a}$ and $\boldsymbol{b}$ and in a direction which forms with $\boldsymbol{a}$, $\boldsymbol{b}$ (in that order) a right-handed triad, that is to say, a right-handed screw motion from $\boldsymbol{a}$ to $\boldsymbol{b}$ gives the direction of $\boldsymbol{n}$ as axis. Then we write the vector product of $\boldsymbol{a}$ and $\boldsymbol{b}$ as $\boldsymbol{a} \times \boldsymbol{b}$ (read " $\boldsymbol{a}$ cross $\boldsymbol{b}$ ") and define it by

$$\boldsymbol{a} \times \boldsymbol{b} = (ab \sin \theta)\boldsymbol{n} \quad . \quad . \quad . \quad . \qquad (1)$$

where θ is the angle between $\boldsymbol{a}$ and $\boldsymbol{b}$ in the sense of a rotation from $\boldsymbol{a}$ to $\boldsymbol{b}$ (v. Fig. 19).

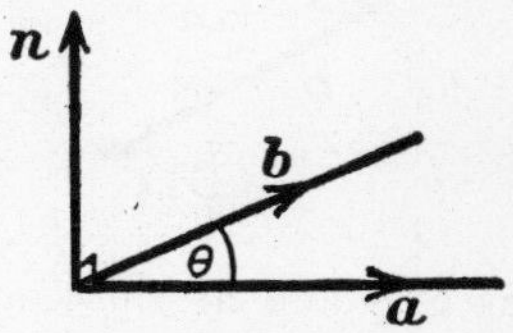

Fig. 19.

We notice that the vector $\boldsymbol{a} \times \boldsymbol{b}$ is perpendicular to the plane of $\boldsymbol{a}$ and $\boldsymbol{b}$ and that, because of the change in the direction of $\boldsymbol{n}$,

$$\boldsymbol{a} \times \boldsymbol{b} = -\boldsymbol{b} \times \boldsymbol{a} \quad . \quad . \qquad (2)$$

Thus the vector product is *not commutative*, in the sense of elementary algebra ($ab = ba$).

Equation (1) immediately implies the following properties :

(i) $\boldsymbol{a} \times \boldsymbol{a} = \boldsymbol{0}$ (all a) since $\theta = 0$.

(ii) $\boldsymbol{a} \times \boldsymbol{b} = \boldsymbol{0}$ implies $\boldsymbol{a} = \boldsymbol{0}$, $\boldsymbol{b} = \boldsymbol{0}$ or $\theta = 0$ (parallelism).

If $\boldsymbol{a}$ and $\boldsymbol{b}$ are in fact parallel we can find a scalar λ such that $\boldsymbol{b} = \lambda\boldsymbol{a}$.

It is clear from the definition that the vector product cannot, in general, be associative, i.e. $\boldsymbol{a} \times (\boldsymbol{b} \times \boldsymbol{c}) \neq (\boldsymbol{a} \times \boldsymbol{b}) \times \boldsymbol{c}$. For $\boldsymbol{a} \times (\boldsymbol{b} \times \boldsymbol{c})$ is a vector in the plane of $\boldsymbol{b}$ and $\boldsymbol{c}$ whereas $(\boldsymbol{a} \times \boldsymbol{b}) \times \boldsymbol{c}$ is in the plane of $\boldsymbol{a}$ and $\boldsymbol{b}$, and except when each equals the vector $\boldsymbol{b}$ these cannot be equal.

It remains only to examine the *distributive law* in relation to the vector product. We shall show that it does, in fact, hold, i.e.

$$\boldsymbol{a} \times (\boldsymbol{b} + \boldsymbol{c}) = \boldsymbol{a} \times \boldsymbol{b} + \boldsymbol{a} \times \boldsymbol{c} \quad . \qquad (3)$$

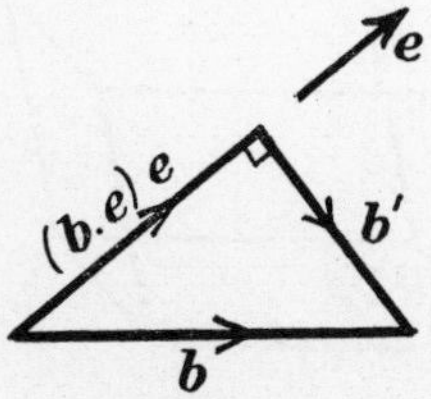

Fig. 20.

First, let $\boldsymbol{e}$ be a given unit vector (e.g. in the direction of $\boldsymbol{a}$, so that $\boldsymbol{a} = a\boldsymbol{e}$). Then any other vector $\boldsymbol{b}$ gives a unique value of $\boldsymbol{b}.\boldsymbol{e}$, so that there is a unique triangle (v. Fig. 20) in which

$$\boldsymbol{b} = \boldsymbol{b} \;+ (\boldsymbol{b}.\boldsymbol{e})\boldsymbol{e} \quad . \quad . \qquad (4)$$

where $\boldsymbol{b}'$ is perpendicular to $\boldsymbol{e}$. For another vector $\boldsymbol{c}$ we can similarly identify a unique $\boldsymbol{c}'$ such that

$$\boldsymbol{c} = \boldsymbol{c}' + (\boldsymbol{c}.\boldsymbol{e})\boldsymbol{e} \quad . \quad . \quad . \quad . \quad (5)$$

Adding (4) and (5) and using the fact that the scalar product obeys the distributive law, we get

$$(\boldsymbol{b} + \boldsymbol{c}) = (\boldsymbol{b}' + \boldsymbol{c}') + \{(\boldsymbol{b} + \boldsymbol{c}).\boldsymbol{e}\}\boldsymbol{e}$$

so that $$(\boldsymbol{b} + \boldsymbol{c})' = \boldsymbol{b}' + \boldsymbol{c}' \quad . \quad . \quad . \quad . \quad . \quad (6)$$

Now, taking $\boldsymbol{a} = a\boldsymbol{e}$, we notice that $\boldsymbol{a} \times \boldsymbol{b} = \boldsymbol{a} \times \boldsymbol{b}'$ since (i) $|\,\boldsymbol{a} \times \boldsymbol{b}\,| = ab \sin\theta = ab' = |\,\boldsymbol{a} \times \boldsymbol{b}'\,|$ and (ii) the direction of $\boldsymbol{a} \times \boldsymbol{b}$ is the same as that of $\boldsymbol{a} \times \boldsymbol{b}'$. From Fig. 21 we see that $\boldsymbol{a} \times \boldsymbol{b}'$ is obtained from $\boldsymbol{a}$ and $\boldsymbol{b}'$ by rotating the vector $\boldsymbol{b}'$ through $\pi/_2$ about $\boldsymbol{a}$

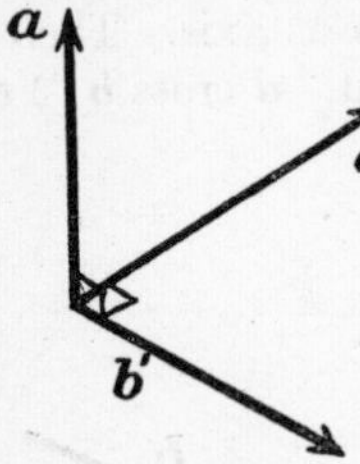

FIG. 21.

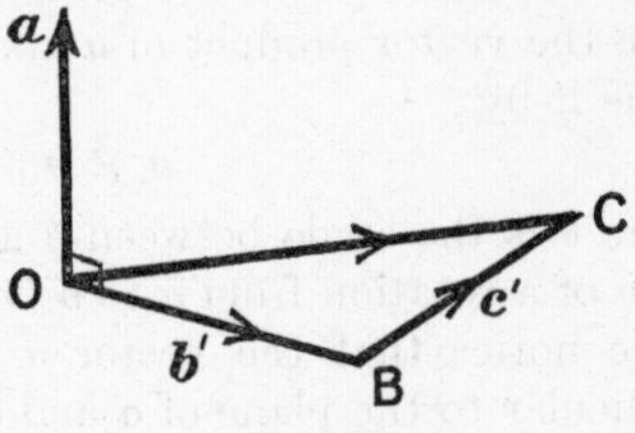

FIG. 22.

as axis and at the same time multiplying $\boldsymbol{b}'$ by the scalar a. The same applies to the products $\boldsymbol{a} \times \boldsymbol{c}'$ and $\boldsymbol{a} \times \overline{OC}$ (which equals $\boldsymbol{a} \times (\boldsymbol{b}' + \boldsymbol{c}')$), using the triangle OBC in Fig. 22. Thus the whole triangle OBC becomes rotated in its own plane about $\boldsymbol{a}$ and in its new position its sides represent $\boldsymbol{a} \times \boldsymbol{b}'$, $\boldsymbol{a} \times \boldsymbol{c}'$ and $\boldsymbol{a} \times \overline{OC}$. We therefore get

$$\boldsymbol{a} \times (\boldsymbol{b}' + \boldsymbol{c}') = \boldsymbol{a} \times \overline{OC} = \boldsymbol{a} \times \boldsymbol{b}' + \boldsymbol{a} \times \boldsymbol{c}'$$

and from (6) we have

$$\boldsymbol{a} \times (\boldsymbol{b}' + \boldsymbol{c}') = \boldsymbol{a} \times (\boldsymbol{b} + \boldsymbol{c})'$$

so that, finally

$$\boldsymbol{a} \times (\boldsymbol{b} + \boldsymbol{c}) = \boldsymbol{a} \times \boldsymbol{b} + \boldsymbol{a} \times \boldsymbol{c} \qquad \text{Q.E.D.}$$

2.9 The triple scalar product $\boldsymbol{a}.(\boldsymbol{b} \times \boldsymbol{c})$

This is an important example of a product formed by three vectors $\boldsymbol{a}$, $\boldsymbol{b}$, $\boldsymbol{c}$; the result is a scalar. Using Fig. 23 we can write

$$\begin{aligned}\boldsymbol{a}.(\boldsymbol{b} \times \boldsymbol{c}) &= \boldsymbol{a}.\boldsymbol{n}\ (bc \sin\theta)\\ &= (a \cos\phi)(bc \sin\theta)\\ &= \text{height} \times \text{area of base}\\ &= \text{volume of the parallelepiped whose coterminus edges are } \boldsymbol{a}, \boldsymbol{b}, \boldsymbol{c}\end{aligned}$$

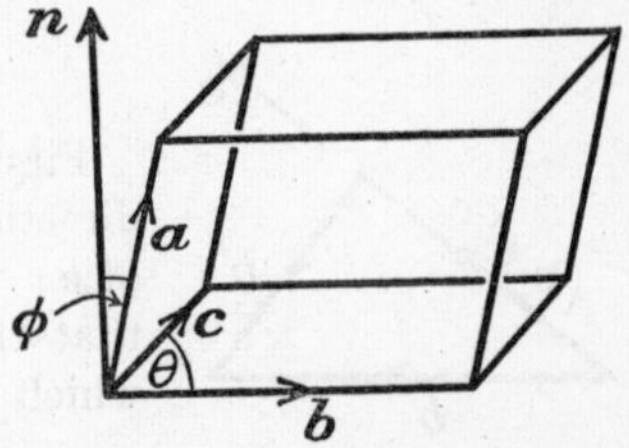

FIG. 23.

It is clear that, depending upon whether the relevant angle ϕ is acute or obtuse, we obtain

$$\begin{aligned} &\boldsymbol{a}.(\boldsymbol{b} \times \boldsymbol{c}) = \boldsymbol{c}.(\boldsymbol{a} \times \boldsymbol{b}) = \boldsymbol{b}.(\boldsymbol{c} \times \boldsymbol{a}) \\ &= -\boldsymbol{a}.(\boldsymbol{c} \times \boldsymbol{b}) = -\boldsymbol{b}.(\boldsymbol{a} \times \boldsymbol{c}) = -\boldsymbol{c}.(\boldsymbol{b} \times \boldsymbol{a}) \quad . \quad (1) \end{aligned}$$

The value of $\boldsymbol{a}.(\boldsymbol{b} \times \boldsymbol{c})$ is therefore unaltered by a cyclic interchange of the letters. For this reason we shall write it as $[\boldsymbol{abc}]$. We now have the results :

(i) $[\boldsymbol{aab}] = 0$ (all $\boldsymbol{a}$, $\boldsymbol{b}$) since the above volume vanishes.

(ii) If the vectors $\boldsymbol{a}$, $\boldsymbol{b}$, $\boldsymbol{c}$ are *coplanar* then $[\boldsymbol{abc}] = 0$.

This means that if $\boldsymbol{r}$ is the position vector of a variable point P the vector equation of the plane through O, B, C will be

$$[\boldsymbol{rbc}] = 0$$

(iii) Since the volume of a tetrahedron is one-sixth of the volume of the circumscribing parallelepiped then, with coterminus edges $\boldsymbol{a}$, $\boldsymbol{b}$, $\boldsymbol{c}$, the volume of a tetrahedron will be $\frac{1}{6}[\boldsymbol{abc}]$.

2.10 Linearly independent vectors

If we can find values of the scalars λ, μ, ν other than $\lambda = \mu = \nu = 0$ and such that

$$\lambda\boldsymbol{a} + \mu\boldsymbol{b} + \nu\boldsymbol{c} = \boldsymbol{0}$$

we say that the vectors $\boldsymbol{a}$, $\boldsymbol{b}$, $\boldsymbol{c}$ are *linearly dependent*. If the only possible values of λ, μ, ν are zero we say that $\boldsymbol{a}$, $\boldsymbol{b}$, $\boldsymbol{c}$ are *linearly independent*.

Theorem 2.10 I. *If* a, b, c *are non-coplanar vectors then they are linearly independent.*

To prove this, suppose that the vectors are linearly dependent and that $\lambda\boldsymbol{a} + \mu\boldsymbol{b} + \nu\boldsymbol{c} = \boldsymbol{0}$, $\lambda \neq 0$. Multiplying in scalar product by the vector $(\boldsymbol{b} \times \boldsymbol{c})$ gives

$$\lambda[\boldsymbol{abc}] + \mu[\boldsymbol{bbc}] + \nu[\boldsymbol{cbc}] = 0$$

which reduces by 2.9 (i) to $[\boldsymbol{abc}] = 0$.
But then 2.9 (ii) implies that $\boldsymbol{a}$, $\boldsymbol{b}$, $\boldsymbol{c}$ are co-planar, which is a contradiction.

Theorem 2.10 II. *If* a, b, c *is a linearly independent triad then any vector* $\boldsymbol{r}$ *can be uniquely written in the form*

$$\boldsymbol{r} = \lambda\boldsymbol{a} + \mu\boldsymbol{b} + \nu\boldsymbol{c}$$

Assume λ, μ, ν exist. Multiplying by $.(\boldsymbol{b} \times \boldsymbol{c})$ then gives

$$[\boldsymbol{rbc}] = \lambda[\boldsymbol{abc}] = \lambda\Delta \quad \text{(say)}$$

Hence

$$\lambda = \frac{1}{\Delta}[\boldsymbol{rbc}], \quad \mu = \frac{1}{\Delta}[\boldsymbol{rca}], \quad \nu = \frac{1}{\Delta}[\boldsymbol{rab}]$$

since $\Delta \neq 0$. These values are unique.

Now we need only show that

$$\boldsymbol{s} = \boldsymbol{r} - \frac{1}{\Delta}\{[\boldsymbol{rbc}]\boldsymbol{a} + [\boldsymbol{rca}]\boldsymbol{b} + [\boldsymbol{rab}]\boldsymbol{c}\}$$
$$= \boldsymbol{0} \quad \text{all } \boldsymbol{r}$$

This follows since $\boldsymbol{s}.(\boldsymbol{b} \times \boldsymbol{c}) = \boldsymbol{s}.(\boldsymbol{c} \times \boldsymbol{a}) = \boldsymbol{s}.(\boldsymbol{a} \times \boldsymbol{b}) = 0$ (all $\boldsymbol{r}$) which implies $\boldsymbol{s} = \boldsymbol{0}$ or $\boldsymbol{s}$ is parallel to $\boldsymbol{c}$, on the one hand, or it implies $\boldsymbol{s} = \boldsymbol{0}$ or $\boldsymbol{s}$ is parallel to $\boldsymbol{a}$, on the other. Hence $\boldsymbol{s} = \boldsymbol{0}$ for all $\boldsymbol{r}$.

Q.E.D.

The uniqueness of this result means that for any two vectors $\boldsymbol{r}_1 = \lambda_1\boldsymbol{a} + \mu_1\boldsymbol{b} + \nu_1\boldsymbol{c}$ and $\boldsymbol{r}_2 = \lambda_2\boldsymbol{a} + \mu_2\boldsymbol{b} + \nu_2\boldsymbol{c}$ equality amounts to the following :

(i) $\boldsymbol{r}_1 = \boldsymbol{r}_2$ implies $\lambda_1 = \lambda_2$, $\mu_1 = \mu_2$, $\nu_1 = \nu_2$.

(ii) $\lambda_1 = \lambda_2$, $\mu_1 = \mu_2$, $\nu_1 = \nu_2$ implies $\boldsymbol{r}_1 = \boldsymbol{r}_2$.

Also it follows that $\boldsymbol{r}_1 \pm \boldsymbol{r}_2 = (\lambda_1 \pm \lambda_2)\boldsymbol{a} + (\mu_1 \pm \mu_2)\boldsymbol{b} + (\nu_1 \pm \nu_2)\boldsymbol{c}$.

Thus the vectors $\boldsymbol{r}$ in space may to some extent be adequately described by a set of three scalars λ, μ, ν provided a linearly independent triad is understood. The rules governing the combination of vectors will also be expressed in terms of these scalars, although not exclusively ; the properties of the *triad of reference* $\boldsymbol{a}$, $\boldsymbol{b}$, $\boldsymbol{c}$ will also enter into such a description. It is therefore of some importance to obtain triads whose properties are most convenient. These turn out to be triads of mutually perpendicular unit vectors, and we shall examine them in the next section.

2.11 The orthonormal triad

This title describes a set of three mutually perpendicular unit vectors which, in addition, we shall agree to take as positive, or right-handed. Let us denote the vectors by $\boldsymbol{i}$, $\boldsymbol{j}$, $\boldsymbol{k}$ and let Fig. 24 denote a typical representation with O as geometrical origin. By definition we have

$$\left.\begin{aligned} &\boldsymbol{i}^2 = \boldsymbol{j}^2 = \boldsymbol{k}^2 = 1 \\ &\boldsymbol{i}.\boldsymbol{j} = \boldsymbol{j}.\boldsymbol{k} = \boldsymbol{k}.\boldsymbol{i} = 0 \\ &\boldsymbol{i} \times \boldsymbol{j} = \boldsymbol{k}, \quad \boldsymbol{j} \times \boldsymbol{k} = \boldsymbol{i}, \quad \boldsymbol{k} \times \boldsymbol{i} = \boldsymbol{j} \end{aligned}\right\} \quad . \quad . \quad (1)$$

Hence $$[\boldsymbol{ijk}] = \boldsymbol{i}.(\boldsymbol{j} \times \boldsymbol{k}) = \boldsymbol{i}.\boldsymbol{i} = 1$$

and $$[\boldsymbol{rjk}] = \boldsymbol{r}.\boldsymbol{i}, \quad [\boldsymbol{rki}] = \boldsymbol{r}.\boldsymbol{j}, \quad [\boldsymbol{rij}] = \boldsymbol{r}.\boldsymbol{k}$$

Then by 2.10 II every vector $\boldsymbol{r}$ can be written

$$\boldsymbol{r} = (\boldsymbol{r}.\boldsymbol{i})\boldsymbol{i} + (\boldsymbol{r}.\boldsymbol{j})\boldsymbol{j} + (\boldsymbol{r}.\boldsymbol{k})\boldsymbol{k} \quad . \quad . \quad . \quad (2)$$

The scalars $(\boldsymbol{r}.\boldsymbol{i})$, $(\boldsymbol{r}.\boldsymbol{j})$, $(\boldsymbol{r}.\boldsymbol{k})$ we shall call the *components* of $\boldsymbol{r}$ in the directions of $\boldsymbol{i}$, $\boldsymbol{j}$, $\boldsymbol{k}$ respectively. This resolution of a vector is unique by 2.10 II. If now we regard $\boldsymbol{r}$ as the position vector of a point P relative to O then it is usual to write $\boldsymbol{r}.\boldsymbol{i} = x$, $\boldsymbol{r}.\boldsymbol{j} = y$, $\boldsymbol{r}.\boldsymbol{k} = z$. Then (2) gives

$$\boldsymbol{r} = x\boldsymbol{i} + y\boldsymbol{j} + z\boldsymbol{k} \quad . \quad . \quad . \quad . \quad (3)$$

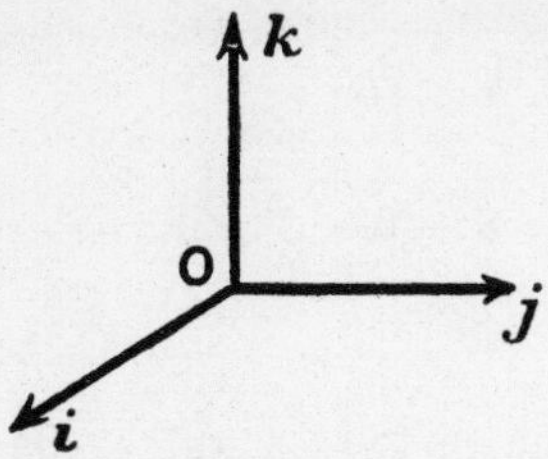

FIG. 24.

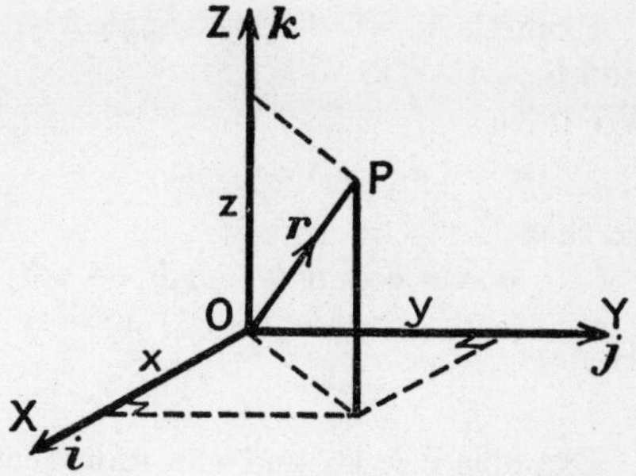

FIG. 25.

The numbers x, y, z are clearly the ordinary Cartesian co-ordinates of the point P w.r.t. the axes OX, OY, OZ, as shown in Fig. 25. Generally, every vector $\boldsymbol{F}$, whether it be a free vector, line vector or position vector, possesses three unique components X, Y, Z w.r.t. any given orthonormal triad $\boldsymbol{i}$, $\boldsymbol{j}$, $\boldsymbol{k}$ and can therefore be written

$$\boldsymbol{F} = X\boldsymbol{i} + Y\boldsymbol{j} + Z\boldsymbol{k} \quad . \quad . \quad . \quad (4)$$

Consider two vectors $\boldsymbol{a} = a_1\boldsymbol{i} + a_2\boldsymbol{j} + a_3\boldsymbol{k}$ and $\boldsymbol{b} = b_1\boldsymbol{i} + b_2\boldsymbol{j} + b_3\boldsymbol{k}$. Then by (1) we get the *scalar product* as

$$\boldsymbol{a}.\boldsymbol{b} = (a_1\boldsymbol{i} + a_2\boldsymbol{j} + a_3\boldsymbol{k}).(b_1\boldsymbol{i} + b_2\boldsymbol{j} + b_3\boldsymbol{k})$$

i.e.

$$\boldsymbol{a}.\boldsymbol{b} = a_1b_1 + a_2b_2 + a_3b_3 \quad . \quad . \quad . \quad . \quad (5)$$

Hence (3) and (5) give

$$|\boldsymbol{r}|^2 = \boldsymbol{r}^2 = x^2 + y^2 + z^2 \quad . \quad . \quad . \quad (6)$$

and when $\boldsymbol{e} = l\boldsymbol{i} + m\boldsymbol{j} + n\boldsymbol{k}$ is a *unit vector* we get

$$l^2 + m^2 + n^2 = 1 \quad . \quad . \quad . \quad . \quad (7)$$

The numbers l, m, n are, in this case, identical with Cartesian *direction cosines* since (e.g.) $l = \boldsymbol{e}.\boldsymbol{i} = \cos\alpha$, where α is the angle between $\boldsymbol{e}$ and the axis $\boldsymbol{i}$.

Also, by using the properties (1), we get the *vector product* in the form

$$\boldsymbol{a} \times \boldsymbol{b} = (a_1\boldsymbol{i} + a_2\boldsymbol{j} + a_3\boldsymbol{k}) \times (b_1\boldsymbol{i} + b_2\boldsymbol{j} + b_3\boldsymbol{k})$$

reducing to

$$\boldsymbol{a} \times \boldsymbol{b} = (a_2b_3 - a_3b_2)\boldsymbol{i} + (a_3b_1 - a_1b_3)\boldsymbol{j} + (a_1b_2 - a_2b_1)\boldsymbol{k} \quad . \quad (8)$$

We can also write (8) as a determinant

$$\boldsymbol{a} \times \boldsymbol{b} = \begin{vmatrix} \boldsymbol{i} & \boldsymbol{j} & \boldsymbol{k} \\ a_1 & a_2 & a_3 \\ b_1 & b_2 & b_3 \end{vmatrix} \quad . \quad . \quad . \quad (9)$$

Now the *triple scalar product* becomes

$$[\boldsymbol{abc}] = \boldsymbol{a}.(\boldsymbol{b} \times \boldsymbol{c}) = \begin{vmatrix} a_1 & a_2 & a_3 \\ b_1 & b_2 & b_3 \\ c_1 & c_2 & c_3 \end{vmatrix} \quad . \quad . \quad . \quad (10)$$

which shows the properties 2.9 (i) very clearly.

Example 1. To find the angle θ between the vectors $\boldsymbol{a} = 2\boldsymbol{i} - 3\boldsymbol{j} + \boldsymbol{k}$ and $\boldsymbol{b} = 4\boldsymbol{i} + 2\boldsymbol{j} - \boldsymbol{k}$.
We have

$$a = |\boldsymbol{a}| = \sqrt{4 + 9 + 1} = \sqrt{14} \quad \text{and} \quad b = |\boldsymbol{b}| = \sqrt{21}$$

so that

$$ab \cos\theta = \boldsymbol{a}.\boldsymbol{b} = a_1b_1 + a_2b_2 + a_3b_3 = 8 - 6 - 1 = 1$$

Hence $$\cos\theta = \frac{1}{\sqrt{14}\sqrt{21}} \quad \text{giving } \theta = 85° \, 45'.$$

Example 2. To find the unit vector $\boldsymbol{e}$ perpendicular to the $\boldsymbol{a}$ and $\boldsymbol{b}$ of Ex. (1).

A vector in the required direction will be $\boldsymbol{a} \times \boldsymbol{b}$ and so write $\boldsymbol{e} = \dfrac{\boldsymbol{a} \times \boldsymbol{b}}{|\boldsymbol{a} \times \boldsymbol{b}|}$. But $\boldsymbol{a} \times \boldsymbol{b} = \boldsymbol{i} + 6\boldsymbol{j} + 16\boldsymbol{k}$ which gives

$$\boldsymbol{e} = \frac{1}{\sqrt{293}}(\boldsymbol{i} + 6\boldsymbol{j} + 16\boldsymbol{k})$$

Example 3. To find the Cartesian equation of the plane through the points (0, 0, 0), (2, − 3, 5) and (− 1, 0, − 4). The equation is $[\boldsymbol{rab}] = 0$ where $\boldsymbol{a} = 2\boldsymbol{i} - 3\boldsymbol{j} + 5\boldsymbol{k}$ and $\boldsymbol{b} = -\boldsymbol{i} - 4\boldsymbol{k}$ and $\boldsymbol{r} = x\boldsymbol{i} + y\boldsymbol{j} + z\boldsymbol{k}$. Hence we get

$$\begin{vmatrix} x & y & z \\ 2 & -3 & 5 \\ -1 & 0 & -4 \end{vmatrix} = 0 \quad \text{giving } 4x + y - z = 0$$

Example 4. To find the equation of a straight line. Let the line pass through a fixed point $\boldsymbol{a}$ and lie in a direction defined by the unit vector $\boldsymbol{e}$, as shown in Fig. 26. If $P(r)$ is a current point on the line and $AP = t$ (positive, negative or zero) we have

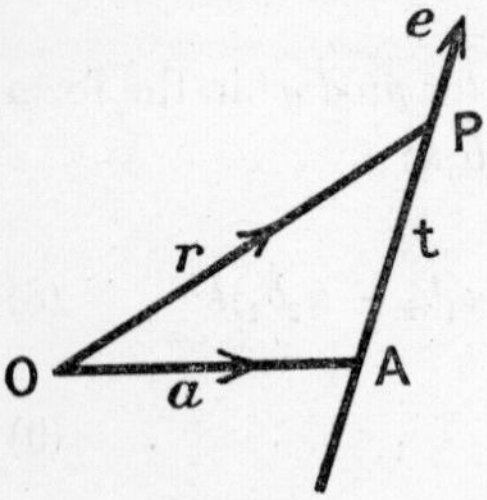

FIG. 26.

$$\boldsymbol{r} = \boldsymbol{a} + \overline{AP} \quad \text{which is } \boldsymbol{r} = \boldsymbol{a} + t\boldsymbol{e}$$

This is the vector equation of the line.

Writing $\boldsymbol{a} = a_1\boldsymbol{i} + a_2\boldsymbol{j} + a_3\boldsymbol{k}$ and $\boldsymbol{e} = l\boldsymbol{i} + m\boldsymbol{j} + n\boldsymbol{k}$ we get the usual Cartesian form, viz.

$$\frac{x - a_1}{l} = \frac{y - a_2}{m} = \frac{z - a_3}{n} = t$$

2.12 The triple vector product a × (b × c)

We shall prove the very important result

$$\boldsymbol{a} \times (\boldsymbol{b} \times \boldsymbol{c}) = (\boldsymbol{a}.\boldsymbol{c})\boldsymbol{b} - (\boldsymbol{a}.\boldsymbol{b})\boldsymbol{c} \quad . \quad . \quad . \quad (1)$$

Take $\boldsymbol{e}$ to be a unit vector defined by $\boldsymbol{b} \times \boldsymbol{c} = \mu\boldsymbol{e}$. Then the vectors

$(\boldsymbol{e} \times \boldsymbol{b})$, $(\boldsymbol{e} \times \boldsymbol{c})$ and $\boldsymbol{e}$ are non-coplanar and linearly independent by 2.10 I. By 2.10 II we can find numbers α, β, γ such that

$$\boldsymbol{a} = \alpha(\boldsymbol{e} \times \boldsymbol{b}) + \beta(\boldsymbol{e} \times \boldsymbol{c}) + \gamma\boldsymbol{e} \quad . \quad . \quad . \qquad (2)$$

whence it follows that

$$\boldsymbol{a} \times (\boldsymbol{b} \times \boldsymbol{c}) = \mu\boldsymbol{a} \times \boldsymbol{e} = \alpha\mu(\boldsymbol{e} \times \boldsymbol{b}) \times \boldsymbol{e} + \beta\mu(\boldsymbol{e} \times \boldsymbol{c}) \times \boldsymbol{e} \;. \qquad (3)$$

Since $\boldsymbol{e}$ is perpendicular to $\boldsymbol{b}$ we have $|\boldsymbol{e} \times \boldsymbol{b}| = b$ and the direction of $\boldsymbol{e} \times \boldsymbol{b}$ is perpendicular to $\boldsymbol{e}$ and to $\boldsymbol{b}$ (v. Fig. 27). Hence we have $(\boldsymbol{e} \times \boldsymbol{b}) \times \boldsymbol{e} = \boldsymbol{b}$ and similarly $(\boldsymbol{e} \times \boldsymbol{c}) \times \boldsymbol{e} = \boldsymbol{c}$ so that (3) becomes

$$\boldsymbol{a} \times (\boldsymbol{b} \times \boldsymbol{c}) = \alpha\mu\boldsymbol{b} + \beta\mu\boldsymbol{c} \quad . \qquad (4)$$

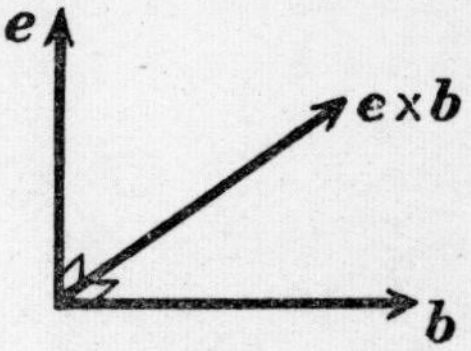

FIG. 27.

But (2) also gives

$$\boldsymbol{a}.\boldsymbol{c} = \alpha[\boldsymbol{ceb}] = \alpha[\boldsymbol{ebc}] = \alpha\mu e^2 = \alpha\mu$$

and

$$\boldsymbol{a}.\boldsymbol{b} = \beta[\boldsymbol{bec}] = -\beta[\boldsymbol{ebc}] = -\beta\mu e^2 = -\beta\mu$$

Substituting in (4) now gives the result (1).

Example 1. To simplify $(\boldsymbol{a} \times \boldsymbol{b}).(\boldsymbol{c} \times \boldsymbol{d})$.

We have

$$\begin{aligned}(\boldsymbol{a} \times \boldsymbol{b}).(\boldsymbol{c} \times \boldsymbol{d}) &= [(\boldsymbol{a} \times \boldsymbol{b})\boldsymbol{c}\boldsymbol{d}] = [\boldsymbol{d}(\boldsymbol{a} \times \boldsymbol{b})\boldsymbol{c}] \\ &= \boldsymbol{d}.\{(\boldsymbol{a} \times \boldsymbol{b}) = \boldsymbol{c}\} \\ &= (\boldsymbol{a}.\boldsymbol{c})(\boldsymbol{b}.\boldsymbol{d}) - (\boldsymbol{a}.\boldsymbol{d})(\boldsymbol{b}.\boldsymbol{c})\end{aligned}$$

Example 2. To simplify the product $(\boldsymbol{a} \times \boldsymbol{b}) \times (\boldsymbol{c} \times \boldsymbol{d})$.

We have

$$\begin{aligned}(\boldsymbol{a} \times \boldsymbol{b}) \times (\boldsymbol{c} \times \boldsymbol{d}) &= \{(\boldsymbol{a} \times \boldsymbol{b}).\boldsymbol{d}\}\boldsymbol{c} - \{(\boldsymbol{a} \times \boldsymbol{b}).\boldsymbol{c}\}\boldsymbol{d} \\ &= [\boldsymbol{abd}]\boldsymbol{c} - [\boldsymbol{abc}]\boldsymbol{d}\end{aligned}$$

Equally well we have

$$(\boldsymbol{a} \times \boldsymbol{b}) \times (\boldsymbol{c} \times \boldsymbol{d}) = [\boldsymbol{cda}]\boldsymbol{b} - [\boldsymbol{cdb}]\boldsymbol{a}$$

The two answers are compatible since four vectors must be linearly dependent, by 2.10 II.

2.13 The suffix notation

We have already seen that, with respect to an orthonormal triad of reference, the behaviour of a vector can be adequately and conveniently represented by its three components X, Y, Z. It is therefore possible to denote a vector either by a single symbol $\boldsymbol{F}$ or by the set of three (say) (X_1, X_2, X_3), where the suffixes refer to an unspecified triad of reference. The advantages of using just one symbol are clearly those which are due to the economy and simplicity involved; but this loss, when we come to using the components instead, is mitigated by a new view of vectors and scalars which we thereby obtain and the latent possibility of a significant generalisation which it contains. The study of vectors through the study of their components leads us to the *tensor calculus*.

Let (x^1, x^2, x^3) be the components of a position vector $\boldsymbol{r}$ w.r.t. a triad of reference $(\boldsymbol{e}_1, \boldsymbol{e}_2, \boldsymbol{e}_3)$. Here the use of the superscripts must not be confused with the notation for powers. Now suppose we change from this triad to a second (say) $(\bar{\boldsymbol{e}}_1, \bar{\boldsymbol{e}}_2, \bar{\boldsymbol{e}}_3)$ as in Fig. 28.

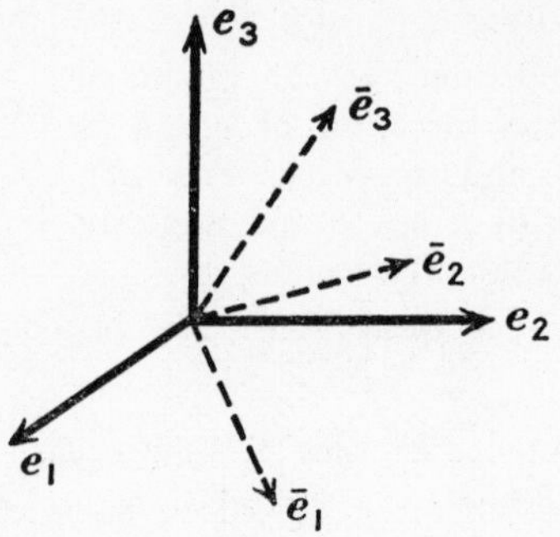

FIG. 28.

Writing the direction cosines of $\bar{\boldsymbol{e}}_r$ as l^r_s $(s = 1, 2, 3)$ we have

$$\bar{\boldsymbol{e}}_r = l^r_1\boldsymbol{e}_1 + l^r_2\boldsymbol{e}_2 + l^r_3\boldsymbol{e}_3 \quad (r = 1, 2, 3) \qquad (1)$$
$$= \sum_{s=1}^{3} l^r_s \boldsymbol{e}_s$$

Here we shall introduce the *summation convention*, viz., whenever a suffix is repeated in a product term we shall assume that summation over the possible values of the suffix is intended. Thus equation (1) will be written

$$\bar{\boldsymbol{e}}_r = l^r_s\boldsymbol{e}_s \qquad (2)$$

If the components of $\boldsymbol{r}$ w.r.t. the triad $\{\bar{\boldsymbol{e}}_r\}$ are written $(\bar{x}^1, \bar{x}^2, \bar{x}^3)$ we get, by 2.11 (2),

$$\bar{x}^1 = \boldsymbol{r}.\bar{\boldsymbol{e}}_1 = \boldsymbol{r}.(l^1_1\boldsymbol{e}_1 + l^1_2\boldsymbol{e}_2 + l^1_3\boldsymbol{e}_3)$$

giving $\quad \bar{x}^1 = l^1_1x^1 + l^1_2x^2 + l^1_3x^3$

and generally $\quad \bar{x}^r = l^r_sx^s \qquad (3)$

The equations (3) can also be written in matrix notation

$$\begin{pmatrix} \bar{x}^1 \\ \bar{x}^2 \\ \bar{x}^3 \end{pmatrix} = \begin{pmatrix} l^1_1 & l^1_2 & l^1_3 \\ l^2_1 & l^2_2 & l^2_3 \\ l^3_1 & l^3_2 & l^3_3 \end{pmatrix} \begin{pmatrix} x^1 \\ x^2 \\ x^3 \end{pmatrix} \qquad (4)$$

Now consider an expression of the form

$$a_mx^m = a_1x^1 + a_1x^2 + a_3x^3 \qquad (5)$$

which remains invariant as we change from x^s to $\bar{x}^r$. Then if the a_m become a_n we get

$$\bar{a}_n\bar{x}^n = a_mx^m \qquad (6)$$

and if we solve equations (3) to give $x^s = \lambda^s_r \bar{x}^r$ (λ^s_r will be the cofactor of l^r_s in the determinant $| l^r_s |$ divided by $| l^r_s |$) equation (6) will become

$$\bar{a}_n \bar{x}^n = a_m \lambda^m_r \bar{x}^r = a_m \lambda^m_n \bar{x}^n$$

i.e.

$$(\bar{a}_n - a_m \lambda^m)\bar{x}^n = 0$$

for all values of the $\bar{x}^n$. Hence we can write

$$\bar{a}_n = \lambda^m_n a_m \qquad (7)$$

and the matrix form of these equations will be

$$(\bar{a}_1 \bar{a}_2 \bar{a}_3) = (a_1 a_2 a_3) \begin{pmatrix} \lambda^1_1 & \lambda^1_2 & \lambda^1_3 \\ \lambda^2_1 & \lambda^2_2 & \lambda^2_3 \\ \lambda^3_1 & \lambda^3_2 & \lambda^3_3 \end{pmatrix} \qquad (8)$$

The matrix (λ^m_n) is the inverse of the matrix (l^r_s) and so (4) and (8) illustrate the equation (6). But also we notice the difference in the formation of the sums on the rhs of equations (3) and (7). If we regard the (a_m) as the components of a vector we say that it is a *covariant vector* and that the (x^r) are the components of a *contravariant vector*. When the two triads of reference are orthonormal it is clear that the matrix (l^r_s) is orthogonal so that, in fact, (λ^m_n) is the transverse of (l^r_s), i.e. $\lambda^s_r = l^r_s$. This means that (7) can be written

$$\bar{a}_r = l^r_s a_s$$

which should be compared with (3).

It would now be possible to define a contravariant vector as a set of symbols (u^r) which transform under a change of axes as in (3). Similarly a covariant vector will be a set of symbols (v_r) which transforms as in (7). More precisely the vector would be the class of all its representations (u^r) or (v_r) which transform as in (3) or (7). We shall prefer to regard these properties under transformation as deducible from our definitions of 2.2 and 2.3.

Physical quantities which possess "components" w.r.t. a set of axes and whose components are of the form u^r or v_r (that is to say, algebraic symbols with a *single suffix*) are called *tensors of the first order* (or vectors). They can be identified by showing that the components obey transformation equations like (3) or (7). The use of superscript and subscript is a convenient way of emphasising the difference between contravariance and covariance.

We can now say that a *scalar is a tensor of zero order*; its value does not depend on the axes of reference.

2.14 The metric tensor

Let us now consider the possibility of tensors of order higher than the first, that is to say, consider the existence of unspecified physical quantities which require for their description algebraic symbols like a_{rs}, b^s_{rt}, . . . ($r, s, t, \ldots = 1, 2, 3$) when referred to a set of axes in space. In particular let us restrict ourselves to *tensors of the second order*, possessing components of the form a^{rs}, a^r_s or a_{rs}.

We shall say that the a^{rs} ($r, s = 1, 2, 3$) are the components of a *contravariant tensor* of the second order if they transform (using the notation of 2.13) according to the equations

$$\bar{a}^{rs} = l^r_p l^s_q a^{pq} \qquad . \quad . \quad . \quad . \quad (1)$$

summation being assumed over $p, q = 1, 2, 3$. Similarly we shall say that the a^r_s are the components of a *mixed tensor*, contravariant in r and covariant in s, when they transform according to

$$\bar{a}^r_s = l^r_p \lambda^q_s a^p_q \qquad . \quad . \quad . \quad . \quad (2)$$

Finally the a_{rs} are the components of a *covariant tensor* of the second order when they transform according to the equations

$$a_{rs} = \lambda^p_r \lambda^q_s a_{pq} \qquad . \quad . \quad . \quad . \quad (3)$$

An important example of a contravariant tensor of the second order is obtained by forming all possible products $(a^r b^s)$ ($r, s = 1, 2, 3$) among the components (a^r) and (b^s) of two contravariant vectors $\boldsymbol{a}$ and $\boldsymbol{b}$. Thus, using 2.13 (3), we get

$$a^r b^s = l^r_p l^s_q a^p b^q \qquad . \quad . \quad . \quad . \quad (3a)$$

and writing a^{rs} for $a^r b^s$ we have, in fact, equation (1).

Now let us consider the square of the distance δ^2 between the origin O and any point P of space. This quantity is invariant, being independent of the choice of axes $\{\boldsymbol{e}_r\}$. If $\overline{OP}$ has components $(\bar{x}^1, \bar{x}^2, \bar{x}^3)$ w.r.t. $(\bar{\boldsymbol{e}}_1, \bar{\boldsymbol{e}}_2, \bar{\boldsymbol{e}}_3)$ then

$$\delta^2 = (\bar{x}^1)^2 + (\bar{x}^2)^2 + (\bar{x}^3)^2$$

and using 2.13 (3) we obtain

$$\delta^2 = g_{rs} x^r x^s \qquad . \quad . \quad . \quad . \quad . \quad (4)$$

where we have written

$$\begin{aligned} g_{rs} &= l^1_r l^1_s + l^2_r l^2_s + l^3_r l^3_s \\ &= l^p_r l^p_s \quad (p = 1, 2, 3) \qquad . \quad . \quad . \quad (5) \end{aligned}$$

The form of δ^2 is called *the metric of the space in which the co-ordinates of a point are* (x^1, x^2, x^3). Since δ^2 is invariant we get

$$\begin{aligned} \bar{g}_{rs} \bar{x}^r \bar{x}^s &= g_{pq} x^p x^q \\ &= g_{pq} \lambda^p_r \lambda^q_s \bar{x}^r \bar{x}^s \end{aligned}$$

so that

$$(\bar{g}_{rs} - g_{pq} \lambda^p_r \lambda^q_s) \bar{x}^r \bar{x}^s = 0 \quad \text{all } \bar{x}^r, \bar{x}^s$$

Hence we see that the g_{rs} transform according to the equations

$$\bar{g}_{rs} = \lambda_r^p \lambda_s^q g_{pq} \quad . \quad . \quad . \quad . \quad (6)$$

which is identical in form with equation (3). Hence g_{rs} are the components of a covariant tensor of the second order : it is called the *metric tensor* associated with the co-ordinate system (x^1, x^2, x^3).

2.15 The general transformation

If we consider a general functional transformation $\bar{x}^r = f^r(x^1, x^2, x^3)$ from one set of axes to another we notice that the differentials $d\bar{x}^r$ and dx^s $(r, s = 1, 2, 3)$ are related linearly, cf. 2.13 (3), viz.,

$$d\bar{x}^r = \frac{\partial \bar{x}^r}{\partial x^1}\, dx^1 + \frac{\partial \bar{x}^r}{\partial x^2}\, dx^2 + \frac{\partial \bar{x}^r}{\partial x^3}\, dx^3$$

or

$$d\bar{x}^r = \frac{\partial \bar{x}^r}{\partial x^s}\, dx^s \quad . \quad . \quad . \quad . \quad . \quad . \quad (1)$$

These differentials represent infinitesimal displacements (contravariant vectors) and the coefficients $\dfrac{\partial \bar{x}^r}{\partial x^s}$ $(r, s = 1, 2, 3)$ take the place of the constant coefficients l_s^r.

The metric will now be $ds^2 = g_{rs}\, dx^r\, dx^s$, being the square of the distance between two neighbouring points defined by (x^1, x^2, x^3) and $(x^1 + dx^1, x^2 + dx^2, x^3 + dx^3)$. The metric tensor will now be

$$g_{rs} = \frac{\partial \bar{x}^p}{\partial x^r} \cdot \frac{\partial \bar{x}^p}{\partial x^s} \quad (p = 1, 2, 3) \quad . \quad . \quad . \quad . \quad (2)$$

If the system of co-ordinates (x^1, x^2, x^3) is an *orthogonal* system at every point the metric ds^2 must be a sum of squares. This will mean

$$g_{rs} = 0 \quad r \neq s$$

and

$$g_{rr} = \left(\frac{\partial \bar{x}^1}{\partial x^r}\right)^2 + \left(\frac{\partial \bar{x}^2}{\partial x^r}\right)^2 + \left(\frac{\partial \bar{x}^3}{\partial x^r}\right)^2 \quad . \quad . \quad (3)$$

If we write $g_{rr} = h_r{}^2$ we shall obtain the metric, in this special orthogonal case only, as

$$ds^2 = h_1{}^2\,(dx^1)^2 + h_2{}^2\,(dx^2)^2 + h_3{}^2\,(dx_3)^2 \quad . \quad . \quad (4)$$

Fortunately certain simple co-ordinate systems are not only useful but also orthogonal. We give three examples below.

Example 1. In *rectangular Cartesian co-ordinates* $x^1 = x$, $x^2 = y$, $x^3 = z$ we have $\delta^2 = x^2 + y^2 + z^2$ and so $g_{11} = g_{22} = g_{33} = 1$ and $g_{rs} = 0$. $r \neq s$. These are summed up in the use of Kronecker's delta δ_r^s, defined by $\delta_r^s = 1$ when $r = s$ and $\delta_r^s = 0$ when $r \neq s$. Thus $g_{rs} = \delta_{rs}$.

Example 2. In *cylindrical polar co-ordinates* $x^1 = r$, $x^2 = \theta$, $x^3 = z$.

Writing $\bar{x}^1 = x = r \cos \theta$, $\bar{x}^2 = y = r \sin \theta$, $\bar{x}^3 = z = z$ and using (3) and (4) we get

$$ds^2 = dr^2 + r^2 \, d\theta^2 + dz^2$$

Here $h_1 = 1$, $h_2 = r$, $h_3 = 1$. The axes are shown in Fig. 29.

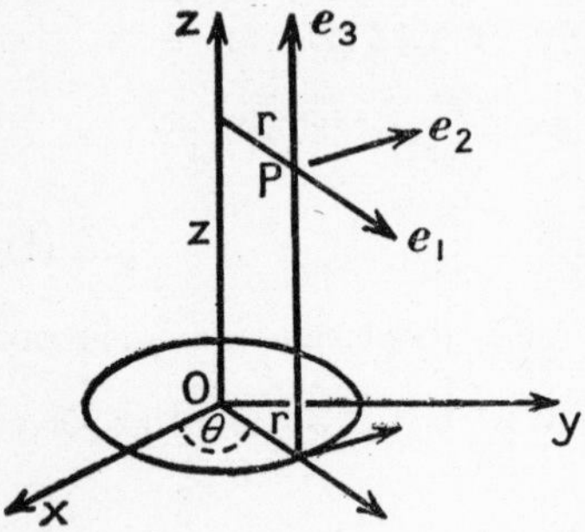

FIG. 29.

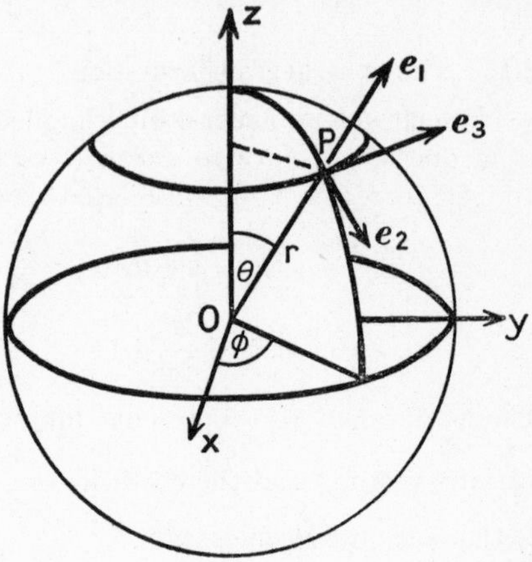

FIG. 30.

Example 3. In *spherical polar co-ordinates* $x^1 = r$, $x^2 = \theta$, $x_3 = \phi$. Writing $\bar{x}^1 = x = r \sin \theta \cos \phi$, $\bar{x}^2 = y = r \sin \theta \sin \phi$, $\bar{x}_3 = z = r \cos \theta$ we get $h_1 = 1$, $h_2 = r$, $h_3 = r \sin \theta$ so that

$$ds^2 = dr^2 + r^2 \, d\theta^2 + r^2 \sin^2 \theta \, d\phi^2$$

The co-ordinates and axes are shown in Fig. 30.

In Examples 2 and 3 we have cases of orthogonal axes in which $ds^2 = h_1{}^2 \, (dx^1)^2 + h_2{}^2 \, (dx^2)^2 + h_3{}^2 \, (dx^3)^2$ so that an infinitesimal displacement $\boldsymbol{dr}$ at any point P of space consists of displacements $h_1 \, dx^1$, $h_2 \, dx^2$, $h_3 \, dx^3$ along the axes $\boldsymbol{e}_1$, $\boldsymbol{e}_2$, $\boldsymbol{e}_3$ at P. Thus the *velocity components* will be $h_r \dfrac{dx^r}{dt}$ $(r = 1, 2, 3)$ at a point P. The fact that the metric is a differential in these cases means that the *directions* of the axes $\{\boldsymbol{e}_r\}$ change from point to point, although they still remain mutually perpendicular. This situation should be compared with that illustrated by Fig. 28 and discussed in 2.14.

Exercise II

1. If $\boldsymbol{a}$, $\boldsymbol{b}$ are given vectors and c is a given scalar, solve the equation

$\boldsymbol{r} \times \boldsymbol{a} + c\boldsymbol{r} = \boldsymbol{b}$ for the vector $\boldsymbol{r}$. (L.U.)

[Hint : Multiply vectorially by $\boldsymbol{a}$.]

2. A vector $\boldsymbol{x}$ satisfies the equations

$$\boldsymbol{x} \times \boldsymbol{b} = \boldsymbol{c} \times \boldsymbol{b} \text{ and } \boldsymbol{x}.\boldsymbol{a} = 0$$

Prove that $\boldsymbol{x} = \boldsymbol{c} - \left(\dfrac{\boldsymbol{a}.\boldsymbol{c}}{\boldsymbol{a}.\boldsymbol{b}}\right)\boldsymbol{b}$ provided that $\boldsymbol{a}.\boldsymbol{b} \neq 0$. (L.U.)

3. P is the foot of the perpendicular from a point B, with position vector $\boldsymbol{b}$, to the line $\boldsymbol{r} = \boldsymbol{a} + \lambda \boldsymbol{t}$. Show that the equation of the line BP is

$$\boldsymbol{r} = \boldsymbol{b} + \mu \boldsymbol{t} \times \{(\boldsymbol{a} - \boldsymbol{b}) \times \boldsymbol{t}\}$$

and find the position vector of P.

4. If $\boldsymbol{a}, \boldsymbol{b}, \boldsymbol{c}$ is a linearly independent triad of vectors and $\boldsymbol{a}' = \dfrac{\boldsymbol{b} \times \boldsymbol{c}}{\Delta}$, $\boldsymbol{b}' = \dfrac{\boldsymbol{c} \times \boldsymbol{a}}{\Delta}$, $\boldsymbol{c}' = \dfrac{\boldsymbol{a} \times \boldsymbol{b}}{\Delta}$, $\Delta = [\boldsymbol{abc}]$, prove $[\boldsymbol{a}'\boldsymbol{b}'\boldsymbol{c}'] = \Delta^{-1}$.

5. Prove that if two pairs of opposite sides of a tetrahedron are perpendicular then so is the third pair. [This includes the theorem "The altitudes of a triangle are concurrent."]

6. The vector $\boldsymbol{r} = (x, y, z)$ satisfies the equation

$$m\frac{d^2\boldsymbol{r}}{dt^2} = e\boldsymbol{E} + \frac{e}{c}\frac{d\boldsymbol{r}}{dt} \times \boldsymbol{H}$$

where $\boldsymbol{E} = (0, \mathrm{E}, 0)$, $\boldsymbol{H} = (0, 0, H)$ and e, m, c, E, H are constants. Find the solution that satisfies the conditions $\boldsymbol{r} = \boldsymbol{0}$, $\dfrac{d\boldsymbol{r}}{dt} = \boldsymbol{0}$ at $t = 0$. (M.T.)

[This is the equation of motion of a particle of mass m, carrying a charge e e.s.n. and subject to the electric field $\boldsymbol{E}$ and the magnetic field $\boldsymbol{H}$.]

7. Determine the vector equation of the plane parallel to two given vectors $\boldsymbol{a}$ and $\boldsymbol{b}$ which passes through the point with position vector $\boldsymbol{c}$ and find the equation of the plane through the three points whose position vectors are $\boldsymbol{a}, \boldsymbol{b}, \boldsymbol{c}$.

Use vector methods to show that the six planes each containing an edge of a given tetrahedron and passing through the mid-point of the opposite edge have a point in common. (L.U.)

8. Prove that, for any three given vectors $\boldsymbol{P}, \boldsymbol{Q}, \boldsymbol{R}$,

$$[(\boldsymbol{Q} \wedge \boldsymbol{R}) \wedge (\boldsymbol{R} \wedge \boldsymbol{P}) \,.\, (\boldsymbol{P} \wedge \boldsymbol{Q})] = [\boldsymbol{P} \wedge \boldsymbol{Q} \,.\, \boldsymbol{R}]^2.$$

Explain when it is possible to express a vector $\boldsymbol{X}$ in the form $\lambda\boldsymbol{P} + \mu\boldsymbol{Q} + \nu\boldsymbol{R}$.

Show that, in general, α, β, γ can be found so that

$$\boldsymbol{X} = \alpha\boldsymbol{Q} \wedge \boldsymbol{R} + \beta\boldsymbol{R} \wedge \boldsymbol{P} + \gamma\boldsymbol{P} \wedge \boldsymbol{Q}$$

Find expressions for λ, μ, ν ; α, β, γ. (L.U.)

CHAPTER III

SOME PRELIMINARY IDEAS

3.1 Work done by a force

Suppose a force $\boldsymbol{F}$ acts upon a particle at a point $P(\boldsymbol{r})$, as in Fig. 31, and moves its point of application to P' through a vectorial distance $\boldsymbol{dr}$. Then the work done by $\boldsymbol{F}$ is defined to be

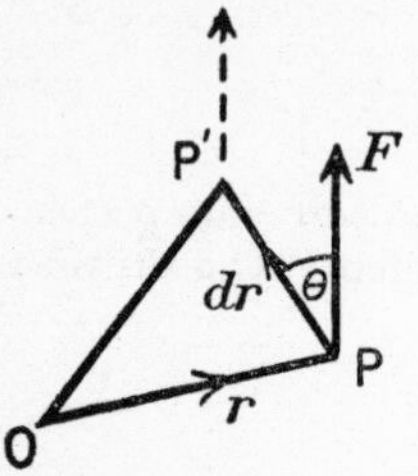

FIG. 31.

$$\delta W = (F \cos \theta)\, dr = \boldsymbol{F}.\boldsymbol{dr} \qquad . \qquad (1)$$

We write this as δW and not, in general, as dW because the rhs of (1) need not be a perfect differential. If F is measured in dynes and dr in cm. the units of work done (or energy) are *ergs*. If the units of force are poundals and those of distance are feet then the unit of energy is the *foot-poundal* (or ft. pdl.).

The work done by $\boldsymbol{F}$ in a finite displacement from $P_1(\boldsymbol{r}_1)$ to $P_2(\boldsymbol{r}_2)$ will now be

$$\sum_{P_1}^{P_2} \delta W = \int_{\boldsymbol{r}_1}^{\boldsymbol{r}_2} \boldsymbol{F}.\boldsymbol{dr} \qquad . \quad . \quad . \quad . \qquad (2)$$

Writing $\boldsymbol{r} = x\boldsymbol{i} + y\boldsymbol{j} + z\boldsymbol{k}$ and $\boldsymbol{F} = x\boldsymbol{i} + y\boldsymbol{j} + z\boldsymbol{k}$ where $\boldsymbol{i}, \boldsymbol{j}, \boldsymbol{k}$ is a fixed triad of reference, (1) becomes

$$\delta W = Xdx + Ydy + Zdz \qquad . \quad . \quad . \qquad (3)$$

If now δW is a perfect differential, and this is frequently the case, there exists a scalar function of position $W(x, y, z)$ such that

$$X = \frac{\partial W}{\partial z},\ Y = \frac{\partial W}{\partial y},\ Z = \frac{\partial W}{\partial z} \qquad . \quad . \quad . \qquad (4)$$

and equation (2) will then give

$$\sum_{P_1}^{P_2} \delta W = \int_{\boldsymbol{r}_1}^{\boldsymbol{r}_2} dW = W(\boldsymbol{r}_2) - W(\boldsymbol{r}_1) \qquad . \quad . \qquad (5)$$

When $W(x, y, z)$, or $\mathrm{W}(\boldsymbol{r})$, exists we call it the *work function* and we say that the force F is a *conservative force*. We also say that the particle at P exists in the *field of force* defined by $\boldsymbol{F}$. When the field is conservative we define its *potential function* $V(x, y, z)$, or $V(\boldsymbol{r})$, by

$$V(x, y, z) = -\ W(x, y, z) \qquad . \quad . \quad . \qquad (6)$$

(4) and (6) then give

$$X = -\ \frac{\partial V}{\partial x},\ Y = -\ \frac{\partial V}{\partial y},\ Z = -\ \frac{\partial V}{\partial z} \qquad . \quad . \qquad (7)$$

It is clear, from the minus sign in (6), that $V(x, y, z)$ measures the energy which is latent in the field of force at $P(x, y, z)$.

Another important property of a conservative field of force is the following.

The value of the rhs of (2) will, in general, depend on the path of integration, say the curve γ, from P_1 to P_2. As an illustration consider the artificial force $\boldsymbol{F} = ay\boldsymbol{i} + x^2\boldsymbol{j}$ and let it move its point of application from $P_1(a, 0, 0)$ to $P_2(0, a, 0)$. In the first instance let γ be the straight line γ_1 with equation $x + y = a$ in the xy-plane, as shown in Fig. 32.

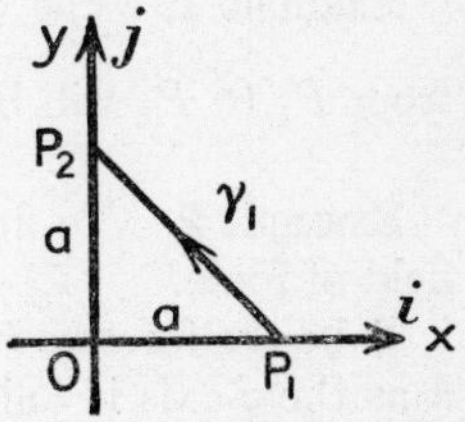

FIG. 32.

$$\text{We now get} \int_{P_1}^{P_2} \boldsymbol{F}\cdot d\boldsymbol{r} = \int_{P_1}^{P_2} (ay\,dx + x^2\,dy)$$

$$= \int_{P_1}^{P_2} (a^2 - ax - x^2)dx \qquad \text{since } x + y = a$$

$$= \int_0^a (x^2 + ax - a^2)dx$$

$$\text{which gives} \quad \int_{P_1}^{P_2} \boldsymbol{F}.d\boldsymbol{r} = -\frac{a^3}{6} \text{ ergs (along } \gamma_1). \qquad (8)$$

Now take γ to be γ_2, viz., the arc of the circle $x^2 + y^2 = a^2$ which joins P_1 and P_2, as shown in Fig. 33. Writing $x = a\cos\theta$, $y = a\sin\theta$ we get

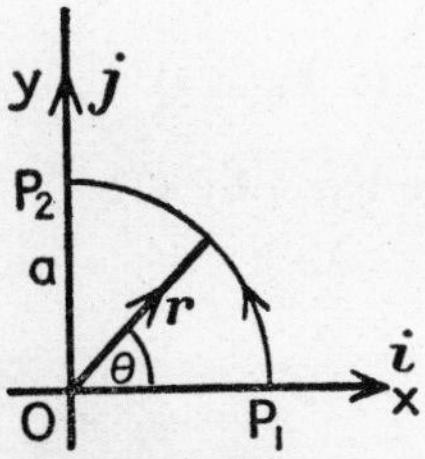

FIG. 33.

$$\boldsymbol{F} = a^2(\sin\theta\boldsymbol{i} + \cos^2\theta\boldsymbol{j})$$

and $\quad \boldsymbol{r} = a(\cos\theta\boldsymbol{i} + \sin\theta\boldsymbol{j})$

Hence $\quad d\boldsymbol{r} = (-\sin\theta\boldsymbol{i} + \cos\theta\boldsymbol{j})a\,d\theta \qquad$ so that

$$\int_{P_1}^{P_2} \boldsymbol{F}.d\boldsymbol{r} = a^3 \int_0^{\pi/2} (-\sin^2\theta + \cos^3\theta)\,d\theta$$

$$= -a^3\left(\frac{\pi}{4} - \frac{2}{3}\right). \qquad (9)$$

In this a work function does not exist since $W(x, y)$ cannot satisfy $\dfrac{\partial W}{\partial x} = ay$ and $\dfrac{\partial W}{\partial y} = x^2$ simultaneously.

When a work function (or potential function) exists we can see that the rhs of (2) is *independent of the curve* γ, for we get

$$\int_{P_1}^{P_2} \boldsymbol{F}.d\boldsymbol{r} = \int_{P_1}^{P_2} \left(\frac{\partial W}{\partial x}dx + \frac{\partial W}{\partial y}dy + \frac{\partial W}{\partial z}dz\right)$$

$$= \int_{P_1}^{P_2} dW = W(P_2) - W(P_1)$$

Thus the work done by $\boldsymbol{F}$ depends only on the initial and final positions of the point of application P. This means that energy, in the form of work done by a force, cannot accumulate in a conservative field.

Finally we notice that δW must be a scalar quantity in the sense of 2.13. Using the suffix notation $\boldsymbol{r} = (x^1, x^2, x^3)$ and $\boldsymbol{F}_1 = (X_1, X_2, X_3)$ we see, by the argument contained in equations (5), (6), (7) of 2.13, that $\boldsymbol{F}$ is a *covariant vector*.

Example 1. The work done by a constant force $\boldsymbol{F}$ in a displacement from P_1 to P_2 will be $\int_{P_1}^{P_2} \boldsymbol{F}.d\boldsymbol{r} = \boldsymbol{F}.\int_{P_1}^{P_2} d\boldsymbol{r} = \boldsymbol{F}.(\boldsymbol{r}_2 - \boldsymbol{r}_1)$

Example 2. To find the potential function $V(x, y, z)$ for a constant field of force.

Take the force as $\boldsymbol{F} = F\boldsymbol{k}$ where $\boldsymbol{k}$ is a constant unit vector. Taking $\boldsymbol{k}$ as the z-axis it follows that $V = -Fz +$ constant satisfies (7). In particular this is applicable to the (constant) gravitational field near the earth's surface. Taking $\boldsymbol{k}$ to be vertically upwards we have $\boldsymbol{F} = -mg\boldsymbol{k}$ so that

$$V = mgz + \text{a constant}$$

Example 3. To find the potential function associated with an elastic string which obeys *Hooke's law.*

Hooke's law states that the tension in an elastic string is proportional to the extension. If the natural (unstretched) length is a and the *modulus of elasticity* (Hooke) is λ, then the tension in the string when it is stretched to a length $a + x$ is given by

$$\boldsymbol{F} = -\frac{\lambda}{a}x\boldsymbol{i} \qquad (v. \text{ Fig. } 34)$$

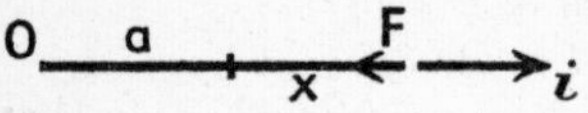

FIG. 34.

Writing $V = V(x)$ we have, by (7)

$$-\frac{dV}{dz} = -\frac{\lambda x}{a}$$

which gives

$$V = \tfrac{1}{2}\frac{\lambda x^2}{a}$$

Example 4. To find the potential function $V(x, y, z)$ for the field of force defined by $\boldsymbol{F} = \frac{\mu}{r^3}\boldsymbol{r}$ (μ being a constant).

This is the *inverse square law* of force, with $\boldsymbol{r}$ the position vector of the point where $\boldsymbol{F}$ acts (v. 1.4). Thus $|\boldsymbol{F}| = \frac{\mu}{r^3}|\boldsymbol{r}| = \frac{\mu}{r^2}$ and when $\mu<0$ we have the case of *attraction towards* 0 (e.g. gravitational attraction) whilst $\mu>0$ corresponds to repulsion (e.g. Conlomb electrostatic repulsion). Writing $\boldsymbol{r} = x\boldsymbol{i} + y\boldsymbol{j} + z\boldsymbol{k}$ we have

$$\boldsymbol{F} = X\boldsymbol{i} + Y\boldsymbol{j} + Z\boldsymbol{k}$$

with

$$X = \boldsymbol{F}.\boldsymbol{i} = \frac{\mu}{r^3}\boldsymbol{r}.\boldsymbol{i} = \frac{\mu x}{r^3} = \frac{\mu x}{(x^3 + y^2 + z^2)^{3/2}}$$

Similarly $Y = \dfrac{\mu y}{(x^2 + y^2 + z^2)^{3/2}}$ and $Z = \dfrac{\mu z}{(x^2 + y^2 + z^2)^{3/2}}$

Then $V(x, y, z)$ exists and is given by

$$V = \frac{\mu}{(x^2 + y^2 + z^2)^{\frac{1}{2}}} = \frac{\mu}{r}$$

since this satisfies (7).

In the important case of *gravitational attraction* let us take $\mu > 0$ and $\boldsymbol{F} = -\dfrac{\mu}{r^3}\boldsymbol{r}$. Then $V = -\dfrac{\mu}{r}$.

3.2 The torque of a force about a point

Suppose a force (or any line vector) acts at a point $P(\boldsymbol{r})$ as shown in Fig. 35. Then we define *the torque of* $\boldsymbol{F}$ *about* 0 as

$$\boldsymbol{\Gamma}(0) = \boldsymbol{r} \times \boldsymbol{F} \quad . \quad . \qquad (1)$$

The magnitude of $\boldsymbol{\Gamma}(0)$ is $\Gamma = rF \sin \theta = Fp$, which equals the *statical moment* of $\boldsymbol{F}$ about 0. The direction of $\boldsymbol{\Gamma}$ is perpendicular to the plane of the diagram (v. 2.8).

This vector $\boldsymbol{\Gamma}(0)$ depends upon 0 but is independent of the choice of P, provided only that P lies in the line of action of $\boldsymbol{F}$. For if Q is any other point on this line of action its position vector will be $\boldsymbol{s} = \boldsymbol{r} + \lambda \boldsymbol{e}$, for some λ and for $\boldsymbol{F} = F\boldsymbol{e}$ (v. 2.11 Ex. 4). Then we have

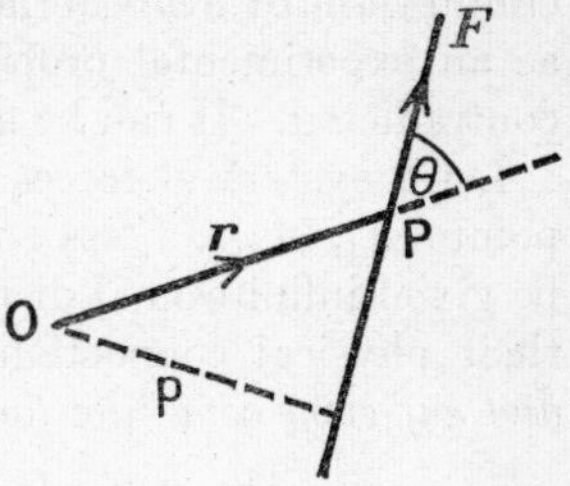

FIG. 35.

$$\begin{aligned} \boldsymbol{s} \times \boldsymbol{F} &= (\boldsymbol{r} + \lambda \boldsymbol{e}) \times F\boldsymbol{e} \\ &= \boldsymbol{r} \times \boldsymbol{F} + \lambda F \boldsymbol{e} \times \boldsymbol{e} \\ &= \boldsymbol{r} \times \boldsymbol{F} \text{ for all values of } \lambda \end{aligned}$$

If we write $\boldsymbol{\Gamma}(0) = L\boldsymbol{i} + M\boldsymbol{j} + N\boldsymbol{k}$ it is clear that, e.g., L measures the moment of $\boldsymbol{F}$ about the axis $\boldsymbol{i}$·

Example 1. Given the constant force $\boldsymbol{F} = 2\boldsymbol{i} + \boldsymbol{j} - 3\boldsymbol{k}$ acting at the point $A(1, -2, 1)$, find (i) the torque of $\boldsymbol{F}$ about the point $B(2, 0, -2)$, and (ii) the moment of $\boldsymbol{F}$ about the line through B which is equally inclined to the axes.

The vector

$$\overline{BA} = (\boldsymbol{i} - 2\boldsymbol{j} + \boldsymbol{k}) - (2\boldsymbol{i} - 2\boldsymbol{k}) = -\boldsymbol{i} - 2\boldsymbol{j} + 3\boldsymbol{k}$$

and so the torque

$$\begin{aligned} \boldsymbol{\Gamma}(B) &= (-\boldsymbol{i} - 2\boldsymbol{j} + 3\boldsymbol{k}) \times (2\boldsymbol{i} + \boldsymbol{j} - 3\boldsymbol{k}) \\ &= 3\boldsymbol{i} + 3\boldsymbol{j} + 3\boldsymbol{k} \end{aligned}$$

The line which is equally inclined to the axes will be in the direction of the unit vector $\boldsymbol{e}=l\boldsymbol{i}+m\boldsymbol{j}+n\boldsymbol{k}$, where $l=m=n$ and $l^2+m^2+n^2=1$, i.e. $l = m = n = \dfrac{1}{\sqrt{3}}$. Hence the required moment will be

$$\boldsymbol{\Gamma}(B).\boldsymbol{e} = \frac{1}{\sqrt{3}}(3+3+3) = \frac{9}{\sqrt{3}}.$$

3.3 The principle of virtual work

This is a principle of Statics but involves a result of some importance in Dynamics. Known also as the *Principle of Virtual Velocities*, it was observed to be true in the equilibrium of pulley-systems by Simon Stevinus (v. *supra*) in the sixteenth century. Galileo also established it in the matter of equilibrium on an inclined plane, and it was first proposed as a *universal* principle in matters of statical equilibrium by Jean Bernoulli * in the year 1717. It must be regarded as an experimental proposition but one which has not, so far, been contradicted. It can be generally formulated as follows.

Let a system of forces $\boldsymbol{F}_1, \boldsymbol{F}_2, \ldots \boldsymbol{F}_n$ act on a physical system at points $A_1, A_2, \ldots A_n$ respectively. Now imagine these points to be given infinitesimal displacements $\boldsymbol{dr}_1, \boldsymbol{dr}_2, \ldots \boldsymbol{dr}_n$ compatible with their physical connections. The principle asserts that *the necessary and sufficient condition for equilibrium* (in the original position) is

$$\delta W = \boldsymbol{F}_1.\boldsymbol{dr}_1 + \boldsymbol{F}_2.\boldsymbol{dr}_2 + \ldots + \boldsymbol{F}_n.\boldsymbol{dr}_n = 0 \qquad . \quad (1)$$

This is equivalent to saying that the work done by the forces is of the second order of small quantities in any (virtual) displacement from equilibrium.

In the important case when all the forces $\boldsymbol{F}_r$ $(r = 1, 2, \ldots n)$ are *conservative* equation (1) becomes

$$dW = 0 = dV \qquad . \quad . \quad . \quad . \quad (2)$$

This amounts to saying that *in equilibrium the potential function (or the work function) has a stationary value.* If the potential function is a function of (say) n independent co-ordinates $q_1, q_2, \ldots q_n$ equilibrium will occur at those values of the q's which satisfy the equations

$$0 = \frac{\partial V}{\partial q_1} = \frac{\partial V}{\partial q_2} = \ldots = \frac{\partial V}{\partial q_n} \qquad . \quad . \quad . \quad (3)$$

Example 1. A uniform square board of side $2a$ rests in a vertical plane with two of its sides in contact with smooth horizontal pegs distant b apart, and in the same horizontal line. Discuss the existence of a non-symmetrical position of equilibrium.

Let G be the centre of gravity of the board and A the corner between

* French mathematician, 1667–1748.

the pegs P, Q. Let the board be in a position with one side making θ with the horizontal, as in Fig. 36. The potential energy of the board is $V = Mgz = V(\theta)$ and so V is stationary where z is stationary. Now we have

$$z = AG \sin(\theta + 45°) - AQ \sin\theta$$

and
$$AQ = b\cos\theta, \quad AG = a\sqrt{2}$$

Hence
$$z(\theta) = a\sqrt{2}\sin(\theta + 45°) - \tfrac{1}{2}b\sin 2\theta$$

In equilibrium

$$\frac{dz}{d\theta} = a\sqrt{2}\cos(\theta + 45°) - b\cos 2\theta = 0$$

which gives
$$b(\cos^2\theta - \sin^2\theta) = a(\cos\theta - \sin\theta)$$

so that, provided $0 < \theta < 45°$, this reduces to

$$b(\cos\theta + \sin\theta) = a$$

or
$$\sin(\theta + 45°) = \frac{a}{b\sqrt{2}} \qquad . \qquad . \qquad . \qquad \text{(i)}$$

Equation (i) gives a position of equilibrium provided

$$\frac{1}{\sqrt{2}} < \frac{a}{b\sqrt{2}} < 1 \quad \text{i.e. provided } \frac{a}{\sqrt{2}} < b < a$$

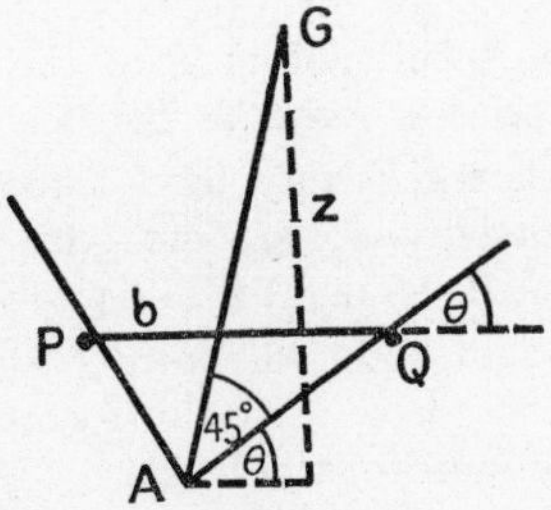

FIG. 36.

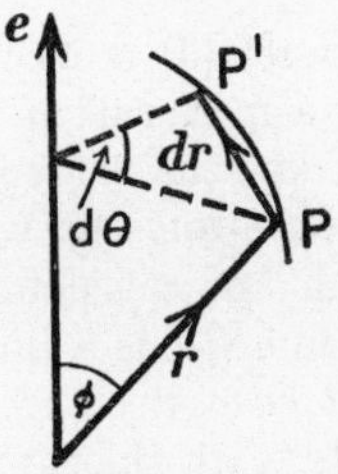

FIG. 37.

3.4 Infinitesimal rotations

Consider a point P of a line (or rigid rod) passing through the origin O, and suppose that the line is turned through an infinitesimal angle $d\theta$ about an axis through O defined by the unit vector $\mathbf{e}$ (v. Fig. 37) Then is $P(\mathbf{r})$ moves to $P'(\mathbf{r} + d\mathbf{r})$ we have

$$PP' = |dr| = r\sin\phi . 2\sin(\tfrac{1}{2}d\theta)$$
$$= r\sin\phi\{d\theta + O(d\theta^3)\}$$

Hence $|d\mathbf{r}| \to r\sin\phi\, d\theta$ as $d\theta \to 0$. Also the direction of $d\mathbf{r}$ tends to be perpendicular to both $\mathbf{e}$ and $\mathbf{r}$ as $d\theta \to 0$. The limit being understood we can therefore write

$$d\mathbf{r} = (d\theta\, \mathbf{e}) \times \mathbf{r} \qquad . \qquad . \qquad . \qquad . \qquad (1)$$

The quantity $d\theta\,\boldsymbol{e}$ looks like a vector, but because it represents a rotation it is not obvious that such a " vector " is commutative with regard to addition. Certainly the *order* of two finite rotations of a body determines the final position. However, we can easily show that infinitesimal rotations are commutative. Consider successive rotations $d\theta_1$ about $\boldsymbol{e}_1$ and $d\theta_2$ about $\boldsymbol{e}_2$. Performed in this order let the final position of P be $\boldsymbol{r}_{12}$. Then, by (1), we get

$$\boldsymbol{r}_1 = \boldsymbol{r} + d\theta_1\,\boldsymbol{e}_1 \times \boldsymbol{r}$$

and so

$$\begin{aligned}\boldsymbol{r}_{12} &= \boldsymbol{r}_1 + d\theta_2\,\boldsymbol{e}_2 \times \boldsymbol{r}_1\\ &= \boldsymbol{r} + d\theta_1\,\boldsymbol{e}_1 \times \boldsymbol{r} + d\theta_2\,\boldsymbol{e}_2 \times \{\boldsymbol{r} + d\theta_1\,\boldsymbol{e}_1 \times \boldsymbol{r}\}\\ &= \boldsymbol{r} + \{d\theta_1\,\boldsymbol{e}_1 + d\theta_2\,\boldsymbol{e}_2\} \times \boldsymbol{r}\end{aligned}$$

to the first order. Clearly $\boldsymbol{r}_{12} = \boldsymbol{r}_{21}$ as $d\theta_1, d\theta_2 \to 0$.

If the rotation $d\theta$ in (1) takes place in a time dt the resulting vector, viz.,

$$\boldsymbol{\omega} = \frac{d\theta}{dt}\boldsymbol{e} = \dot{\theta}\boldsymbol{e} \quad . \quad . \quad . \quad . \quad (2)$$

is called the *angular velocity vector.* Equation (1) then gives the velocity $\boldsymbol{v}$ of the point P, viz.,

$$\boldsymbol{v} = \frac{d\boldsymbol{r}}{dt} = \boldsymbol{\omega} \times \boldsymbol{r} \quad . \quad . \quad . \quad . \quad (3)$$

This formula (3) is clearly applicable to all points P of the line OP and so we may call $\boldsymbol{\omega}$ the *angular velocity vector of the line OP*. It follows from the above argument that OP may have two or more simultaneous angular velocities defined by $\boldsymbol{\omega}_1$, $\boldsymbol{\omega}_2$, etc. In this case the velocity of any point in this line will be (e.g.) $\boldsymbol{v} = (\boldsymbol{\omega}_1 + \boldsymbol{\omega}_2) \times \boldsymbol{r}$.

If the line OP is a line fixed in a rigid body which may turn about the point O of itself it is necessary to prove that the formula (3) is applicable, with the same $\boldsymbol{\omega}$, to every point of the body.

3.5 The angular velocity of a rigid body

We shall say that a material system is a *rigid body* when the distance between any pair of its points is a constant w.r.t. the time t. Suppose such a rigid body is free to turn about a point O of itself, and let $\boldsymbol{r}_1$, $\boldsymbol{r}_2$ be position vectors of any two points of the body w.r.t. O as origin. Then

$$\boldsymbol{r}_1^2 = \text{constant}, \quad \boldsymbol{r}_2^2 = \text{constant}, \quad (\boldsymbol{r}_1 - \boldsymbol{r}_2)^2 = \text{constant}$$

Differentiating w.r.t. the time t and writing $\dot{\boldsymbol{r}}$ for $\dfrac{d\boldsymbol{r}}{dt}$ gives

$$\boldsymbol{r}_1.\dot{\boldsymbol{r}}_1 = \boldsymbol{r}_2.\dot{\boldsymbol{r}}_2 = (\boldsymbol{r}_1 - \boldsymbol{r}_2).(\dot{\boldsymbol{r}}_1 - \dot{\boldsymbol{r}}_2) = 0 \quad . \quad . \quad (1)$$

These imply

$$\boldsymbol{r}_1.\dot{\boldsymbol{r}}_2 + \boldsymbol{r}_2.\dot{\boldsymbol{r}}_1 = 0 \quad . \quad . \quad . \quad . \quad (2)$$

We shall now show that for any two non-parallel vectors $\boldsymbol{r}_1$ and $\boldsymbol{r}_2$

there exists an angular velocity vector $\boldsymbol{\omega}$ satisfying 3.4 (3). We shall then show that such an $\boldsymbol{\omega}$ will serve for all points of the rigid body.

Assume an $\boldsymbol{\omega}$ exists for which $\dot{\boldsymbol{r}}_1 = \boldsymbol{\omega} \times \boldsymbol{r}_1$ and $\dot{\boldsymbol{r}}_2 = \boldsymbol{\omega} \times \boldsymbol{r}_2$. This $\boldsymbol{\omega}$ is therefore perpendicular to both $\dot{\boldsymbol{r}}_1$ and $\dot{\boldsymbol{r}}_2$ and so we can write

$$\boldsymbol{\omega} = \lambda(\dot{\boldsymbol{r}}_1 \times \dot{\boldsymbol{r}}_2) \quad \text{for some } \lambda$$

Then, by (1) and 2.12(1), we get

$$\dot{\boldsymbol{r}}_1 = \boldsymbol{\omega} \times \boldsymbol{r}_1 = -\lambda \boldsymbol{r}_1 \times (\dot{\boldsymbol{r}}_1 \times \dot{\boldsymbol{r}}_2) = -\lambda \dot{\boldsymbol{r}}_1(\dot{\boldsymbol{r}}_2 . \boldsymbol{r}_1)$$

and similarly $$\dot{\boldsymbol{r}}_2 = +\lambda \dot{\boldsymbol{r}}_2(\dot{\boldsymbol{r}}_1 . \dot{\boldsymbol{r}}_2)$$

Both of these values are compatible with the ' condition of rigidity " (2). We can therefore write

$$\boldsymbol{\omega} = \frac{\dot{\boldsymbol{r}}_1 \times \dot{\boldsymbol{r}}_2}{\dot{\boldsymbol{r}}_2 . \boldsymbol{r}_2}$$

Now let $P(\boldsymbol{r})$ be any third point of the body. The conditions of rigidity will give

$$\boldsymbol{r} . \dot{\boldsymbol{r}} = \boldsymbol{r} . \dot{\boldsymbol{r}}_1 + \dot{\boldsymbol{r}} . \boldsymbol{r}_1 = \boldsymbol{r} . \dot{\boldsymbol{r}}_2 + \dot{\boldsymbol{r}} . \boldsymbol{r}_2 = 0 \quad . \quad . \quad (3)$$

If we write $\boldsymbol{u} = \boldsymbol{\omega} \times \boldsymbol{r}$ equation (3) implies

$$(\boldsymbol{u} - \dot{\boldsymbol{r}}) . \boldsymbol{r} = 0 \quad \text{(v. 2.9(i))}$$

and $$(\boldsymbol{u} - \dot{\boldsymbol{r}}) . \boldsymbol{r}_1 = (\boldsymbol{\omega} \times \boldsymbol{r}) . \boldsymbol{r}_1 - \dot{\boldsymbol{r}} . \boldsymbol{r}_1 = -\dot{\boldsymbol{r}}_1 . \boldsymbol{r} - \dot{\boldsymbol{r}} . \boldsymbol{r}_1 = 0$$

and, similarly, $$(\boldsymbol{u} - \dot{\boldsymbol{r}}) . \boldsymbol{r}_2 = 0$$

If now $\boldsymbol{r}, \boldsymbol{r}_1, \boldsymbol{r}_2$ are non-coplanar the vector $(\boldsymbol{u} - \dot{\boldsymbol{r}})$ cannot be perpendicular to each of them and so it must be the nul vector, i.e.

$$\boldsymbol{u} = \dot{\boldsymbol{r}} \quad (\text{all } \boldsymbol{r})$$

If $\boldsymbol{r}, \boldsymbol{r}_1, \boldsymbol{r}_2$ are coplanar we can write $\boldsymbol{r} = a\,\boldsymbol{r}_1 + b\,\boldsymbol{r}_2$ for some a, b whence

$$\dot{\boldsymbol{r}} = a\,\dot{\boldsymbol{r}}_1 + b\,\dot{\boldsymbol{r}}_2 = \boldsymbol{\omega} \times (a\,\boldsymbol{r}_1 + b\,\boldsymbol{r}_2) = \boldsymbol{\omega} \times \boldsymbol{r}$$

Hence a vector $\boldsymbol{\omega}$ exists which satisfies 3.4(3) for all points of the body. This $\boldsymbol{\omega}$ is a *unique vector* for if there is another (say) $\boldsymbol{\omega}'$ we can find non-parallel vectors $\boldsymbol{r}_1, \boldsymbol{r}_2$ for which

$$(\boldsymbol{\omega} - \boldsymbol{\omega}') \times \boldsymbol{r}_1 = \dot{\boldsymbol{r}}_1 - \dot{\boldsymbol{r}}_1 = \boldsymbol{0}$$

and $$(\boldsymbol{\omega} - \boldsymbol{\omega}') \times \boldsymbol{r}_2 = \boldsymbol{0}$$

These imply that $\boldsymbol{\omega} - \boldsymbol{\omega}' = \boldsymbol{0}$ or $\boldsymbol{\omega} - \boldsymbol{\omega}'$ is parallel to both $\boldsymbol{r}_1$ and $\boldsymbol{r}_2$. Hence $\boldsymbol{\omega}' = \boldsymbol{\omega}$.

3.6 Rotating frames of reference

Let us consider a general linearly independent triad of vectors $\boldsymbol{a}, \boldsymbol{b}, \boldsymbol{c}$ forming a frame of reference S at an origin O. By 2.10 II every other vector $\boldsymbol{x}$ can be uniquely expressed in the form

$$\boldsymbol{x} = \lambda\,\boldsymbol{a} + \mu\,\boldsymbol{b} + \nu\,\boldsymbol{c} \quad . \quad . \quad . \quad (1)$$

Now consider a second frame S_0 at the same origin O but defined by a triad $\boldsymbol{a}_0, \boldsymbol{b}_0, \boldsymbol{c}_0$ and such that

(i) S is moving about O with angular velocity $\boldsymbol{\omega}$ relative to S_0, which we regard as fixed ; and

(ii) S and S_0 are momentarily coincident.

Because of (ii) equation (1) will be equally true with $\boldsymbol{a}_0$, $\boldsymbol{b}_0$, $\boldsymbol{c}_0$ in place of $\boldsymbol{a}$, $\boldsymbol{b}$, $\boldsymbol{c}$ respectively. On the other hand, the rate of change of $\boldsymbol{x}$ w.r.t. the time t will be different in S and S_0. In fact we get, from (1),

$$\frac{d\boldsymbol{x}}{dt} = (\dot{\lambda}\,\boldsymbol{a} + \dot{\mu}\,\boldsymbol{b} + \dot{\nu}\,\boldsymbol{c}) + (\lambda\,\dot{\boldsymbol{a}} + \mu\,\dot{\boldsymbol{b}} + \nu\,\dot{\boldsymbol{c}}) \qquad . \quad (2)$$

and from 3.4(3) we get, relative to S_0,

$$\dot{\boldsymbol{a}} = \boldsymbol{\omega} \times \boldsymbol{a}, \quad \dot{\boldsymbol{b}} = \boldsymbol{\omega} \times \boldsymbol{b}, \quad \dot{\boldsymbol{c}} = \boldsymbol{\omega} \times \boldsymbol{c}$$

so that (2) becomes

$$\frac{d\boldsymbol{x}}{dt} = (\dot{\lambda}\,\boldsymbol{a} + \dot{\mu}\,\boldsymbol{b} + \dot{\nu}\,\boldsymbol{c}) + \boldsymbol{\omega} \times \boldsymbol{x} \qquad . \quad . \quad (3)$$

and this rate of change is w.r.t. the fixed frame in space S_0. Now $\dot{\lambda}\,\boldsymbol{a} + \dot{\mu}\,\boldsymbol{b} + \dot{\nu}\,\boldsymbol{c}$ is the rate of change of $\boldsymbol{x}$ regarding S as fixed, i.e. relative to S ; we shall therefore write, after E. A. Milne,

$$\dot{\lambda}\,\boldsymbol{a} + \dot{\mu}\,\boldsymbol{b} + \dot{\nu}\,\boldsymbol{c} = \frac{\partial \boldsymbol{x}}{\partial t}$$

We now write (3) as

$$\frac{d\boldsymbol{x}}{dt} = \frac{\partial \boldsymbol{x}}{\partial t} + \boldsymbol{\omega} \times \boldsymbol{x} \quad . \quad . \quad . \quad . \quad (4)$$

It is most important to remember that, in (4), $\frac{\partial \boldsymbol{x}}{\partial t}$ means the rate of change of $\boldsymbol{x}$ relative to the moving frame S and $\frac{d\boldsymbol{x}}{dt}$ is relative to the fixed frame S_0. In the case when $\boldsymbol{x} = \boldsymbol{r}$, the position vector of a particle P, we get

$$\frac{d\boldsymbol{r}}{dt} = \boldsymbol{v}\ (\text{w.r.t. } S_0) = \frac{\partial \boldsymbol{r}}{\partial t} + \boldsymbol{\omega} \times \boldsymbol{r}$$

and so

$$\frac{d^2\boldsymbol{r}}{dt^2} = \boldsymbol{f}\ (\text{acceleration w.r.t. } S_0) = \frac{\partial \boldsymbol{v}}{\partial t} + \boldsymbol{\omega} \times \boldsymbol{v}$$

This gives

$$\frac{d^2\boldsymbol{r}}{dt^2} = \frac{\partial^2 \boldsymbol{r}}{\partial t^2} + 2\boldsymbol{\omega} \times \frac{\partial \boldsymbol{r}}{\partial t} + \frac{\partial \boldsymbol{\omega}}{\partial t} \times \boldsymbol{r} + \boldsymbol{\omega} \times (\boldsymbol{\omega} \times \boldsymbol{r}) \quad . \quad (5)$$

Applying (4) to the vector $\boldsymbol{\omega}$ itself also gives

$$\frac{d\boldsymbol{\omega}}{dt} = \frac{\partial \boldsymbol{\omega}}{\partial t} \quad . \quad . \quad . \quad . \quad (6)$$

3.7 Kinematics and kinetics

When we are analysing the *geometry of motion* we call it the study of *kinematics*. This will involve an analysis of the velocities and accelerations of the body or bodies : it will not involve any discussion of the forces which are acting, that is to say, the causes of the motion.

When we analyse the motion of a system by introducing the forces and deducing the accelerations and velocities, then we call it a study of *kinetics*.

From this it is clear that some kinematic knowledge is essential before we can contemplate the kinetics of a system, for the statement that "$\dfrac{dx}{dt}$ is a measure of velocity" is a kinematic statement. Equation 3.6(4) is a kinematic result, where Law II of 1.3 and equation 1.5(1) are examples of kinetic statements.

Exercise III

1. Is the force defined by $\boldsymbol{F} = (xyz)^n \{x^p\boldsymbol{i} + y^q\boldsymbol{j} + z^s\boldsymbol{k}\}$ conservative, when (i) $p = q = s = 1$; n a positive integer : (ii) p, q, s all different ; n an arbitrary constant : (iii) $p = q = s = -n$; n a positive integer ?

2. Find the work done by the $\boldsymbol{F}$ of Example 1, given by $p = q = s = n = 1$, when it moves its point of application from $P_1(1, -3, 0)$ to $P_2(4, 2, -1)$.

3. $\boldsymbol{F}$ is the force on a particle placed in a field of force. If the field is conservative, i.e. if the work done on the particle in moving it from a given point to another given point is independent of the path taken, show that curl $\boldsymbol{F} = 0$. Determine whether this condition is satisfied when

$$\text{(i) } \boldsymbol{F} = \frac{\mu\boldsymbol{r}}{|\boldsymbol{r}|^3}\,; \qquad \text{(ii) } \boldsymbol{F} = \boldsymbol{k}\,(\boldsymbol{k}.\boldsymbol{r})\,;$$

where $\boldsymbol{k}$ is a constant vector and $\boldsymbol{r}$ is the radius vector. (C.)

[When $\boldsymbol{F} = X\boldsymbol{i} + Y\boldsymbol{j} + Z\boldsymbol{k}$, curl $\boldsymbol{F} = \left(\dfrac{\partial Z}{\partial y} - \dfrac{\partial Y}{\partial z}\right)\boldsymbol{i} + \left(\dfrac{\partial X}{\partial z} - \dfrac{\partial Z}{\partial x}\right)\boldsymbol{j} + \left(\dfrac{\partial Y}{\partial x} - \dfrac{\partial X}{\partial y}\right)\boldsymbol{k}$, by definition.]

4. Five equal uniform rods AB, BC, CD, DE, EA, each of weight W and length $2a$, are smoothly jointed together at A, B, C, D, E and rest in equilibrium in a vertical plane with the joint A uppermost, and AB, AE equally inclined to the vertical and in contact with two smooth fixed pegs, on the same horizontal level and distant $2c$ ($< 2a$) apart. If E and B are joined by a light rod of length $2a$, show by the principle of virtual work that the compression in the rod is $2W\left(1 - \dfrac{5c}{a}\right)\Big/\sqrt{3}$. (L.U.)

5. A bead of mass M slides on a smooth wire in the form of a circle, of radius a, with its plane vertical. One end of a light elastic string, of modulus λ and unstretched length l (where $0 < l < 2a$) is tied to the bead, and the other end of the string is attached to the highest point of the wire. Show that a position of equilibrium exists, in which the string is inclined to the vertical at an angle θ given by $\cos\theta = \frac{1}{2}\lambda l/(\lambda a - Mgl)$, provided that this fraction lies between 0 and 1.

Show that if this position of equilibrium exists it is stable. (M.T.)

6. Four uniform rods, each of length a and weight w, are freely jointed to form a rhombus $ABCD$ which is freely suspended from A. A smooth uniform disc, of radius r and weight w, rests between the rods CB and CD and in the same vertical plane. The joints B and D are connected by a light elastic string of natural length $3a/4$ and, in equilibrium, $BD = a$. Use the principle of virtual work to show that the modulus of elasticity of the string is $3(2r - \sqrt{3}a)w/a$ if $r > \sqrt{3}a/2$. (L.U.)

7. Establish the vectorial character of infinitesimal rotations of a rigid body.

Prove from first principles that three infinitesimal rotations represented by $\overline{BC}$, $\overline{CA}$ and $\overline{AB}$ are equivalent to a translation normal to the plane ABC, of amount proportional to the area of the triangle ABC. (L.U.)

8. Discuss the existence of an angular velocity of a rigid body moving about a fixed point O.

If $\mathbf{r}_1$, $\mathbf{r}_2$ are the position vectors, measured from O, of two particles of the body, prove that the angular velocity of the body is

$$\frac{\dot{\mathbf{r}}_1 \times \dot{\mathbf{r}}_2}{\dot{\mathbf{r}}_1 \cdot \mathbf{r}_2}$$

Inside a perfectly rough cone of angle 2α, which is rotating with constant spin ω_1 about its axis, rolls a cone of angle 2β $(\beta < \alpha)$. The axis of the inner cone rotates about that of the outer cone with constant spin ω_2. Find the angular velocity $\mathbf{\Omega}$ of the inner cone. (L.U.)

9. Two axes Ox, Oy are inclined at an angle α and rotate with angular velocityω about O. Show that the component velocities are

$$\dot{x} - \omega x \cot\alpha - \omega y \operatorname{cosec}\alpha, \quad \dot{y} + \omega y \cot\alpha + \omega x \operatorname{cosec}\alpha.$$

If the position of a point is defined by the perpendiculars ξ, η drawn to the instantaneous positions of Ox, Oy, prove that the component velocities u, v in these directions are given by

$$\left.\begin{aligned} u &= (\dot{\xi} + \dot{\eta}\cos\alpha)/\sin^2\alpha + \omega\eta/\sin\alpha \\ v &= (\dot{\eta} + \dot{\xi}\cos\alpha)/\sin^2\alpha - \omega\xi/\sin\alpha \end{aligned}\right\},$$

and that the component accelerations are

$$\begin{aligned} &\dot{u} - \omega u \cot\alpha + \omega v \operatorname{cocec}\alpha, \\ &\dot{v} + \omega v \cot\alpha - \omega u \operatorname{cosec}\alpha. \end{aligned}$$

(C.)

10. The motion of each of two points relative to a certain frame is uniform rectilinear motion, and the straight paths intersect. Prove that the acceleration with which the distance between the points increases is inversely proportional to the cube of that distance, and find the path of either point relative to the other. (C.)

11. Relatively to a certain frame a point O describes a straight line uniformly with velocity V, and a second point P describes a curve in such a way that the line OP describes areas uniformly; prove that the resolved part perpendicular to OP of the acceleration of P is $2Vv \sin \phi/OP$, where v is the velocity of P, and ϕ the angle which the tangent to its path makes with that of O. (C.)

12. Relatively to a certain frame, a point A describes a circle (centre O) uniformly, and a point B moves with an acceleration always directed to A. If the area covered by the line AB is described uniformly, prove that the resolved part parallel to OA of the velocity of B is proportional to the perpendicular from B on OA produced. (C.)

13. (i) Define the scalar product $\boldsymbol{a}.\boldsymbol{b}$ and the vector product $\boldsymbol{a} \times \boldsymbol{b}$ of the vectors $\boldsymbol{a}$ and $\boldsymbol{b}$, and show that

$$\boldsymbol{a} \times \boldsymbol{b}.\boldsymbol{c} = \boldsymbol{b} \times \boldsymbol{c}.\boldsymbol{a} = \boldsymbol{c} \times \boldsymbol{a}.\boldsymbol{b}.$$

(ii) Define the vector moment of a force about a point, and show that the resultant moment of two intersecting forces is equal to the vector sum of the moments of the separate forces.

Show that the moment of a force about an axis OX through a point O is equal to the resolute along OX of the vector moment of the force about O. (U.L.)

CHAPTER IV

THE KINEMATICS OF PARTICLE MOTION

4.1 Motion in a straight line

Take a fixed point O in the line as origin. Then a particle P is defined by a co-ordinate x. Its position vector $\overline{OP} = \boldsymbol{r}$ will be simply

$$\boldsymbol{r} = x\,\boldsymbol{i} \quad (\text{v. Fig. } 38)$$

FIG. 38.

The **velocity** of P is the vector $\dot{\boldsymbol{r}} = \dot{x}\,\boldsymbol{i}$, or simply $\dot{x}$ since the direction cannot be mistaken.

The **acceleration** of P is the vector $\ddot{\boldsymbol{r}} = \ddot{x}\,\boldsymbol{i}$, or writing only the magnitude we have $\ddot{x}$. If we put $v = \dot{x}$ we get alternative forms for the acceleration, viz.,

$$\text{acceleration} = \frac{dv}{dt} = \frac{d^2x}{dt^2} = v\frac{dv}{dx} \quad . \quad . \quad (1)$$

4.2 Motion in a plane

Here we have a choice among different co-ordinate systems, the advantages of one system over another being largely determined kinetically.

(a) **Rectangular Cartesian co-ordinates.** Taking axes OX, OY defined by unit vectors $\boldsymbol{i}, \boldsymbol{j}$ (v. Fig. 39) we have, for any P,

$$\overline{OP} = \boldsymbol{r} = x\,\boldsymbol{i} + y\,\boldsymbol{j} \quad . \quad (1)$$

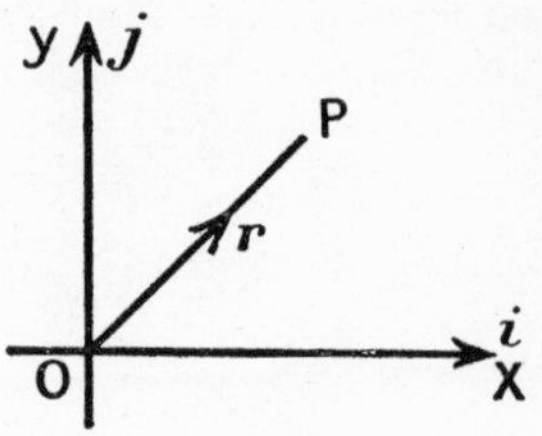

FIG. 39.

The **velocity** of P is $\boldsymbol{v} = \dot{\boldsymbol{r}} = \dot{x}\,\boldsymbol{i} + \dot{y}\,\boldsymbol{j}$, that is a line vector at P with components $\dot{x}$ and $\dot{y}$ parallel to the axes.

The **acceleration** of P is $\boldsymbol{f} = \dot{\boldsymbol{v}} = \ddot{\boldsymbol{r}} = \ddot{x}\,\boldsymbol{i} + \ddot{y}\,\boldsymbol{j}$, a line vector with components $\ddot{x}$, $\ddot{y}$. If we write $u_1 = \dot{x}$ and $u_2 = \dot{y}$ we can also write by 4.1(1),

$$\ddot{x} = u_1\frac{du_1}{dx} \quad \text{and} \quad \ddot{y} = u_2\frac{du_2}{dy}$$

If we refer the motion of P to a *moving frame* OX, OY which is rotating about the third axis OZ (or $\boldsymbol{k}$, perpendicular to the plane of $\boldsymbol{i}, \boldsymbol{j}$) with a constant angular velocity ω, we get by 3.6(4),

$$\boldsymbol{v} = \dot{x}\,\boldsymbol{i} + \dot{y}\,\boldsymbol{j} + \boldsymbol{\omega} \times (x\,\boldsymbol{i} + y\,\boldsymbol{j})$$

and since $\boldsymbol{\omega} = \omega\,\boldsymbol{k}$ this gives

$$\boldsymbol{v} = (\dot{x} - \omega y)\boldsymbol{i} + (\dot{y} + \omega x)\boldsymbol{j} \quad . \quad . \quad . \quad . \quad (2)$$

The acceleration will now be

$$\boldsymbol{f} = \frac{\partial \boldsymbol{v}}{\partial t} + \omega\, \boldsymbol{k} \times \boldsymbol{v}$$

$$= (\ddot{x} - \omega \dot{y})\boldsymbol{i} + (\ddot{y} + \omega \dot{x})\boldsymbol{j} + \omega\, \boldsymbol{k} \times \boldsymbol{v}$$

giving $$\boldsymbol{f} = (\ddot{x} - 2\omega\dot{y} - \omega^2 x)\boldsymbol{i} + (\ddot{y} + 2\omega\dot{x} - \omega^2 y)\boldsymbol{j} \quad . \quad (3)$$

These equations (2) and (3) would be useful, for example, in describing the motion of a particle which is moving on a plane lamina which is itself rotating in its own plane.

(b) Plane polar co-ordinates. Let P be defined by co-ordinates (r, θ) as shown in Fig. 40. Take axes $\boldsymbol{e}_1$ and $\boldsymbol{e}_2$ along $\overline{OP}$ (radially) and perpendicular to $\overline{OP}$ (transversally), as shown. These axes may be regarded as rotating in the plane about the perpendicular axis $\boldsymbol{k}$ through O with angular velocity $\dot{\theta}\, \boldsymbol{k}$: $\boldsymbol{k}$ forms an orthonormal triad with both $\boldsymbol{e}_1$, $\boldsymbol{e}_2$ and $\boldsymbol{i}, \boldsymbol{j}$ and is not shown in Fig. 40.

Now $$\overline{OP} = \boldsymbol{r} = r\, \boldsymbol{e}_1$$

and the **velocity** is $$\boldsymbol{v} = \frac{\partial \boldsymbol{r}}{\partial t} + \dot{\theta}\, \boldsymbol{k} \times \boldsymbol{r}$$

giving $$\boldsymbol{v} = \dot{r}\, \boldsymbol{e}_1 + r\dot{\theta}\, \boldsymbol{e}_2 \quad . \quad . \quad . \quad . \quad (4)$$

Thus P has velocity components $\dot{r}$ radially and $r\dot{\theta}$ transversally. The **acceleration** is

$$\boldsymbol{f} = \ddot{r}\, \boldsymbol{e}_1 + (r\ddot{\theta} + r\dot{\theta})\boldsymbol{e}_2 + \dot{\theta}\, \boldsymbol{k} \times \boldsymbol{v}$$

giving $$\boldsymbol{f} = (\ddot{r} - r\dot{\theta}^2)\boldsymbol{e}_1 + (r\ddot{\theta} + 2\dot{r}\dot{\theta})\boldsymbol{e}_2$$

This can be written

$$\boldsymbol{f}\, (\ddot{r} - r\dot{\theta}^2)\boldsymbol{e}_1 + \frac{1}{r}\frac{d}{dt}\, (r^2\dot{\theta})\boldsymbol{e}_2 \quad . \quad . \quad . \quad . \quad (5)$$

showing the radial and transverse components.

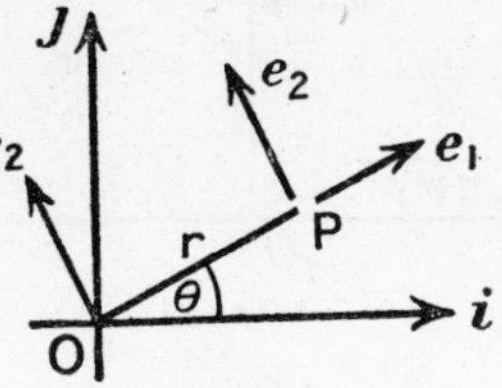

FIG. 40.

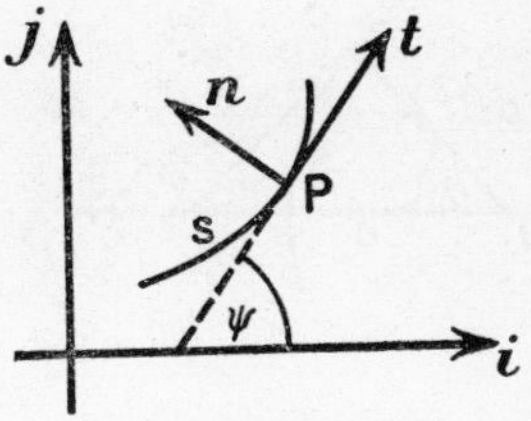

FIG. 41.

4.3 Motion on a fixed plane curve

Let P be the position of a particle on a plane curve, as shown in Fig. 41. The vectors $\boldsymbol{t}$ and $\boldsymbol{n}$ are unit vectors in the directions of the tangent and normal (in the sense of ψ increasing) at the point P. Let s be the arc length measured from a fixed point on the curve.

Let $\boldsymbol{k}$ be a unit vector perpendicular to the plane so as to form an orthonormal triad with $\boldsymbol{t}, \boldsymbol{n}$.

Using 4.2(a), the velocity of P is of magnitude v where

$$v^2 = \left(\frac{dx}{dt}\right)^2 + \left(\frac{dy}{dt}\right)^2 = \left(\frac{ds}{dt}\right)^2 .$$

and the direction of $\boldsymbol{v}$ is inclined to the axis $\boldsymbol{i}$ at an angle θ where $\tan\theta = \dot{y}/\dot{x} = \tan\psi$. Thus the velocity of P can be written

$$\boldsymbol{v} = \dot{s}\,\boldsymbol{t} \quad . \quad . \quad . \quad . \quad . \quad (1)$$

Regard the frame $(\boldsymbol{t}, \boldsymbol{n})$ at P as a rotating frame of reference with $\boldsymbol{\omega} = \dot{\psi}\,\boldsymbol{k}$ whence, by 3.6(4), the acceleration is

$$\boldsymbol{f} = \frac{\partial \boldsymbol{v}}{\partial t} + \dot{\psi}\,\boldsymbol{k} \times \boldsymbol{v}$$

giving

$$\boldsymbol{f} = \ddot{s}\,\boldsymbol{t} + \dot{s}\dot{\psi}\,\boldsymbol{n} \quad . \quad . \quad . \quad . \quad (2)$$

But $\dot{s}\dot{\psi} = \dfrac{ds}{dt}\cdot\dfrac{d\psi}{dt} = \left(\dfrac{ds}{dt}\right)^2\dfrac{d\psi}{ds}$ and writing $v = \dfrac{ds}{dt}$ we get the usual form

$$\boldsymbol{f} = \frac{dv}{dt}\boldsymbol{t} + \frac{v^2}{\rho}\boldsymbol{n} \quad . \quad . \quad . \quad . \quad (3)$$

where $\rho = \dfrac{ds}{d\psi}$ is the *radius of curvature* of the curve at P. Because of the form of (3) it is clearly an advantage to know the *intrinsic equation* of the plane curve, that is, the relation between s and ψ, say, $s = f(\psi)$. The following examples illustrate the properties of some simple curves, being those which are popular among examiners.

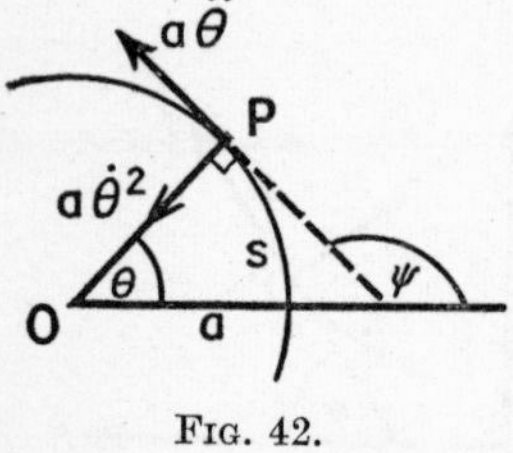

FIG. 42.

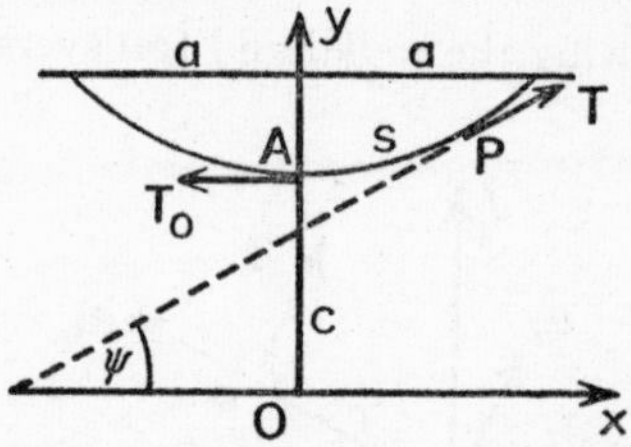

FIG. 43.

Example 1. Motion in a circle (v. Fig. 42). Since $s = a\theta = a(\psi - \pi/_2)$ we have $\rho = \dfrac{ds}{d\psi} = a$ (constant), a well-known property. The acceleration of P will consist of $\ddot{s} = a\ddot{\theta}$ along the tangent, and $a\dot{\theta}^2$ towards the centre O. This result also follows by writing $r = a$ (constant) in 4.2(5).

Example 2. The catenary (v. Fig. 43). This is the shape adopted by a uniform perfectly flexible heavy chain suspended under gravity by fixing its two ends on the same horizontal level. Considering the equilibrium of the portion AP, let $w =$ density per unit length, $T =$ tension at P and $T_0 =$ tension at A, and choose c so that $T_0 = wc$. Then $T \sin \psi = ws$, $T \cos \psi = T_0 = wc$ imply the intrinsic equation $s = c \tan \psi$. This gives $\rho = \dfrac{ds}{d\psi} = c \sec^2 \psi$. Also $\dfrac{dx}{ds} = \sec \psi = \dfrac{1}{c}\sqrt{c^2+s^2}$ implies that $s = c \sinh\left(\dfrac{x}{c}\right)$ whilst the equation $\dfrac{dx}{dy} = \dfrac{s}{c} = \sinh\left(\dfrac{x}{c}\right)$ implies $y = c \cosh\left(\dfrac{x}{c}\right)$. Finally these results imply $y = \sqrt{c^2 + s^2} = c \sec \psi$ and $x = c \log(\sec \psi + \tan \psi)$. The line $y = 0$ is commonly called the *directrix* of the catenary

Example 3. The cycloid (*v.* Fig. 44). This is the curve described by a point P on the circumference of a circle, centre C, radius a, which rolls on a base line—in the diagram we imagine the circle to

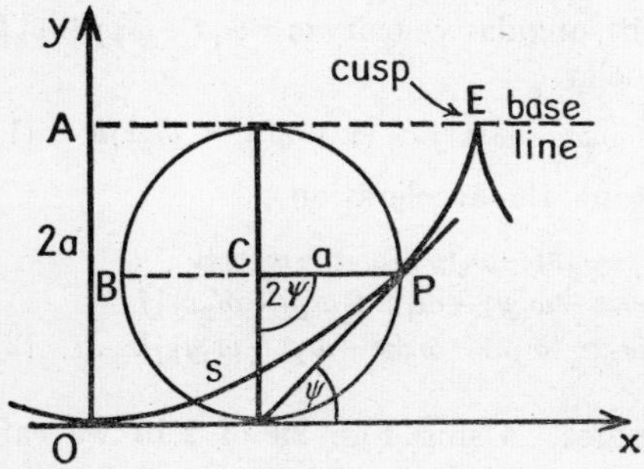

FIG. 44.

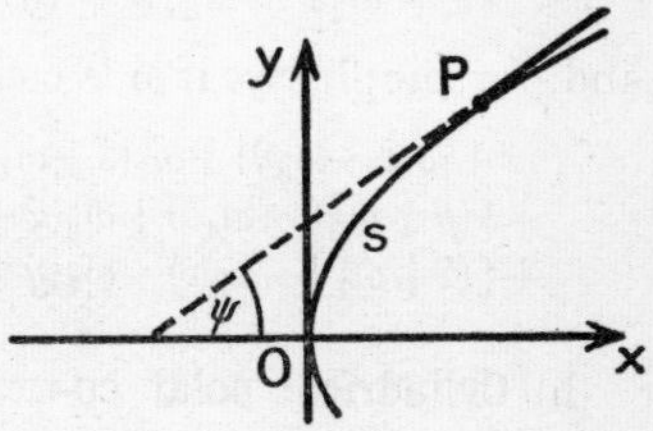

FIG. 45.

roll from left to right and underneath the base line. Then P moves from O to E while the *generating circle* turns through π. At $t = 0$ B coincides with A. Let PT make an angle ψ with the x-axis and let (x, y) be the co-ordinates of P.

Then and

$$\left.\begin{aligned} x &= AD + a \sin 2\psi = a(2\psi + \sin 2\psi) \\ y &= a(1 - \cos 2\psi) \end{aligned}\right\} \quad . \quad . \quad (4)$$

It follows that $\dfrac{dy}{dx} = \dfrac{2 \sin 2\psi}{2(1 + \cos 2\psi)} = \tan \psi$, so that PT is also the tangent to the cycloid at P. The normal is therefore along PD. Since $ds^2 = dx^2 + dy^2$ the intrinsic equation is

$$s = 4a \sin \psi \quad . \quad . \quad . \quad . \quad (5)$$

Example 4. The parabola (*v.* Fig. 45). Take the standard equation as $y^2 = 4ax$. Although the intrinsic equation is unwieldy it is possible to find the radius of curvature ρ in a convenient form. For the equation

$$\frac{dy}{dx} = \frac{2a}{y} = \tan\psi$$

implies that $$-\frac{2a}{y^2}\cdot\frac{dy}{ds} = -\frac{2a}{y^2}\sin\psi = \sec^2\psi\,\frac{d\psi}{ds}$$

Hence $$\rho = -\frac{y^2\sec^2\psi}{2a\sin\psi} = -2a\,\mathrm{cosec}^3\,\psi \quad . \quad . \quad (6)$$

4.4 Motion in space

Here again we have the possibility of different co-ordinate systems. We shall discuss three systems.

(a) **Rectangular Cartesian co-ordinates.** Using a fixed triad **i**, **j**, **k** we get simply

for position, $\boldsymbol{r} = x\,\boldsymbol{i} + y\,\boldsymbol{j} + z\,\boldsymbol{k}$
for velocity, $\boldsymbol{v} = \dot{\boldsymbol{r}} = \dot{x}\,\boldsymbol{i} + \dot{y}\,\boldsymbol{j} + \dot{z}\,\boldsymbol{k}$
for acceleration, $\boldsymbol{f} = \dot{\boldsymbol{v}} = \ddot{\boldsymbol{r}} = \ddot{x}\,\boldsymbol{i} + \ddot{y}\,\boldsymbol{j} + \ddot{z}\,\boldsymbol{k}$

If the triad is turning about O with angular velocity $\boldsymbol{\omega}=\omega_1\boldsymbol{i}+\omega_2\boldsymbol{j}+\omega_3\boldsymbol{k}$ we get, by using 3.6(4), the velocity

$$\boldsymbol{v} = (\dot{x} + \omega_2 z - \omega_3 y)\boldsymbol{i} + (\dot{y} + \omega_3 x - \omega_1 z)\boldsymbol{j} + (\dot{z} + \omega_1 y - \omega_2 x)\boldsymbol{k} \quad (1)$$

and, for simplicity, if $\boldsymbol{\omega}$ is constant, the acceleration

$$\begin{aligned}&= \{(\ddot{x}+\omega_2\dot{z}-\omega_3\dot{y})+\omega_2(\dot{z}+\omega_1 y-\omega_2 x)-\omega_3(\dot{y}+\omega_3 x-\omega_1 z)\}\boldsymbol{i}\\ &\quad+\{(\ddot{y}+\omega_3\dot{x}-\omega_1\dot{z})+\omega_3(\dot{x}+\omega_2 z-\omega_3 y)-\omega_1(\dot{z}+\omega_1 y-\omega_2 x)\}\boldsymbol{j}\\ &\quad+\{(\ddot{z}+\omega_1\dot{y}-\omega_2\dot{x})+\omega_1(\dot{y}+\omega_3 x-\omega_1 z)-\omega_2(\dot{x}+\omega_2 z-\omega_3 y)\}\boldsymbol{k} \quad . \quad (2)\end{aligned}$$

(b) **Cylindrical polar co-ordinates.** Using Fig. 29 of 2.15 we can write the position

$$\boldsymbol{r} = r\,\boldsymbol{e}_1 + z\,\boldsymbol{e}_3 \quad (r \neq |\,\boldsymbol{r}\,|)$$

Regarding these axes as rotating with angular velocity $\boldsymbol{\omega} = \dot{\theta}\,\boldsymbol{e}_3$ we get, by 3.6(4),

$$\boldsymbol{v} = \dot{r}\,\boldsymbol{e}_1 + \dot{z}\,\boldsymbol{e}_3 + \dot{\theta}\,\boldsymbol{e}_3 \times (r\,\boldsymbol{e}_1 + z\,\boldsymbol{e}_3)$$

giving $$\boldsymbol{v} = \dot{r}\,\boldsymbol{e}_1 + r\dot{\theta}\,\boldsymbol{e}_2 + \dot{z}\,\boldsymbol{e}_3 \quad . \quad . \quad . \quad . \quad . \quad (3)$$

a result already obtained in 2.15. The acceleration will be

$$\boldsymbol{f} = \ddot{r}\,\boldsymbol{e}_1 + (r\ddot{\theta} + \dot{r}\dot{\theta})\boldsymbol{e}_2 + \ddot{z}\,\boldsymbol{e}_3 + \dot{\theta}\,\boldsymbol{e}_3 \times \boldsymbol{v}$$

which becomes

$$\boldsymbol{f} = (\ddot{r} - r\dot{\theta}^2)\boldsymbol{e}_1 + \frac{1}{r}\frac{d}{dt}(r^2\dot{\theta})\boldsymbol{e}_2 + \ddot{z}\,\boldsymbol{e}_3 \quad . \quad . \quad . \quad (4)$$

Example 1. If a particle P moves on the surface of a right circular cylinder, $r = a$, it will have an acceleration

$$\boldsymbol{f} = -a\dot{\theta}^2\,\boldsymbol{e}_1 + a\ddot{\theta}\,\boldsymbol{e}_2 + \ddot{z}\,\boldsymbol{e}_3 \quad . \quad . \quad . \quad (5)$$

(c) Spherical polar co-ordinates. Here P is defined by r, θ, ϕ (v. Fig. 30 of 2.15). Writing $\boldsymbol{r} = r\,\boldsymbol{e}_1$ we see that the triad (e_1, e_2, e_3) possesses an angular velocity

$$\boldsymbol{\omega} = \dot{\theta}\,\boldsymbol{e}_3 + \dot{\phi}\,\boldsymbol{k}$$

where $\boldsymbol{k}$ is a unit vector along the z-axis. Hence, see Fig. 46,

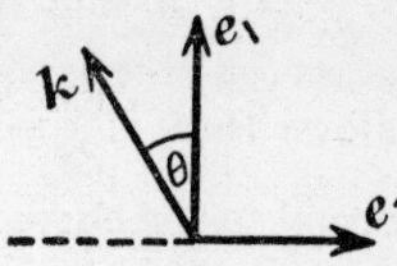

FIG. 46.

$$\boldsymbol{k} = \cos\theta\,\boldsymbol{e}_1 - \sin\theta\,\boldsymbol{e}_2$$

This gives
$$\boldsymbol{\omega} = \dot{\phi}\cos\theta\,\boldsymbol{e}_1 - \dot{\phi}\sin\theta\,\boldsymbol{e}_2 + \dot{\theta}\,\boldsymbol{e}_3 \quad . \quad . \quad (6)$$

The velocity of P will now be

$$\boldsymbol{v} = \dot{r}\,\boldsymbol{e}_1 + \boldsymbol{\omega} \times r\,\boldsymbol{e}_1$$

which is
$$\boldsymbol{v} = \dot{r}\,\boldsymbol{e}_1 + r\dot{\theta}\,\boldsymbol{e}_2 + r\sin\theta\dot{\phi}\,\boldsymbol{e}_3 \quad . \quad . \quad . \quad (7)$$

The acceleration will be

$$\boldsymbol{f} = \ddot{r}\,\boldsymbol{e}_1 + (\dot{r}\dot{\theta} + r\ddot{\theta})\boldsymbol{e}_2 + \frac{dt}{d}(r\sin\theta\dot{\phi})\boldsymbol{e}_3 + \boldsymbol{\omega} \times \boldsymbol{v}$$

which gives

$$\begin{aligned}\boldsymbol{f} = &\{\ddot{r} - r\dot{\theta}^2 - r\dot{\phi}^2\sin^2\theta\}\boldsymbol{e}_1 \\ &+ \{r\ddot{\theta} + 2\dot{r}\dot{\theta} - r\dot{\phi}^2\sin\theta\cos\theta\}\boldsymbol{e}_2 \\ &+ \left\{\frac{1}{r\sin\theta}\frac{d}{dt}(r^2\sin^2\theta\dot{\phi})\right\}\boldsymbol{e}_3 \quad . \quad . \quad . \quad (8)\end{aligned}$$

These components are in the directions of r increasing, θ increasing and ϕ increasing, respectively.

Example 2. Motion on the surface of a sphere. To obtain this we put $r = a$, $\dot{r} = 0$, $\ddot{r} = 0$ in (7) and (8), whence

$$\boldsymbol{v} = a\dot{\theta}\,\boldsymbol{e}_2 + a\sin\theta\,\dot{\phi}\,\boldsymbol{e}_3 \quad . \quad . \quad . \quad . \quad . \quad . \quad (9)$$

and
$$\begin{aligned}\boldsymbol{f} = &-a(\dot{\theta}^2 + \dot{\phi}^2\sin^2\theta)\boldsymbol{e}_1 + a(\ddot{\theta} - \dot{\phi}^2\sin\theta\cos\theta)\boldsymbol{e}_2 \\ &+ \frac{a}{\sin\theta}\frac{d}{dt}(\dot{\phi}\sin^2\theta)\boldsymbol{e}_3 \quad . \quad . \quad . \quad (10)\end{aligned}$$

Example 3. Motion on the surface of a cone. Take the origin O at the vertex of the cone so that its equation is $\theta = \alpha$ (constant). Hence, putting $\dot{\theta} = \ddot{\theta} = 0$ in (7) and (8), we get

$$\boldsymbol{v} = \dot{r}\,\boldsymbol{e}_1 + (\sin\alpha)\,r\dot{\phi}\,\boldsymbol{e}_3 \quad . \quad . \quad . \quad (11)$$

and

$$\boldsymbol{f} = (\ddot{r} - r\dot{\phi}^2\sin^2\alpha)\boldsymbol{e}_1 - r\dot{\phi}^2\sin\alpha\cos\alpha\,\boldsymbol{e}_2 + \frac{\sin\alpha}{r}\frac{d}{dt}(r^2\dot{\phi})\boldsymbol{e}_3 \quad . \quad (12)$$

4.5 Motion on a fixed curve in space

Let P describe a twisted curve in space and regard its position vector $\boldsymbol{r}$ as a function of arc length s. Now as $ds \to 0$ $|\,\boldsymbol{dr}\,| \to ds$ and so $\dfrac{d\boldsymbol{r}}{ds} = \boldsymbol{t}$, a unit vector along the tangent at P. Since $\boldsymbol{t}^2 = 1$ it follows that $\boldsymbol{t}.\dfrac{d\boldsymbol{t}}{ds} = 0$ (v. 2.7) and so $\dfrac{d\boldsymbol{t}}{ds}$ is a vector along (say) $\boldsymbol{n}$, a normal to the curve. This vector $\boldsymbol{n}$ is called the *principal normal* at P : the unit vector $\boldsymbol{b}$, which completes the orthonormal triad at P, is called the *binormal*. The plane of $\boldsymbol{t}$ and $\boldsymbol{n}$ is called the *osculating plane* of the curve at P.

It is clear that as P moves along the curve the " moving triad " of $\boldsymbol{t}$, $\boldsymbol{n}$, $\boldsymbol{b}$ will twist with (say) an angular velocity $\boldsymbol{\omega} = \omega_1 \boldsymbol{t} + \omega_2 \boldsymbol{n} + \omega_3 \boldsymbol{b}$.

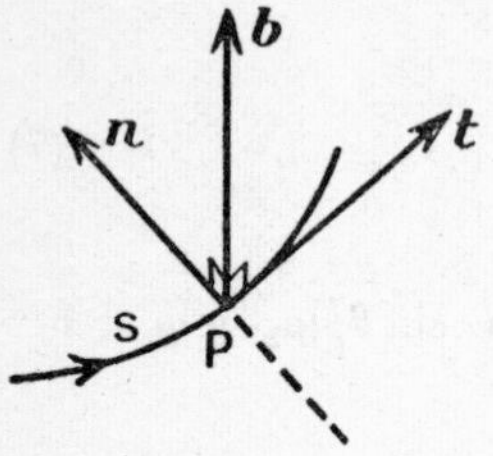

FIG. 47.

Now if P has a velocity $v = \dfrac{ds}{dt}$ we have

$$\frac{d\boldsymbol{t}}{dt} = v\frac{d\boldsymbol{t}}{ds} = \boldsymbol{\omega} \times \boldsymbol{t}$$

and since $\boldsymbol{n}$ is parallel to $\dfrac{d\boldsymbol{t}}{ds}$, this implies

$$\boldsymbol{n} \times (\boldsymbol{\omega} \times \boldsymbol{t}) = -(\boldsymbol{n}.\boldsymbol{\omega})\boldsymbol{t} = \boldsymbol{0}$$

Hence $\boldsymbol{n}.\boldsymbol{\omega} = 0 = \omega_2$ and $\boldsymbol{\omega} = \omega_1 \boldsymbol{t} + \omega_3 \boldsymbol{b}$. The rate of turn, w.r.t. arc-length s, of the triad about $\boldsymbol{b}$ is called the *curvature* and that about $\boldsymbol{t}$ is called the *torsion*. Writing $\dfrac{1}{\rho}$ = curvature and $\dfrac{1}{\sigma}$ = torsion, we can write $\omega_1 = \dfrac{v}{\sigma}$ and $\omega_2 = \dfrac{v}{\rho}$. Writing $\boldsymbol{\omega} = v\left(\dfrac{1}{\sigma}\boldsymbol{t} + \dfrac{1}{\rho}\boldsymbol{b}\right)$ we can readily deduce the Serret-Frenet formulæ, viz.,

$$\left.\begin{aligned} \frac{d\boldsymbol{t}}{ds} &= \frac{1}{v}\boldsymbol{\omega} \times \boldsymbol{t} = \frac{1}{\rho}\boldsymbol{n} \\ \text{and} \qquad \frac{d\boldsymbol{b}}{ds} &= -\frac{1}{\sigma}\boldsymbol{n}, \quad \frac{d\boldsymbol{n}}{ds} = \frac{1}{\sigma}\boldsymbol{b} - \frac{1}{\rho}\boldsymbol{t} \end{aligned}\right\} \quad . \quad . \quad . \quad (1)$$

Now the velocity of P is

$$\frac{d\boldsymbol{r}}{dt} = v\frac{d\boldsymbol{r}}{ds} = v\,\boldsymbol{t}$$

and the acceleration is $\boldsymbol{f}$ where

$$\boldsymbol{f} = v\dot{\boldsymbol{t}} + \boldsymbol{\omega} \times v\,\boldsymbol{t} = \dot{v}\,\boldsymbol{t} + v^2\left(\frac{1}{\sigma}\boldsymbol{t} + \frac{1}{\rho}\boldsymbol{b}\right) \times \boldsymbol{t}$$

which gives

$$\boldsymbol{f} = \dot{v}\,\boldsymbol{t} + \frac{v^2}{\rho}\boldsymbol{n} \quad . \quad . \quad . \quad . \quad (2)$$

Thus the acceleration is entirely in the osculating plane.

Exercise IV

1. A particle of mass m moves through a medium which offers resistance $av + bv^3$ where v is the velocity and a, b are constants. If this be the only force acting and if the particle be given an initial velocity u, prove that it will come to rest after traversing a distance

$$\frac{m}{\sqrt{ab}}.\tan^{-1}\left\{u\sqrt{\frac{b}{a}}\right\}.$$

Show also that the velocity becomes $\frac{1}{2}u$ after a time t given by

$$\frac{2at}{m} = \log\left\{\frac{4a + bu^2}{a + bu^2}\right\}$$ (L.U.)

2. The acceleration of a particle P moving in a straight line is given by $n^2x - 3n^2x^2/2a$, where x is the distance of P from a fixed point O of the line. If the velocity of P is zero when $x = a$, describe the general nature of the subsequent motion and show that the time elapsed when $x = 3a/4$ is $(\log_e 3)/n$. (M.T.)

3. Prove that, if rectangular axes Ox, Oy revolve with uniform angular velocity ω, and the component velocities of a point (x, y) parallel to the axes are A/x and B/y, then the square of the distance of the point from the origin increases uniformly with the time. (C.)

4. The sides CA, CB of a triangle are fixed in position, and the side AB is of constant length c. The velocities of A and B along CA and CB are u and v, the corresponding accelerations are U, V, and ω is the angular velocity of AB; prove that

$$u\cos A + v\cos B = 0 \qquad u\sin A \sim v\sin B = c\omega$$
$$U\cos A + V\cos B = -c\omega^2 \qquad U\sin A \sim V\sin B = c\dot{\omega}$$ (C.)

5. A particle moves with an acceleration μy^{-3} towards the axis x, starting from the point $(0, k)$ with velocities U, V parallel to the axes of x, y. Prove that it will not strike the axis x unless $\mu > V^2k^2$, and that, in this case, it strikes it at a distance $Uk^2/(\sqrt{\mu} - Vk)$ from the origin. (C.)

6. Obtain the radial and transverse components of the acceleration of a particle, which describes the plane curve $r = f(\theta)$, in the forms

$$\ddot{r} - r\dot{\theta}^2, \quad \frac{1}{r}\frac{d}{dt}(r^2\dot{\theta})$$

If the curve is the equiangular spiral $r = ae^{\theta\cot\alpha}$, and if the radius vector to the particle has constant angular velocity, show that the resultant acceleration of the particle makes an angle 2α with the radius vector and is of magnitude v^2/r, where v is the speed of the particle. (L.U.)

7. A particle moves with constant speed v along the cardioid $r = a(1 + \cos\theta)$. Show that the radial component of the acceleration is constant, and that both $\frac{d\theta}{dt}$ and the magnitude of the resultant acceleration are proportional to $r^{-1/2}$. (L.U.)

8. A particle describes a cycloid with an acceleration always perpendicular to the base, prove that its magnitude is proportional to the inverse fourth power of the radius of curvature at each point of the curve. (C.)

9. Show that a particle can describe an equiangular spiral of angle α and pole S with an acceleration μ/SP^n whose direction makes a constant angle β with the tangent to the spiral provided that

$$\tan \alpha = \tfrac{1}{2}(n - 1) \tan \beta \qquad \text{(C.)}$$

10. Two fixed points are taken on a circle and any point on the circle is at distances r_1, r_2 from them, the radii vectores r_1, r_2 containing an angle α ; prove that the component velocities in the directions of r_1 and r_2 are u_1, u_2 where

$$u_1 + u_2 \cos \alpha = \dot{r}_1, \qquad u_2 + u_1 \cos \alpha = \dot{r}_2$$

and that the component accelerations in the same directions are

$$\dot{u}_1 - u_2\dot{r}_2/r_1 \text{ and } \dot{u}_2 - u_1\dot{r}_1/r_2 \qquad \text{(C.)}$$

11. The radii vectores from two fixed points distant c apart to the position of a particle are r_1, r_2, and the velocities in these directions are u_1, u_2 ; prove that the accelerations in the same directions are

$$\dot{u}_1 + \frac{u_1u_2}{2r_1{}^2r_2}(r_1{}^2 - r_2{}^2 + c^2) \text{ and } \dot{u}_2 + \frac{u_1u_2}{2r_1r_2{}^2}(r_2{}^2 - r_1{}^2 + c^2) \qquad \text{(C.)}$$

12. The radii vectores from three fixed points to the position of a particle are r_1, r_2, r_3, and the velocities in these directions are u_1, u_2, u_3 ; prove that the accelerations in these directions are

$$\dot{u}_2 + u_2\left(\frac{u_2}{r_2} + \frac{u_3}{r_3}\right) - \frac{u_1}{r_1}(u^2 \cos \theta_{12} + u_3 \cos \theta_{13})$$

and the two similar expressions, in which θ_{23}, θ_{31}, θ_{12} are the angles contained by the directions of (r_2, r_3), (r_3, r_1) and (r_1, r_2). (C.)

13. An infinite earthed cylindrical conductor of radius a is enclosed by a concentric infinite cylindrical conductor of radius b whose potential is V ; a uniform magnetic field H is applied parallel to the common axis of the conductors. An electron of mass m whose charge is $-e(e > 0)$ leaves the inner conductor with zero velocity. Show that it cannot reach the outer conductor of

$$V < \frac{eH^2}{8mc^2}\left(\frac{b^2 - a^2}{b}\right)^2 .$$

[The force on a particle carrying a charge e moving with velocity $\boldsymbol{v}$ in an electric field $\boldsymbol{E}$ and a magnetic field $\boldsymbol{H}$ is $e\left(\boldsymbol{E} + \frac{1}{c}\boldsymbol{v} \times \boldsymbol{H}\right)$.] (M.T.)

CHAPTER V

KINETICS OF PARTICLE MOTION (I)

5.1 Forces which act on a particle

A single body may be acted upon by any or all of the following kinds of forces.

(a) **Field of force.** This is defined by a line vector, say $\boldsymbol{F}(\boldsymbol{r})$, which exists at every point $\boldsymbol{r}$ of some region of space. The most important example is the *gravitational field* (v. 3.1 Ex. 4) with $\boldsymbol{F} = -\frac{\mu}{r^3}\boldsymbol{r}$ $(\mu > 0)$, this being the force acting per unit mass on a body at $\boldsymbol{r}$ and due to another mass at the origin O (v. 1.4). If r is very large and the particle at $P(\boldsymbol{r})$ only moves in a limited region between, say, $r_0 + \epsilon$ and $r_0 - \epsilon$ where ϵ/r_0 is very small, then it is possible to regard the gravitational force as effectively constant. This is, in fact, what we do when we say that a particle has constant acceleration near the surface of the earth : here we put r_0 = radius of earth = 4,000 miles (approx.) and ϵ is of the order of hundreds of feet.

(b) **Tension in an inelastic string.** Whenever the particle is fastened to one end of an inelastic string which is taut then the tension in the string, say T, acts on the particle and also acts along the string. The magnitude of T may vary between zero, when the string is slack, and (say) T_0, when the string breaks.

(c) **Tension in an elastic string.** Unless otherwise stated we shall assume that an elastic string is one which obeys Hooke's Law (v. 3.1 Ex. 3), *viz.* tension $= \frac{\lambda}{a}$ (extension), where λ is a constant called the *modulus of elasticity* (Hooke), and a = the natural (unstretched) length.

(d) **Stress in a light rod.** A particle connected to a light rod and in motion will experience the *thrust* or *tension* transmitted by the rod. Such forces act along the line of the rod.

(e) **Reaction at a smooth surface.** If we consider a particle P in motion and in contact with a smooth surface (v. Fig. 48), then a mutual force of reaction R must act along the normal to the surface (which includes a curve). *The particle will leave the surface at the moment when $R = 0$.*

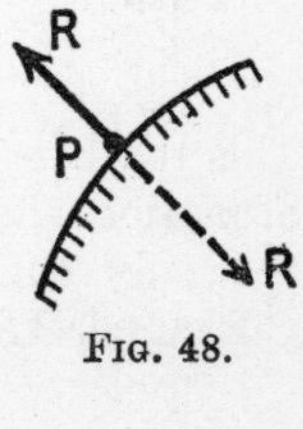

FIG. 48.

(f) **Frictional force.** Whenever two surfaces are in *sliding contact* we know, from experiment, that a tangential force F is brought into play in such a way as to oppose the relative motion. This force F is called a *force of friction* (v. Fig. 49) and always acts opposite to the direction of motion of P, that is to say, opposite to the velocity v. The value of F is known to depend upon (i) the nature (roughness) of the surfaces in contact, and (ii) the reaction R. In statical problems where P does not move on the surface, F may take all values between O and μR, where μ is a constant called the *coefficient of friction*, and when $F = \mu R$ the equilibrium is on the point of breaking (limiting equilibrium). In our dynamical problems with P actually *sliding on the surface* we therefore assume $F = \mu R$.

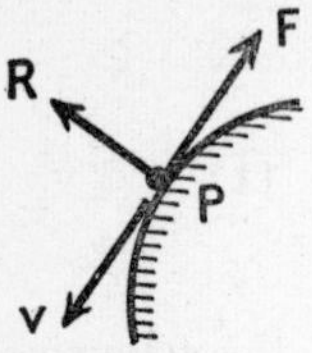

FIG. 49.

(g) **Forces of resistance.** These include all other forces which tend to oppose the motion. In particular we have in mind those forces offered by a *resisting medium*, which means anything from fresh air to a jar of treacle. It is an experimental fact that the resisting forces in these cases are generally *functions of velocity*, e.g. of magnitude $R = kv^p$, where k, p are constants. The directions of the forces are in the line of and opposite to the velocity at any instant.

5.2 Motion in a straight line

Take the straight line as the x-axis and let the particle P, of mass m, be acted upon by a force F in the positive sense. The *equation of motion* will be (v. 1.6)

$$m\frac{dv}{dt} = F \quad . \quad . \quad . \quad . \quad (1)$$

Knowing F as a function of time, or of position, or of velocity, enables us to solve (1) (at least theoretically) and so determine the motion.

Assuming F to be a *conservative field of force* (v. 3.1 and 5.1(a)) (1) gives, writing V for the potential energy,

$$m\,v\frac{dx}{dv} = -\frac{dV}{dx}$$

Hence

$$\tfrac{1}{2}mv^2 + V(x) = \text{Constant} \quad . \quad . \quad . \quad (2)$$

We call $\frac{1}{2}mv^2$ the **Kinetic Energy,** T, of the particle, whence (2) can be written

$$T + V = \text{Constant} \quad . \quad . \quad . \quad (3)$$

This result is called the *energy equation* and establishes, for this type of motion, the *principle of the conservation of energy*.

It only remains for us to study some typical and illustrative problems.

Example 1. Motion under gravity (Galileo's problem). Let a particle of mass m fall vertically in the (constant) gravitational field near the earth's surface. Taking the x-axis downwards we get

$$m\frac{d^2x}{dt^2} = mg = \text{constant}$$

Hence $\ddot{x} = g$, which gives

$$\ddot{x} = u + gt \quad . \quad . \quad . \quad . \quad . \quad (4)$$

and

$$\ddot{x} = ut + \tfrac{1}{2}gt^2 \quad . \quad . \quad . \quad . \quad . \quad (5)$$

where $u = \dot{x}$, at $t = 0$, $=$ initial downward velocity. Reversing the sign of g accounts for upwards motion.

Example 2. Simple Harmonic Motion (S.H.M.). This is motion under the force $F = -\omega^2 x$ per unit mass, with ω a real constant. We usually write $-\omega^2 x$ and not (say) $-kx$ for algebraic convenience (v. *seq.*).

We have

$$\ddot{x} = -\omega^2 x$$

or

$$\ddot{x} + \omega^2 x = 0 \quad . \quad . \quad . \quad . \quad . \quad (6)$$

Hence

$$x = A\cos\omega t + B\sin\omega t \quad . \quad . \quad . \quad (7)$$

A, B arbitrary constants. Take the simple case of $\dot{x} = 0$, $x = a$ at $t = 0$. Then (7) gives $A = a$, $B = 0$. The solution is therefore

$$x = a\cos\omega t \quad . \quad . \quad . \quad . \quad . \quad (8)$$

The potential function is $V = \frac{1}{2}\omega^2 x^2$ and so the energy equation is

$$\dot{x}^2 + \omega^2 x^2 = \text{constant} = \omega^2 a^2$$

since $\dot{x} = 0$ when $x = a$. This gives

$$\dot{x}^2 = \omega^2(a^2 - x^2) \quad . \quad . \quad . \quad . \quad . \quad (9)$$

a result which also follows from (8), or from (6) by myltiplying by $2\dot{x}$ and integrating w.r.t. time.

Now (8) implies that the *motion is oscillatory*, since $-a \leqslant x \leqslant +a$ for all t. The distance a is called the *amplitude* of the motion ; O is the centre of oscillation ; 2π is the period of ωt, so that the *periodic time* is

$$\tau = \frac{2\pi}{\omega} \quad . \quad . \quad . \quad . \quad . \quad (10)$$

Example 3. S.H.M. in a resisting medium. Here we consider only the case of resistance $= 2k\dot{x}$ per unit mass, where k is a positive constant.

We have

$$\ddot{x} = -\omega^2 x - 2k\dot{x}$$

or

$$\ddot{x} + 2k\dot{x} + \omega^2 x = 0 \quad . \quad . \quad . \quad (11)$$

This gives

$$x = e^{-kt}\{A\cos nt + B\sin nt\} \quad . \quad . \quad . \quad (12)$$

if $n^2 = \omega^2 - k^2 > 0$, i.e. the oscillatory case,

or

$$x = e^{-kt}\{A\cosh nt + B\sinh nt\} \quad . \quad . \quad (13)$$

if $n^2 = k^2 - \omega^2 > 0$,

or

$$x = e^{-kt}\{A + Bt\} \quad . \quad . \quad . \quad . \quad . \quad (14)$$

if $k^2 - \omega^2 = 0$.

The oscillatory case is illustrated in Fig. 50. It is commonly referred to as "damped S.H.M." The curve lies between the two curves $x = \pm ce^{-kt}$ since (12) can be written

$$x = Ce^{-kt}\cos(nt - \alpha) \quad . \quad . \quad . \quad . \quad (15)$$

where C, α are new constants.

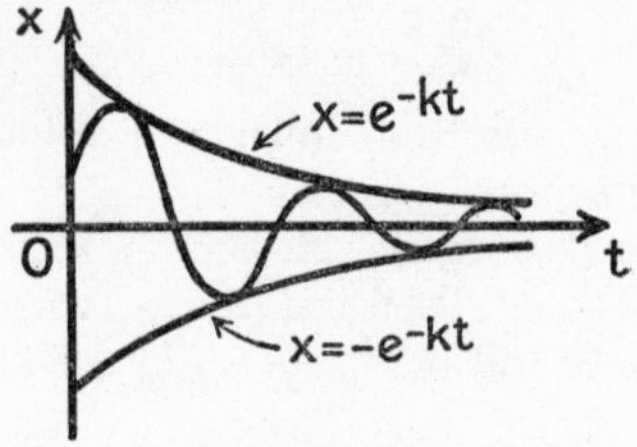

FIG. 50.

Example 4. Forced vibrations in a resisting medium. This is the case of Ex. 3 with an additional force per unit mass of magnitude $F = F_0 \cos(pt + \alpha)$, with α, p, F_0 constants. The equation of motion is

$$\ddot{x} + 2k\dot{x} + \omega^2 x = F_0 \cos(pt + \alpha) \quad . \quad . \quad (16)$$

with solution

$$x = e^{-kt}g(t) + \text{Particular Integral} \quad . \quad . \quad (17)$$

and where $g(t)$ is given by (12), (13) or (14).

The Particular Integral is given in terms of the operator $D = \dfrac{d}{dt}$,

$$\begin{aligned} x &= \frac{F_0}{D^2 + 2kD + \omega^2}.\cos(pt + \alpha) \\ &= \frac{F_0}{2kD + (\omega^2 - p^2)}.\cos(pt + \alpha) \quad (p \neq \omega) \\ &= -\frac{F_0\{2kD - (\omega^2 - p^2)\}}{(\omega^2 - p^2)^2 + 4k^2p^2}\cos(pt + \alpha) \end{aligned}$$

which can be written

$$x = RF_0 \cos(pt + \alpha - \delta) \quad . \quad . \quad . \quad . \quad . \quad (18)$$

where $R^2 = (\omega^2 - p^2)^2 + 4k^2p^2$ and $\tan\delta = \dfrac{2kp}{\omega^2 - p^2}$. Since $|e^{-kt}(gt)| \to 0$ as $t \to \infty$, we see that (18) gives the *steady state*, or *forced vibrations* of the particle.

Example 5. Vertical motion under gravity in a resisting medium. Let us first consider a general resistance per unit mass of kv^p, where k, p are constants and v is the velocity. Then

(i) *motion downwards* : the equation is

$$\ddot{x} = g - k\dot{x}^p \quad . \quad . \quad . \quad . \quad . \quad (19)$$

We notice that the velocity becomes constant when $\ddot{x} = 0$, i.e. when $\dot{x} = \sqrt[p]{\frac{g}{k}} = U$, the *terminal velocity.* Writing $g = kU^p$, (19) becomes

$$\left.\begin{aligned} \ddot{x} = \frac{dv}{dt} &= k(U^p - v^p) \\ \text{or} \qquad v\frac{dv}{dx} &= k(U^p - v^p) \end{aligned}\right\} \quad . \quad . \quad . \quad (20)$$

(ii) *motion upwards* : we merely measure x upwards and reverse the sign of g, giving

$$\left.\begin{aligned} \frac{dv}{dt} &= -\,k(U^p + v^p) \\ \text{and} \qquad v\frac{dv}{dx} &= -\,k(U^p + v^p) \end{aligned}\right\} \quad . \quad . \quad . \quad (21)$$

Example 6. A particle is projected vertically upwards with velocity u and moves in a medium offering resistance kv^4 per unit mass, where v is the velocity. Prove that the greatest height reached above the point of projection is $\frac{\alpha}{2\sqrt{kg}}$, where $g \tan^2 \alpha = ku^4$.

If the particle has velocity w downwards on regaining the point of projection, show that $w^2 = \sqrt{\frac{g}{k}} \tanh \alpha$. (M.T.)

On the way up, using (21), we have

$$v\frac{dv}{dx} = -\,k(U^4 + v^4)$$

and if h is the height reached,

$$\int_u^0 \frac{v\,dv}{U^4 + v^4} = -\,k\int_0^h dx$$

or

$$kh = \int_0^u \frac{v\,dv}{U^4 + v^4} = \int_0^{u^2} \frac{dz}{2(U^4 + z^2)} \quad . \quad . \quad (22)$$

where $z = v^2$. Hence we get

$$kh = \frac{1}{2U^2}.\tan^{-1}\left(\frac{u^2}{U^2}\right)$$

which is

$$h = \frac{\alpha}{2\sqrt{kg}}, \quad \text{with } \tan^2 \alpha = \frac{ku^4}{g}$$

On the way down, we get simply,

$$\int_0^w \frac{v\,dv}{U^4 - v^4} = \int_0^h dx$$

which gives $$\frac{1}{U^2}\tanh^{-1}\left(\frac{\omega^2}{U^2}\right) = 2h = \frac{a}{\sqrt{kg}}$$

or $$w^2 = \sqrt{\frac{g}{k}}\tanh a$$

Example 7. An elastic string AB of length l is fixed at A and would be stretched to $2l$ if a mass m were fastened to B and gently lowered. A mass $\frac{m}{10}$ is fastened to B and let fall from A. Find the distance it will fall and prove that the period of the subsequent motion is

$$2\sqrt{\frac{l}{10g}}\left\{2\sqrt{5} + \pi - \cos^{-1}\frac{1}{\sqrt{21}}\right\}$$

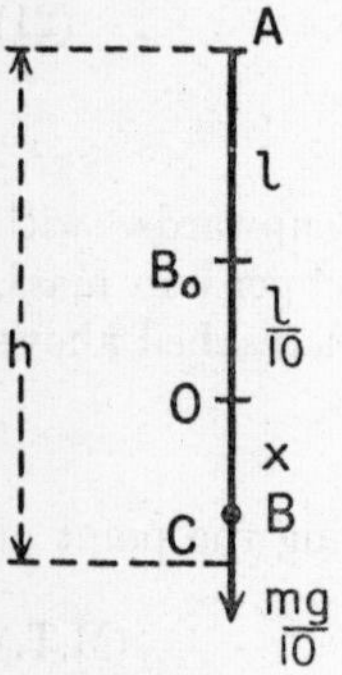

FIG. 51.

Let O, of Fig. 51, be the statical position of equilibrium for the particle of mass $\frac{m}{10}$ attached at B. Then, since $\lambda = mg$, we get $\frac{mg}{10} = \frac{mg}{l}(B_0O)$, giving $B_0O = \frac{l}{10}$; AB_0 being the unstretched length l of the string. For a general position with $OB = x$, we get

$$\frac{m}{10}.\ddot{x} = \frac{mg}{10} - \frac{mg}{l}(B_0O + x) = -\frac{mg}{l}x$$

which gives $$\ddot{x} + \omega^2 x = 0, \quad \omega^2 = \frac{10g}{l} \qquad . \quad . \quad . \quad (23)$$

Thus, while the string is stretched (i.e. B below B_0) the motion is S.H.M. of period $2\pi\sqrt{\frac{l}{10g}}$. To find the depth, h, which B initially falls we have the energy equation (v. 5.2(3) and 3.1 Ex. 3),

$$\tfrac{1}{2}.\frac{mg}{l}.(h - l)^2 - \frac{mg}{10}.h = 0$$

giving $$5h^2 - 11hl + 5l^2 = 0$$

and so $$\frac{h}{l} = \frac{11}{10} + \frac{\sqrt{21}}{10} \qquad . \quad . \quad . \quad . \quad (24)$$

Since $AO = \frac{11}{10}.l$ it follows that B falls to a depth $\frac{\sqrt{21}}{10}.l$ below O, i.e. the amplitude of the S.H.M. is $\frac{\sqrt{21}}{10}.l$, and so for $-\frac{l}{10} \leqslant x \leqslant a$

we have $x = a \cos \omega t$ with $a = \dfrac{\sqrt{21}}{10}.l$. Now B moves continually between A and C and for only part of this path is the motion S.H.M., *viz.* between B_0 and C. The periodic time is therefore τ where

$$\tau = 2t_1 + 2t_2 \quad . \quad . \quad . \quad . \quad (24)$$

with t_1 = time from A to B_0 (or B_0 to A),
t_2 = time from C to B_0.

Hence $$t_1 = \sqrt{\frac{2l}{g}} \quad (\text{from } x = \tfrac{1}{2}gt^2)$$

and $$-\frac{l}{10} = a \cos \omega t_2 = \frac{\sqrt{21}}{10}.l \cos \omega t_2$$

which gives $$t_2 = \frac{1}{\omega}\left\{\cos^{-1}\frac{-1}{\sqrt{21}}\right\} = \frac{1}{\omega}\left\{\pi - \cos^{-1}\frac{+1}{\sqrt{21}}\right\}$$

Hence $$\tau = 2\sqrt{\frac{l}{10g}}\left\{2\sqrt{5} + \pi - \cos^{-1}\frac{1}{\sqrt{21}}\right\} \quad \text{Q.E.D.}$$

5.3 Motion in a plane

Here it is as well to define certain kinetic quantities which are not peculiar to plane motion, but as soon as we leave the very special and limited motion of 5.2 these quantities play a more important part. We define

(a) **linear momentum** as the line vector $\boldsymbol{p} = m\boldsymbol{v}$, with a point of application $\boldsymbol{r}$, that is the position of the particle itself.

(b) **angular momentum** about a *fixed point* O, as the line vector $\boldsymbol{H}(O) = \boldsymbol{r} \times \underline{\boldsymbol{p}} = \boldsymbol{r} \times m\,\boldsymbol{v}$ where $\overline{OP} = \boldsymbol{r}$. This is the torque of the linear momentum about O. In the special case of motion in a plane we can take $\boldsymbol{i}, \boldsymbol{j}$ as defining the plane, whence

$$\boldsymbol{H}(O) = (x\,\boldsymbol{i} + y\,\boldsymbol{j}) \times m(\dot{x}\,\boldsymbol{i} + \dot{y}\,\boldsymbol{j})$$

giving $$\boldsymbol{H}(O) = m(x\dot{y} - y\dot{x})\boldsymbol{k} \quad . \quad . \quad . \quad . \quad (1)$$

a vector with only one component and that perpendicular to the plane.

(c) **kinetic energy** as the scalar quantity $T = \tfrac{1}{2}mv^2$, where $\boldsymbol{v}$ is the velocity of the particle.

These definitions are applicable to 1, 2 or 3 dimensions.

Newton's equation of motion is now, for constant mass m,

$$\frac{d}{dt}\boldsymbol{p} = m\frac{d\boldsymbol{v}}{dt} = \boldsymbol{F} \quad . \quad . \quad . \quad . \quad (2)$$

and, with it, $$\boldsymbol{r} \times m\frac{d\boldsymbol{v}}{dt} = \frac{dt}{dt}(\boldsymbol{r} \times m\,\boldsymbol{v}) = \boldsymbol{r} \times \boldsymbol{F}$$

which is $$\frac{d}{dt}\boldsymbol{H}(O) = \boldsymbol{r} \times \boldsymbol{F} \quad . \quad . \quad . \quad . \quad . \quad (3)$$

(Note : $\frac{d}{dt}(\boldsymbol{r} \times \boldsymbol{v}) = \frac{d}{dt}(\boldsymbol{r} \times \dot{\boldsymbol{r}}) = \dot{\boldsymbol{r}} \times \dot{\boldsymbol{r}} + \boldsymbol{r} \times \ddot{\boldsymbol{r}} = \boldsymbol{r} \times \ddot{\boldsymbol{r}}$.) It is clear that (3) is only applicable when $\boldsymbol{r}$ is taken from a fixed origin O for only then can we write $\dot{\boldsymbol{r}} = \boldsymbol{v}$. Now $\boldsymbol{r} \times \boldsymbol{F}$ = the torque of $\boldsymbol{F}$ about O $= \boldsymbol{\Gamma}(O)$ and so we can write (3) as

$$\frac{d}{dt}\boldsymbol{H}(O) = \Gamma(O) \qquad (4)$$

Again, if $\boldsymbol{F}$ is a conservative force, (2) gives

$$m\,\boldsymbol{v}.\frac{d\boldsymbol{v}}{dt} = \boldsymbol{F}.\boldsymbol{v} = \boldsymbol{F}.\frac{d\boldsymbol{r}}{dt}$$

so that $$\int m\,\boldsymbol{v}.d\boldsymbol{v} = \int \boldsymbol{F}.d\boldsymbol{r} + \text{Constant}$$

which is $$\tfrac{1}{2}m\,v^2 + V = \text{Constant} \qquad (5)$$

This expresses the conservation of energy ; and again, equations (2), (4), (5) are applicable in 1, 2 and 3 dimensions.

We shall now solve some examples which illustrate the use of rectangular and polar co-ordinates in the plane (v. 4.2).

Example 1. The projectile (Galileo). Let a particle P of mass m be projected in a vertical plane from O with an initial velocity V_0 inclined at α to the horizontal. Writing $\boldsymbol{r} = x\,\boldsymbol{i} + y\,\boldsymbol{j}$ and $\boldsymbol{F} = -mg\,\boldsymbol{j}$ we get $\ddot{\boldsymbol{r}} = -g\,\boldsymbol{j}$ for the equation of motion,

and this gives, on integration,

$$\dot{\boldsymbol{r}} = V_0(\cos\alpha\,\boldsymbol{i} + \sin\alpha\,\boldsymbol{j}) - gt\,\boldsymbol{j}$$

and $$\boldsymbol{r} = V_0 t\cos\alpha\,\boldsymbol{i} + (V_0 t\sin\alpha - \tfrac{1}{2}gt^2)\boldsymbol{j} \qquad (6)$$

Hence $$x = V_0 t\cos\alpha\,; \quad y = V_0 t\sin\alpha - \tfrac{1}{2}gt^2$$

imply $$y = x\tan\alpha - \frac{gx^2}{2V_0^2\cos^2\alpha} \qquad (7)$$

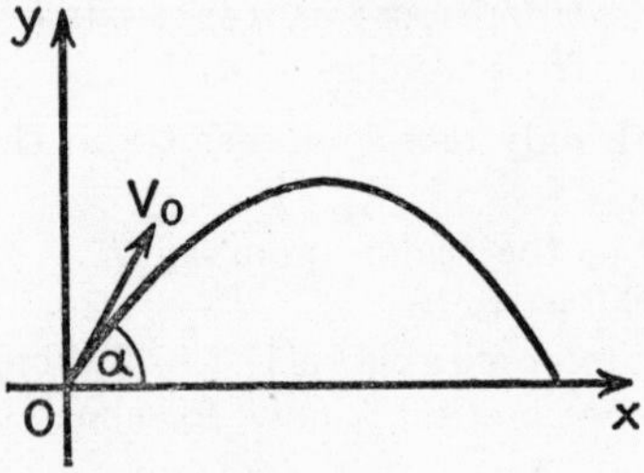

FIG. 52.

which is a parabola. For fixed V_0, x, y there are two possible angles of projection α, given by

$$\frac{gx^2}{2V_0^2}\tan^2\alpha - x\tan\alpha + \left(y + \frac{gx^2}{2V_0^2}\right) = 0 \qquad (8)$$

since $\sec^2 \alpha = 1 + \tan^2 \alpha$. Equation (8) also shows us that for a fixed V_0 the *envelope* of the possible parabolas is given by

$$x^2 = 4 . \frac{gx^2}{2V_0^2}\left(y + \frac{gx^2}{2V_0^2}\right)$$

that is

$$x^2 = -\frac{2V_0^2}{g}\left\{y - \frac{V_0^2}{2g}\right\} \quad . \quad . \quad . \quad (9)$$

This is also a parabola of latus rectum $\dfrac{2V_0^2}{g}$, axis along $x = 0$, vertex at $y = \dfrac{V_0^2}{2g}$ and focus at $y = 0$.

Equation (7) can be written

$$X^2 = -\frac{2V_0^2 \cos^2 \alpha}{g}\left\{y - \frac{V_0^2 \sin^2 \alpha}{2g}\right\} \quad . \quad . \quad (10)$$

with $X = x - \dfrac{V_0^2}{g} \sin \alpha \cos \alpha$.

Equation (10) shows that for a given V_0 and α the parabolic path has latus rectum $\dfrac{2V_0^2}{g} \cos^2 \alpha$ and directrix $y = \dfrac{V_0^2}{2g}$. Thus the directrix of every parabola, for fixed V_0, passes through the vertex of the enveloping parabola.

Finally, putting $y = 0$ in (7) gives the *horizontal range* R, viz.

$$R = \frac{2V_0^2}{g} \cos^2 \alpha \tan \alpha = \frac{V_0^2}{g} \sin 2\alpha \quad . \quad . \quad (11)$$

The *maximum height* follows from (10), viz.

$$h = \frac{V_0^2}{2g} \sin^2 \alpha \quad . \quad . \quad . \quad . \quad (12)$$

and the *time of flight* is

$$t = \frac{R}{V_0 \cos \alpha} = \frac{2V_0}{g} \sin \alpha \quad . \quad . \quad . \quad (13)$$

Equation (11) shows that the maximum range corresponds to $\alpha = 45°$.

Example 2. A particle of unit mass is projected with velocity V and inclination α in a medium whose resistance is $k \times$ (velocity). Show that if k is small the equation of the path is approximately

$$y = x \tan \alpha - \frac{gx^2}{2V^2 \cos^2 \alpha} - \frac{kgx^3}{3V^3 \cos^3 \alpha}$$

The particle is projected in the same medium from a point on a plane which is inclined at β to the horizontal. Prove that the range is approximately

$$\frac{2V^2}{g} \cdot \frac{\sin(\alpha-\beta)\cos\alpha}{\cos^2\beta}\left\{1-\frac{4}{3} \cdot \frac{kV\sin(\alpha-\beta)}{g\cos\beta}\right\} \qquad \text{(L.U.)}$$

The equations of motion will be

$$\ddot{x}+k\dot{x}=0 \qquad . \quad . \quad . \quad . \quad (14)$$

$$\ddot{y}+k\dot{y}=-g \qquad . \quad . \quad . \quad . \quad (15)$$

with $\dot{x}=V\cos\alpha$, $\dot{y}=V\sin\alpha$ at $t=0$.

(14) gives $$\dot{x}+kx=V\cos\alpha$$

and $$x=\frac{V}{k}\cos\alpha\{1-e^{-kt}\} \qquad . \quad . \quad . \quad . \quad . \quad (16)$$

This also gives

$$t=-\frac{1}{k}\log\left\{1-\frac{kx}{V\cos\alpha}\right\}$$

that is, $$t=\frac{x}{V\cos\alpha}+\frac{kx^2}{2V^2\cos^2\alpha}+\frac{k^2x^3}{3V^3\cos^3\alpha}+\cdots \qquad . \quad (17)$$

From (15) we get $$\dot{y}+ky=V\sin\alpha-gt$$

which gives

$$y=\left\{\frac{V}{k}\sin\alpha+\frac{g}{k^2}\right\}(1-e^{-kt})-\frac{g}{k}t \qquad . \quad . \quad . \quad (18)$$

Then (16) and (18) give

$$y=x\tan\alpha+\frac{gx}{Vk\cos\alpha}-\frac{g}{k}t$$

and using (17), this becomes

$$y=x\tan\alpha-\frac{gx^2}{2V^2\cos^2\alpha}-\frac{kgx^3}{3V^3\cos^3\alpha} \qquad \text{Q.E.D.}$$

To find the range on the plane $y=x\tan\beta$ we need R, where $x=R\cos\beta$ and $y=R\sin\beta$. Substituting in the above we get

$$\sin\beta=\cos\beta\tan\alpha-\frac{gR\cos^2\beta}{2V^2\cos^2\alpha}-\frac{kgR^2\cos^3\beta}{3V^3\cos^3\alpha}$$

which is

$$\left(\frac{kg}{3V^3}\right)R^2\cos^3\beta+\left(\frac{g}{2V^2}\right)R\cos^2\beta\cos\alpha-\cos^2\alpha\sin(\alpha-\beta)=0$$

Solving by the formula, we get

$$R=\frac{-3V\cos\alpha}{4k\cos\beta}+\frac{3V\cos\alpha}{4k\cos\beta}\left\{1+\frac{16}{3} \cdot \frac{Vk\sin(\alpha-\beta)}{g\cos\beta}\right\}^{\frac{1}{2}}$$

reducing to

$$R=\frac{3V\cos\alpha}{4k\cos\beta}\left\{\frac{8}{3}\frac{Vk\sin(\alpha-\beta)}{g\cos\beta}-\frac{32}{9} \cdot \frac{V^2k^2\sin^2(\alpha-\beta)}{g^2\cos^2\beta}\right\} \text{(approx.)}$$

that is

$$R = \frac{2V^2}{g} \cdot \frac{\sin(\alpha - \beta)\cos\alpha}{\cos^2\beta}\left\{1 - \frac{4}{3} \cdot \frac{kV\sin(\alpha - \beta)}{g\cos\beta}\right\} \quad \text{Q.E.D.}$$

Example 3. Two equal particles P, Q are joined by a smooth light string passing through a hole, O, in a smooth horizontal table so that P rests on the table and Q hangs beneath. When held at rest with $OP = a$, P is given a horizontal velocity $\sqrt{2nga}$ perpendicular to the string. Assuming the string is sufficiently long to prevent Q hitting the table, show that in the subsequent motion the string remains taut and Q moves between two levels at a vertical distance apart of

$$\tfrac{1}{2}a\,|\,(n^2 + 4n)^{\frac{1}{2}} + n - 2\,| \qquad \text{(M.T.)}$$

Let $OP = r$, $OQ = x$ at any time t and let P be defined in position by plane polar co-ordinates r, θ (v. Fig. 53(i) and (ii)). Let the tension

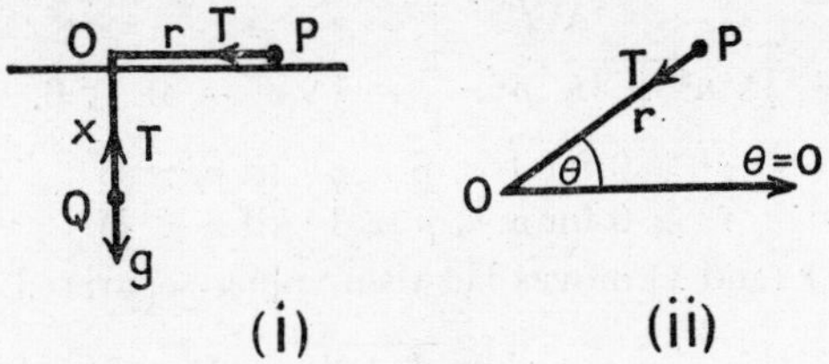

FIG. 53.

in the string be T and take the particles to be of unit mass. We now have, using 4.2(5),

for the motion of P:
$$\ddot{r} - r\dot{\theta}^2 = -T. \qquad (19)$$
$$\frac{1}{r}\frac{d}{dt}(r^2\dot{\theta}) = 0 \qquad (20)$$

for the motion of Q:
$$\ddot{x} = g - T \qquad (21)$$

and since the string is of constant length, say l,

$$r + x = l \qquad (22)$$

Equation (20) implies that

$$r^2\dot{\theta} = \text{constant} = a\sqrt{2nga} \qquad (23)$$

(v. 4.2(4)), which gives

$$\dot{\theta} = \frac{a}{r^2}\sqrt{2nga} \qquad (24)$$

Subtracting (21) from (19) and substituting $\ddot{x} = -\ddot{r}$ from (22), gives

$$2\ddot{r} - r\dot{\theta}^2 + g = 0$$

and (24) then implies

$$2\ddot{r} - 2ng\frac{a^3}{r^3} + g = 0 \qquad (25)$$

From (25) and (21) we see that if the string slackens $T = 0$, $\ddot{x} = g = -\ddot{r}$ and so $r^3 < 0$, which is not possible.

Writing $\ddot{r} = \dot{r}\dfrac{d\dot{r}}{dr}$ (v. 4.1(1)), (25) gives

$$\dot{r}^2 + ng\frac{a^3}{r^2} + gr = \text{constant} = (n+1)ga \quad . \quad . \quad (26)$$

by using the initial conditions, $\dot{r} = 0$, $r = a$ at $t = 0$. Writing $\dfrac{r}{a} = p$ (26 becomes

$$\frac{\dot{r}^2}{ag} = -\left(\frac{a}{r}\right)^2\{p^3 - (n+1)p^2 + n\}$$

$$= -\left(\frac{a}{r}\right)^2(p-1)(p^2 - np - n)$$

$$= -\left(\frac{a}{r}\right)^2(p-1)(p-\alpha)(p-\beta) \quad . \quad . \quad (27)$$

where $\alpha = \dfrac{n}{2} + \frac{1}{2}\sqrt{n^2+4n}$, $p = \dfrac{n}{2} - \frac{1}{2}\sqrt{n^2+4n} < 0$. Hence

$$\dot{r}^2 \geqslant 0 \text{ for } 1 \leqslant p \leqslant \alpha \quad (\text{if } n > \tfrac{1}{2})$$

or

$$\dot{r}^2 \geqslant 0 \text{ for } \alpha \leqslant p \leqslant 1 \quad (\text{if } n < \tfrac{1}{2})$$

In either case r (and x) moves between values separated by a distance

$$a\left|\frac{n}{2} + \tfrac{1}{2}\sqrt{n^2+4n} - 1\right| \qquad \text{Q.E.D.}$$

Example 4. A smooth plane inclined at an angle α to the horizontal is rigidly connected with a fixed vertical axis about which it revolves with uniform angular velocity ω. A heavy particle moves under gravity on the plane. Prove that if x is the displacement of the particle from the point of the plane on the axis, measured upwards along the line of greatest slope, then

$$\frac{d^4x}{dt^4} + \omega^2(3\cos^2\alpha - 1)\frac{d^2x}{dt^2} + x\omega^4\cos^2\alpha = g\omega^2\sin\alpha \qquad \text{(L.U.)}$$

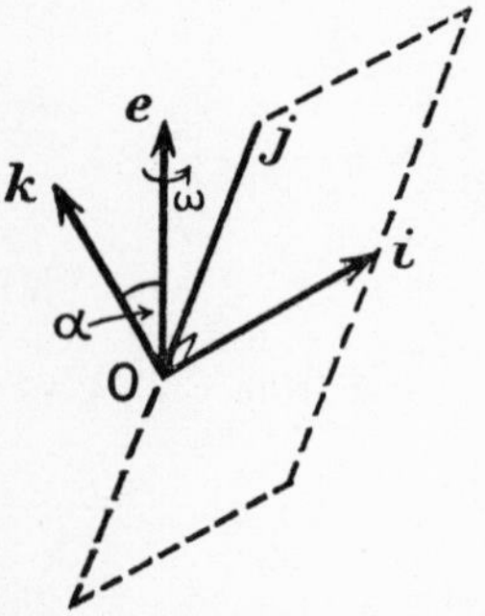

FIG. 54.

Fig. 54 shows the plane, with the unit vector $\boldsymbol{i}$ along the line of greatest slope, $\boldsymbol{k}$ along the normal, and $\boldsymbol{e}$ is a unit vector along the upward vertical. Taking the mass of the particle as unity, the total force acting on it will be

$$\boldsymbol{F} = -g\,\boldsymbol{e} + R\,\boldsymbol{k} \quad . \quad . \quad (28)$$

where R is the normal reaction (v. 5.1(e)). The position of the particle will be defined by $\boldsymbol{r} = x\,\boldsymbol{i} + y\,\boldsymbol{j}$, and the axes $(\boldsymbol{i}, \boldsymbol{j}, \boldsymbol{k})$ are rotating with angular velocity $\boldsymbol{\omega} = \omega\,\boldsymbol{e}$ about O.

Using the theory of 3.6 (see also 4.2), we have

$$\frac{\partial^2 \boldsymbol{r}}{\partial t^2} + 2\omega\, \boldsymbol{e} \times \frac{\partial \boldsymbol{r}}{\partial t} + \omega^2 \boldsymbol{e} \times (\boldsymbol{e} \times \boldsymbol{r}) = \boldsymbol{F} \quad . \quad . \quad (29)$$

Since $\boldsymbol{e} = \sin \alpha\, \boldsymbol{i} + \cos \alpha\, \boldsymbol{k}$, we get

$$\begin{aligned} \boldsymbol{e} \times (\boldsymbol{e} \times \boldsymbol{r}) = (\boldsymbol{e}.\boldsymbol{r})\boldsymbol{e} - \boldsymbol{r} &= x \sin \alpha\, \boldsymbol{e} - x\, \boldsymbol{i} - y\, \boldsymbol{j} \\ &= -x \cos^2 \alpha\, \boldsymbol{i} - y\, \boldsymbol{j} + x \sin \alpha \cos \alpha\, \boldsymbol{k} \end{aligned}$$

and

$$\boldsymbol{e} \times \frac{\partial \boldsymbol{r}}{\partial t} = \boldsymbol{e} \times (\dot{x}\, \boldsymbol{i} + \dot{y}\, \boldsymbol{j}) \quad = -\dot{y} \cos \alpha\, \boldsymbol{i} + \dot{x} \cos \alpha\, \boldsymbol{j} + \dot{y} \sin \alpha\, \boldsymbol{k}$$

Hence (29) gives the three equations

$$\ddot{x} - 2\omega \cos \alpha\, \dot{y} - \omega^2 x \cos^2 \alpha + g \sin \alpha = 0 \quad . \quad . \quad (30)$$

$$\ddot{y} + 2\omega \cos \alpha\, \dot{x} - \omega^2 y \qquad = 0 \quad . \quad . \quad (31)$$

$$2\omega \sin \alpha\, \dot{y} + \omega^2 x \sin \alpha \cos \alpha + g \cos \alpha = R \quad . \quad . \quad (32)$$

Eliminating y and its derivatives from (30) and (31) by successive differentiation quickly gives the required differential equation for x.

Example 5. An elastic string has one end fastened to a smooth horizontal table at O, the other end being attached to a particle P, of mass m. The natural length of the string is a and the modulus of elasticity is λ. When $OP = 2a$ the particle is projected along the table at right angles to the string. Prove that subsequently the string will never attain its natural length if more than one quarter of the total energy is initially kinetic.

If one fifth of the total energy is initially kinetic and if at some instant the string attains its natural length, prove that it will remain slack for a time $\frac{4}{5}\sqrt{\frac{ma}{\lambda}}$. (L.U.)

Fig. 53(ii) illustrates the position with the string taut if we take $\frac{\lambda}{a}(r - a)$ for the tension. The equations of motion (v. 4.2(5)) are

$$m(\ddot{r} - r\dot{\theta}^2) = -\frac{\lambda}{a}(r - a) \quad . \quad . \quad . \quad (33)$$

and

$$\frac{m}{r}\frac{d}{dt}(r^2\dot{\theta}) = 0 \quad . \quad . \quad . \quad . \quad . \quad (34)$$

Let the initial velocity of P perpendicular to OP be u. Then (34) gives

$$r^2\dot{\theta} = 2au$$

and so

$$r\dot{\theta}^2 = \frac{4a^2u^2}{r^3}$$

Hence (33) becomes

$$\ddot{r} - \frac{4a^2u^2}{r^3} + \frac{\lambda}{ma}(r - a) = 0$$

whence $$\dot{r}^2 + \frac{4a^2u^2}{r^2} + \frac{\lambda}{ma}(r^2 - 2ar) = \text{constant}$$
$$= u^2 \quad . \quad . \quad . \quad (35)$$

We therefore have

$$\dot{r}^2 = f(r) = u^2\left\{1 - \frac{4a^2}{r^2}\right\} - \frac{\lambda}{ma}r(r - 2a) \quad . \quad . \quad (36)$$

Now the string can never attain its natural length, $r = a$, if $f(a) < 0$, since $\dot{r}$ would then be complex. This means that

$$0 > f(a) = -3u^2 + \frac{\lambda a}{m}$$

which is $$u^2 > \tfrac{1}{3}\cdot\frac{\lambda a}{m} \quad . \quad . \quad . \quad . \quad (37)$$

But the *total energy* at any time is (v. 3.1 Ex. 3)

$$H = T + V = \tfrac{1}{2}m(\dot{r}^2 + r^2\dot{\theta}^2) + \tfrac{1}{2}\cdot\frac{a}{\lambda}(r - a)^2$$

and initially

$$H_0 = T_0 + V_0 = \tfrac{1}{2}mu^2 + \tfrac{1}{2}\lambda a = \tfrac{1}{2}m\left(u^2 + \frac{\lambda a}{m}\right)$$

Hence (37) implies

$$T_0 > \tfrac{1}{3}V_0, \quad \text{or } T_0 > \tfrac{1}{4}H_0 \qquad \text{Q.E.D.}$$

Now suppose that $T_0 = \frac{1}{5}H_0$; then $T_0 = \frac{1}{4}V_0$ and that means that

$$\frac{\lambda a}{m} = 4u^2 \quad . \quad . \quad (38)$$

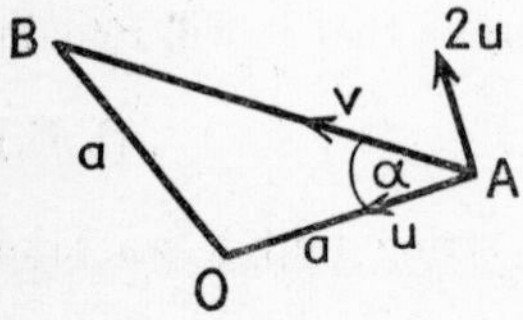

FIG. 55.

Let the string go slack at A (v. Fig. 55). Then the particle travels with constant velocity along the straight line AB. Equation (36) shows that, at A, $\dot{r}^2 = -3u^2 + 4u^2$ giving $\dot{r} = -u$ and the transverse velocity will be $a\dot{\theta} = \frac{2au}{a} = 2u$. The velocity of AB will be $v = u\sqrt{5}$ and $\tan\alpha = \frac{2u}{u} = 2$. Hence the required time will be

$$t = \frac{AB}{v} = \frac{2a\cos\alpha}{v} = \frac{2a}{5u} = \frac{4}{5}\sqrt{\frac{ma}{\lambda}}$$

by equation (38). Q.E.D.

Exercise V

1. A gun is fired from a point O at a car which is moving horizontally with uniform speed U directly away from O; at the instant when the gun is fired the distance of the car from O is b. Prove that, if the car is to be hit, the horizontal and vertical components (u, v) of the velocity of projection of the shell must satisfy the relation

$$v(u - U) = a^2 = \tfrac{1}{2}gb$$

Prove that, if the car is to be hit, and if the velocity of projection is as small as possible, then $u = k^3a$, $v = ka$, where k is the positive root of the equation

$$k^4 - \left(\frac{U}{a}\right)k - 1 = 0 \qquad \text{(M.T.)}$$

2. Two inclined planes intersect in a horizontal line and are inclined to the horizontal at angles α and β. A particle is projected from a point in the former, distant a from the intersection, so as to strike the latter at right angles ; show that the velocity of projection is

$$\sqrt{(2ga)} \sin \beta / \sqrt{\{\sin \alpha - \sin \beta \cos (\alpha + \beta)\}} \qquad \text{(C.)}$$

3. A railway truck carrying a gun is moving with velocity U on a horizontal track directly towards a target, which is not necessarily at ground level. When the truck is at a horizontal distance l from the target the gun is fired with velocity V relative to the truck. If α is the angle at which the gun should be elevated in order to to hit the target, and α_0 is the corresponding elevation when the truck is not moving, show that, when U/V is small,

$$\alpha_0 - \alpha = \frac{\mu \sec \alpha_0 - \sin \alpha_0}{1 - \mu \tan \alpha_0} \cdot \frac{U}{V}$$

approximately, where $\mu = gl/V^2$. (M.T.)

4. Two particles describe the same parabola under gravity. Prove that the intersection of the tangents at their positions at any instant describes a coaxial parabola as if under gravity. Prove also that, if τ is the interval between the instants when they pass through the vertex, the distance between the vertices of the two parabolas is $\frac{1}{8}g\tau^2$. (C.)

5. A particle moves under gravity from the highest point of a sphere of radius c. Prove that it cannot clear the sphere unless its initial velocity exceeds $\sqrt{(\frac{1}{2}gc)}$.

6. Prove that the greatest range on an inclined plane through the point of projection is equal to the distance through which the particle would fall during the time of flight. (C.)

7. A particle moves in the axis x with acceleration μ/x^2 towards the origin, starting from rest at $x = a$. Show that the time of arriving at a distance x is

$$\sqrt{\left(\frac{a^3}{2\mu}\right)}\left\{\cos^{-1}\sqrt{\frac{x}{a}} + \sqrt{\left(\frac{x}{a} - \frac{x^2}{a^2}\right)}\right\}. \qquad \text{(C.)}$$

8. A particle moves in a straight line under a force tending to a fixed point in the line which, at distance r, is equal to $\mu/r^2 - b^2\mu/(r^3a)$, and starts from rest at distance $a + \sqrt{(a^2 - b^2)}$. Prove that it will come to rest at distance $a - \sqrt{(a^2 - b^2)}$ in time $\pi a^{\frac{3}{2}}/\sqrt{\mu}$, and will oscillate between these distances. (C.)

9. A particle moves along the axis x, starting from rest at $x = a$; for an interval t_1 from the beginning of the motion the acceleration is $-\mu x$, for a subsequent interval t_2 the acceleration is μx, and at the end of this interval the particle is at the origin; prove that

$$\tan (t_1\sqrt{\mu}) \tanh (t_2\sqrt{\mu}) = 1 \qquad \text{(C.)}$$

10. A particle falls from rest under gravity through a distance x in a medium whose resistance varies as the square of the velocity; v is the velocity acquired by the particle, V the terminal velocity, and v_0 the velocity that would be acquired by falling through a distance x *in vacuo*; prove that

$$v^2/v_0^2 = 1 - \tfrac{1}{2}v_0^2/V^2 + \frac{1}{2.3}v_0^4/V^4 - \frac{1}{2.3.4}v_0^6/V^6 + \ldots \qquad \text{(C.)}$$

11. A particle is projected vertically upwards from the surface of the Earth with velocity u, and when its velocity is v and its height above the surface is z the resistance is $\kappa v^2/(a + z)$, where a is the Earth's radius. Prove that, if z is always small compared with a, the velocity V with which it returns to the point of projection is approximately given by the equation

$$V^2/u^2 = 1 - \kappa v^2/ga + (4\kappa^2 - \tfrac{2}{3}\kappa)(v^2/2ga)^2$$

variations of gravity with height being taken into account. (C.)

12. A particle of unit mass moves in a straight line under an attraction μ (distance) to a point in the line, and a resistance κ (velocity)^2. Prove that, if it starts from rest at a distance a from the centre of force, it will first come to rest at a distance b, where

$$(1 + 2a\kappa)\, e^{-2a\kappa} = (1 - 2\kappa b)\, e^{2\kappa b} \qquad \text{(C.)}$$

13. The bob of a simple pendulum moves under gravity in a medium of which the resistance per unit of mass is κ (velocity)^2, and starts from the lowest point with such velocity that if it were unresisted the angle of oscillation would be α. Prove that it comes to rest after describing an angle θ which satisfies the equation

$$(1 + 4\kappa^2 l^2) \cos \alpha = 4\kappa^2 l^2 - 2\kappa l \sin \theta\, e^{2\kappa l\theta} + \cos \theta\, e^{2\kappa l\theta},$$

where l is the length of the pendulum. (C.)

14. A particle is projected vertically upwards in a resisting medium which produces a retardation kv^2 when the velocity is v. The terminal velocity is w, and the velocity of projection is v_0. Show that, during the ascent, the velocity at time t after projection is $w \tan (\alpha - kwt)$, where α is the acute angle defined by $\tan \alpha = v_0/w$.

Hence find the relation between position and time during the ascent, and show that the greatest height above the point of projection which is reached by the particle is $(\log \sec \alpha)/k$. (M.T.)

15. A particle of mass m lies in a rough fixed horizontal tube, and is attached to one end of a light spiral spring. The other end of the spring is attached to a fixed point of the tube and lies along the tube. When the spring is extended a distance x the tension is mn^2x. Initially the spring is compressed by an amount c. If the coefficient of friction between m and the tube is $n^2c/6g$, determine the subsequent motion, and show that m eventually remains at rest with the spring neither extended nor compressed.

Find the time during which m is in motion. (M.T.)

16. A heavy particle is tied to the mid-point C of an elastic string of natural length $2l$ with ends attached to fixed points A and B at the same horizontal level distant $2l$ apart. When the particle hangs in equilibrium the points A, B, C form the vertices of an equilateral triangle. Show that, if the particle is slightly displaced in a vertical direction from its equilibrium position, it performs simple harmonic oscillations of period $4\pi(3l^2/49g^2)^{\frac{1}{4}}$.

(L.U.)

17. A ring of mass M, which slides on a smooth rod inclined to the vertical at an angle α, is attached by means of an elastic string to a point so situated that its least distance from the rod is equal to the natural length l of the string. Prove that, if θ is the inclination of the string to the rod when in equilibrium,

$$\cot\theta - \cos\theta = Mg\cos\alpha/\lambda$$

where λ is the modulus of the string.

Show that, if the ring is slightly displaced, the time of a small oscillation is

$$2\pi\left(\frac{Ml}{\lambda}\frac{1}{1-\sin^3\theta}\right)^{\frac{1}{2}} \qquad \text{(L.U.)}$$

18. The co-ordinates of a point P, moving in a plane, are (x, y) relative to rectangular axes Ox, Oy fixed in the plane. If the plane rotates with constant angular velocity ω about a normal through O, prove that the components of the acceleration of P in the directions Ox, Oy are $\ddot{x} - x\omega^2 - 2\dot{y}\omega$ and $\ddot{y} - y\omega^2 + 2\dot{x}\omega$ respectively.

A particle can move along a straight groove cut on a plane and the plane can rotate about a normal which is horizontal and at a perpendicular distance a from the groove. Initially the groove is horizontal and the particle at rest vertically over the axis of rotation. If the plane is then constrained to rotate with constant angular velocity ω, find the distance the particle moves along the groove in time t assuming the coefficient of friction between the particle and the groove to be μ. (L.U.)

19. A particle is placed at a point P of a rough plane inclined at an angle α to the horizontal. Prove that the particle will remain at rest at P if the coefficient of friction μ at P satisfies the condition

$$\mu \geqslant \tan\alpha$$

A particle slides on a plane inclined at an angle α to the horizontal. The coefficient of friction μ is not constant, but is proportional to the distance r from a point O of the plane, $\mu = kr$. A particle is projected from O with velocity u up the line of greatest slope. Prove that the particle will remain at rest when it first comes to rest if

$$u^2 \geqslant 3g \sin^2 \alpha/(k \cos \alpha) \qquad \text{(M.T.)}$$

20. From all points on the circumference of a circle, to the centre of which tends a force varying as the distance, particles are projected towards a point on the circumference with velocities varying as their distances from the point. Prove that at any instant the particles lie on a circle. (C.)

21. A smooth rigid wire bent in the form of the cardioid with polar equation $r = a(1 + \cos \theta)$ is held with axis vertical and cusp above the vertex. A bead is projected horizontally at the lowest point and slides up the wire until it comes to rest at the level of the cusp. Find the velocity of projection and prove that the pressure of the bead on the wire vanishes when $r = 6a/5$. (M.T.)

22. Verify that in a plane field of force of which the potential referred to polar co-ordinates is

$$\frac{\alpha}{r^4} + \frac{\beta}{r^6}(1 + 3 \sin^2 \theta)$$

a particle, if projected in the proper direction with the velocity from infinity, will describe a curve of the form

$$(r - a \sin \theta)(r - b \sin \theta) = ab$$

provided that

$$\frac{2}{ab} + \frac{4}{(a + b)^2} + \frac{\alpha}{\beta} = 0 \qquad \text{(C.)}$$

CHAPTER VI

KINETICS OF PARTICLE MOTION (II)

6.1 Central orbits

A central orbit is the path described by a particle which is acted upon by a force $\boldsymbol{F}$ which always acts in a line through a fixed point O. This type of force (defining a field of force) is called a *central force* and the point O is called the *centre of force*.

The motion of a planet about its sun is an important example of a central orbit (v. 1.4), and in this case the field of force is $\boldsymbol{F} = -\frac{\mu}{r^3}\boldsymbol{r}$ $(\mu > 0)$. Other examples are usually of an artificial nature and frequently occur on university examination papers : even so, they can often be of great mathematical interest.

The first thing we shall prove is that *a central orbit is a plane curve.* Let the central force be $\boldsymbol{F}$ per unit mass, acting on the particle P where $\overline{OP} = \boldsymbol{r}$ (v. Fig. 56). The equation of motion becomes

$$\ddot{\boldsymbol{r}} = \frac{d^2\boldsymbol{r}}{dt^2} = \boldsymbol{F} \quad . \quad (1)$$

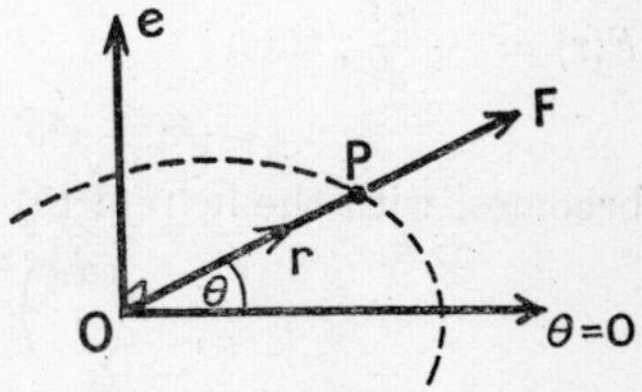

FIG. 56.

Since $\boldsymbol{F}$ is parallel to $\boldsymbol{r}$ (1) gives

$$\boldsymbol{r} \times \ddot{\boldsymbol{r}} = \boldsymbol{r} \times \boldsymbol{F} = \boldsymbol{0} \quad \text{(all } t\text{)}$$

which means that $$\frac{d}{dt}(\boldsymbol{r} \times \dot{\boldsymbol{r}}) = \boldsymbol{0}$$

and so $\boldsymbol{r} \times \dot{\boldsymbol{r}}$ = angular momentum per unit mass about O
= a constant vector (all t), v. 5.3(b)

that is $\boldsymbol{r} \times \dot{\boldsymbol{r}} = h\,\boldsymbol{e}$ . . . . (2)

where $\boldsymbol{e}$ is a unit vector of constant direction and $h = |\boldsymbol{r} \times \dot{\boldsymbol{r}}|$. Now (2) implies $\boldsymbol{r}.\boldsymbol{e} = 0$ (all t) so that $\boldsymbol{r}$ lies in the plane perpendicular to $\boldsymbol{e}$ for all values of t. Q.E.D.

Introducing polar co-ordinates in the plane of the orbit, and using 4.2(5), we get the equations

$$\ddot{r} - r\dot{\theta}^2 = F(r) \quad . \quad . \quad . \quad . \quad (3)$$

$$\frac{1}{r}\frac{d}{dt}(r^2\dot{\theta}) = 0 \quad . \quad . \quad . \quad . \quad (4)$$

where we have written $F = |\boldsymbol{F}|$, $r = |\boldsymbol{r}|$. Equation (4) is really equivalent to (2) since it implies

$$r^2\dot{\theta} = r(r\dot{\theta}) = h \text{ (constant)} \quad . \quad . \quad . \quad (5)$$

To find the orbit we need r as a function of θ and since (3) relates r with t we make the substitution $r = \frac{1}{u}$. Then using (5), we get

$$\dot{r} = -\frac{1}{u^2}\dot{u} = -\frac{1}{u^2}.\frac{du}{d\theta}.\dot{\theta} = -h\frac{du}{d\theta} \quad . \quad . \quad (6)$$

Hence $$\ddot{r} = -h\frac{d^2u}{d\theta^2}\dot{\theta} = -h^2u^2\frac{d^2u}{d\theta^2} \quad . \quad . \quad . \quad . \quad (7)$$

If $F(r)$ becomes $f(u)$ on writing $r = \frac{1}{u}$, (6), (7) and (3) give

$$-h^2u^2\frac{d^2u}{d\theta^2} - h^2u^3 = f(u)$$

which reduces to $$\frac{d^2u}{d\theta^2} + u = -\frac{f(u)}{h^2u^2} \quad . \quad . \quad . \quad (8)$$

This is the *differential equation of the orbit*, given the field of force $f(u)$.

On the other hand, we can obtain (8) by starting from the *energy equation*. Suppose the potential function of the field is $V(r)$, so that $F(r) = -\frac{dV}{dr}$, then

$$\tfrac{1}{2}(\dot{r}^2 + r^2\dot{\theta}^2) + V = K \text{ (constant)}$$

becomes, with the help of (5) and (6),

$$\left(\frac{du}{d\theta}\right)^2 + u^2 = \frac{2}{h^2}(K - V) \quad . \quad . \quad . \quad (9)$$

Differentiating (9) w.r.t. θ and cancelling out $\frac{du}{d\theta}$, we get

$$\frac{d^2u}{d\theta^2} + u = \frac{-1}{h^2u^2}.\frac{-dV}{dr}$$

which is (8).

Example 1. Planetary orbits. A planet moves under a force $\frac{-\mu}{r^2} = F(r)$ towards the sun at O. Hence (8) gives

$$\frac{d^2u}{d\theta^2} + u = \frac{\mu}{h^2} \quad . \quad . \quad . \quad . \quad . \quad . \quad . \quad (10)$$

This has solution $$u = \frac{\mu}{h^2} + A\cos(\theta - \alpha)$$

with A, α arbitrary constants, and this can be written

$$\frac{h^2/\mu}{r} = 1 + B\cos(\theta - \alpha) \quad . \quad . \quad . \quad (11)$$

But the equation of a *conic section*, focus at O, of semi-latus rectum l and eccentricity e, is

$$\frac{l}{r} = 1 + e\cos(\theta - \alpha) \qquad . \quad . \quad . \quad (12)$$

Clearly (11) and (12) prove that the planets describe conic sections about the sun at one focus.

In particular, if the orbit is an ellipse of axes $2a$ and $2b$ we have

$$l = \frac{b^2}{a} = \frac{h^2}{\mu} \qquad . \quad . \quad . \quad . \quad (13)$$

It also follows from (5), for any orbit,

$$\begin{aligned}\tfrac{1}{2}h &= \tfrac{1}{2}r^2\frac{d\theta}{dt}\\ &= \text{rate of description of sectorial area mapped out by}\\ &\qquad \text{the radius vector } OP\\ &= \text{a constant (v. 1.3)} \qquad . \quad . \quad . \quad . \quad . \quad . \quad (14)\end{aligned}$$

Hence the *periodic time* of description of an elliptic orbit will be

$$\tau = \frac{\text{area of ellipse}}{\tfrac{1}{2}h} = \frac{2\pi ab}{\sqrt{\mu l}} \quad \text{by (13)}$$

and this gives

$$\tau = \frac{2\pi a^{3/2}}{\sqrt{\mu}} \qquad . \quad . \quad . \quad . \quad (15)$$

This is Kepler's 3rd law.

Example 2. A particle moves in a plane under an attraction $\frac{\mu}{r^5}$ per unit mass towards a centre of attraction O in the plane. It is projected from a point A at distance a from O with velocity u at right angles to OA. Prove that the differential equation of the orbit is

$$\left(\frac{dr}{d\theta}\right)^2 = \frac{1}{a^2u^2}(r^2 - a^2)\left\{\left(u^2 - \frac{\mu}{2a^4}\right)r^2 - \frac{\mu}{2a^2}\right\}$$

Prove that in the special case when $u^2 = \frac{\mu}{2a^4}$ the orbit is the circle on OA as diameter, and that the time from A to O is $\pi a^3/\sqrt{8\mu}$. (M.T.)

Since $F(r) = -\frac{\mu}{r^5}$ we have $V(r) = -\frac{\mu}{4r^4}$ and the energy equation is

$$\dot{r}^2 + r^2\dot{\theta}^2 - \frac{\mu}{2r^4} = \text{constant} = K \qquad . \quad . \quad (16)$$

together with

$$r^2\dot{\theta} = \text{constant} = au \qquad . \quad . \quad (17)$$

(16) and (17) give

$$\dot{r}^2 + \frac{a^2u^2}{r^2} - \frac{\mu}{2r^4} = u^2 - \frac{\mu}{2a^4}$$

and since $\frac{dr}{d\theta} = \dot{r}/\dot{\theta}$ we get

$$\left(\frac{dr}{d\theta}\right)^2 = \frac{r^4}{a^2u^2}\left\{u^2 - \frac{\mu}{2a^4} - \frac{a^2u^2}{r^2} + \frac{\mu}{2r^4}\right\}$$

$$= \frac{1}{a^2u^2}(r^2 - a^2)\left\{\left(u^2 - \frac{\mu}{2a^4}\right)r^2 - \frac{\mu}{2a^2}\right\} \quad \text{Q.E.D.}$$

When $u^2 = \frac{\mu}{2a^4}$ we get $\quad \left(\frac{dr}{d\theta}\right)^2 = (a^2 - r^2)$

so that $-a \leqslant r \leqslant +a$ and $\frac{dr}{d\theta} = -\sqrt{a^2 - r^2}$. Hence $r = a\cos\theta$, which is the circle on OA as diameter, and the time from A to O will be

$$t = \tfrac{1}{2}.\frac{\pi(a/2)^2}{\tfrac{1}{2}h} = \pi a^3/\sqrt{8\mu} \qquad \text{Q.E.D.}$$

Example 3. A particle P of unit mass is attracted towards O by a central force $f(u) = \mu u^5$ $(\mu > 0)$ where $\frac{1}{u} = r = OP$. It is projected from infinity along a line at a distance $a\sqrt{2}$ from O with angular momentum $\sqrt{\mu}/a$ about O. Prove that the equation of the orbit of P is of the form

$$r = a\coth(\theta/\sqrt{2}) \qquad \text{(L.U.)}$$

Take the initial line parallel to the initial direction of projection as shown in Fig. 57. If the initial velocity of projection is v_0 we have $v_0^2 = \dot{r}_0^2 + (r^2\dot{\theta}^2)_0$ and also $(r^2\dot{\theta})_0 = h = \sqrt{\mu}/a$. Hence (as $r \to \infty$ at $t = 0$) we get

$$(r^2\dot{\theta}^2)_0 = 0 \quad \text{and} \quad \dot{r}_0 = -v_0 = -\frac{h}{a\sqrt{2}} \quad . \quad . \quad (18)$$

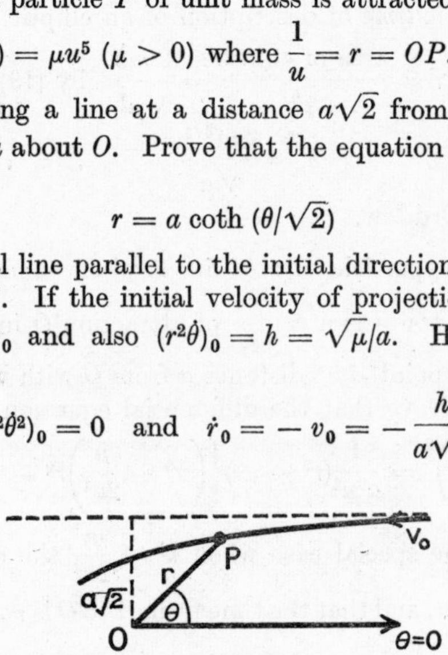

FIG. 57.

The orbit is given by

$$\frac{d^2u}{d\theta^2} + u = \frac{f}{h^2u^2} = a^2u^3$$

so that $$\left(\frac{du}{d\theta}\right)^2 = a^2\frac{u^4}{2} - u^2 + \text{constant} \quad . \quad . \quad (19)$$

Initially (18) shows that

$$\left(\frac{du}{d\theta}\right)_0 = -\frac{\dot{r}_0}{h} = \frac{1}{a\sqrt{2}}$$

Hence (19) becomes

$$\left(\frac{du}{d\theta}\right)^2 = \frac{1}{2a^2}(a^4u^4 - 2a^2u^2 + 1)$$

$$= \frac{1}{2a^2}(a^2u^2 - 1)^2 \quad . \quad . \quad . \quad . \quad (20)$$

Now the point of *nearest approach* is an example of what is called an **apse,** that is to say, a point of the orbit at which $\dot{r} = 0$ (so that $\dot{\boldsymbol{r}}$ is perpendicular to $\boldsymbol{r}$). Hence apses occur where $\frac{du}{d\theta} = 0$ (v. equation (6)).

Equation (20) shows that the point of nearest approach occurs at $u = \frac{1}{a}$, i.e. $r = a$. Hence, generally, $r > a$. Also, since $\frac{du}{d\theta} = -\frac{1}{h}\dot{r}$ and $\dot{r} < 0$ as P approaches O we must take $\frac{du}{d\theta} > 0$. Then (20) leads to

$$\frac{du}{d\theta} = \frac{1}{a\sqrt{2}}(1 - a^2u^2), \quad a^2u^2 < 1$$

This integrates to give

$$\frac{1}{a}\tanh^{-1}(au) = \frac{\theta}{a\sqrt{2}}$$

so that

$$r = a \coth(\theta/\sqrt{2}) \qquad \text{Q.E.D.}$$

Example 4. A particle of unit mass moves in a plane under the action of a central force of attraction $\lambda^2(8au^2 + a^4u^5)$ where $u = \frac{1}{r}$. It is projected with velocity 9λ from an apse at a distance $\frac{a}{3}$ from the centre of force. Show that the equation to its path is

$$\frac{1}{\sqrt{3}}\left\{\frac{5r + a}{a - 3r}\right\}^{\frac{1}{2}} = \cot\left(\frac{\theta}{\sqrt{6}}\right)$$

The equation of the orbit is given by

$$\frac{d^2u}{d\theta^2} + u = \frac{\lambda^2(8au^2 + a^4u^5)}{h^2u^2}$$

and $h = 9\lambda.\frac{a}{3} = 3a\lambda$, hence

$$\frac{d^2u}{d\theta^2} + u = \frac{8}{9a} + \frac{a^2u^3}{9}$$

This gives

$$\left(\frac{du}{d\theta}\right)^2 = \frac{16u}{9a} + \frac{a^2u^4}{18} - u^2 + \text{constant}$$

and $\frac{du}{d\theta} = 0$, $u = \frac{3}{a}$ at $t = 0$. The constant $= -\frac{5}{6a^2}$ therefore, and writing $x = au$ we get

$$18\left(\frac{dx}{d\theta}\right)^2 = x^4 - 18x^2 + 32x - 15$$
$$= (x-1)^2(x-3)(x+5)$$

Hence
$$\frac{dx}{d\theta} = \frac{1}{\sqrt{18}}(x-1)\sqrt{(x-3)(x+5)} \quad . \quad (21)$$

Put $z = \sqrt{\frac{x+5}{x-3}}$ so that $\frac{dz}{dx} = \frac{-4}{(x-3)\sqrt{(x-3)(x+5)}}$ and $x - 1 = 2\frac{(z^2+3)}{(z^2-1)}$, $x - 3 = \frac{8}{z^2-1}$, and so (21) gives

$$\frac{dz}{d\theta} = \frac{-4}{\sqrt{18}} \cdot \frac{(x-1)}{(x-3)} = -\frac{(z^2+3)}{\sqrt{18}}$$

Hence
$$\int \frac{dz}{3+z^2} = -\int \frac{d\theta}{\sqrt{18}} + \frac{\alpha}{\sqrt{3}} \quad (\alpha \text{ a constant})$$

that is
$$\tan^{-1}\frac{z}{\sqrt{3}} = \alpha - \frac{\theta}{\sqrt{6}}$$

Since $z \to \infty$ as $\theta \to 0$ we must take $\alpha = \pi/2$, and so

$$\frac{1}{\sqrt{3}} \cdot \sqrt{\frac{au+5}{au-3}} = \cot\frac{\theta}{\sqrt{6}} \qquad \text{Q.E.D.}$$

6.2 The use of (p-r) equations

The " tangential-polar " equation of a curve is the relation between the radius vector, r, and the perpendicular from the pole to the tangent, i.e. p (v. Fig. 58.) If we know the equation of the curve in the form $r = f(\theta)$ than we can find the tangential-polar equation by eliminating θ and ϕ between

$$\left.\begin{aligned} r &= f(\theta) \\ p &= r\sin\phi \\ \frac{1}{r}\frac{dr}{d\theta} &= \cot\phi \end{aligned}\right\} \quad . \quad . \quad . \quad . \quad (1)$$

Writing $u = \frac{1}{r}$ we have $\frac{du}{d\theta} = -\frac{1}{r^2}\frac{dr}{d\theta}$ and from (1) we get

$$\frac{1}{p^2} = \frac{1}{r^2}(1 + \cot^2 p) = \frac{1}{r^2} + \frac{1}{r^4}\left(\frac{d\theta}{dr}\right)^2$$

which is
$$\frac{1}{p^2} = u^2 + \left(\frac{du}{d\theta}\right)^2 \quad . \quad . \quad . \quad . \quad (2)$$

It follows immediately from 6.1(9) that we can write down the $(p\text{–}r)$ equation of a central orbit in the form

$$\frac{h^2}{p^2} = -2V + C \quad . \quad (3)$$

where C is a constant, and where (v. Fig. 58)

$$h = pv \quad . \quad . \quad (4)$$

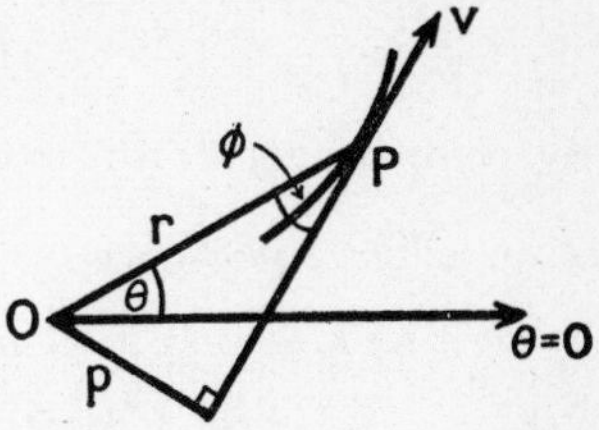

FIG. 58.

In terms of the force $F(r)$ we have, from (3),

$$\frac{h^2}{p^3}\frac{dp}{dr} = +\frac{dV}{dr} = -F(r) \quad . \quad . \quad . \quad (5)$$

Hence $\dfrac{h^2}{p^3}\dfrac{dp}{dr}$ represents the acceleration of a point P along the radius vector, in terms of p and r. We notice also that (3) is not a differential equation, unlike 6.1(9), but is the equation of the orbit : it is therefore extremely useful, provided we can recognise the curve from its equation.

The following is a useful list of $(p - r)$ equations. If the reader has any difficulty in proving them he should consult (e.g.) H. Lamb, *Infinitesimal Calculus*, § 129, Ch. IX (C.U.P.). The *conic sections* with *pole at a focus* :

parabola (latus rectum $4a$), $p^2 = ar$ . . . . . (6)

ellipse (axes $2a$, $2b$), $\dfrac{b^2}{p^2} = \dfrac{2a}{r} - 1$ . . . . (7)

hyperbola (axes $2a$, $2b$), $\dfrac{b^2}{p^2} = \pm\dfrac{2a}{r} + 1$ . . . . (8)

In (8) the upper sign gives the nearer branch, the lower sign the further branch.

With the *pole at the centre* :

ellipse (axes $2a$, $2b$), $\dfrac{a^2b^2}{p^2} = a^2 + b^2 - r^2$ . . . (9)

hyperbola (axes $2a$, $2b$), $\dfrac{a^2b^2}{p^2} = b^2 - a^2 + r^2$ . . . (10)

rectangular hyperbola ($a = b$), $pr = a^2$ . . . . . (11)

Example 1. A particle moves under a central force of attraction $\dfrac{\mu}{r^2}$ per unit mass, and is projected with velocity V at an angle α to the radius vector, and when it is a distance R from the centre of force. To examine the motion.

Equation (3) gives us

$$\frac{h^2}{p^2} = \frac{2\mu}{r} + C = v^2 \quad . \quad . \quad . \quad . \quad (12)$$

Put $r = R$, $v = V$, whence

$$C = \left(V^2 - \frac{2\mu}{R}\right) \quad . \quad . \quad . \quad . \quad (13)$$

By comparing (12) with (6), (7) and (8) we can say that the orbit is an ellipse, parabola or hyperbola according as $V^2 <, =, > \frac{2\mu}{R}$.

By writing $h = (pv)_o = VR \sin \alpha$ we get the curve

$$\frac{V^2R^2 \sin^2 \alpha}{p^2} = \frac{2\mu}{r} + \left(V^2 - \frac{2\mu}{R}\right)$$

and comparing this with the appropriate equation of (6), (7) or (8) we can find all the details of the curve.

Example 2. A particle P is repelled from a fixed point O by a force $\frac{\mu}{r^2}$ where $r = OP$. Prove that P describes one branch of a hyperbola with O as the outer focus and that the speed v is given by $v^2 = \mu\left\{\frac{1}{a} - \frac{2}{r}\right\}$, where $2a$ is the major axis of the orbit.

The particle is projected from infinity with velocity V along a line which is at a perpendicular distance c from O. Prove that the particle eventually returns to infinity along a direction making an angle $2 \tan^{-1}\left\{\frac{\mu}{cV^2}\right\}$ with the initial direction of motion. (L.U.)

The potential function for a force $+\frac{\mu}{r^2}$ is $+\frac{\mu}{r}$ and so (3) gives an orbit

$$v^2 = \frac{h^2}{p^2} = C - \frac{2\mu}{r} \quad . \quad . \quad . \quad . \quad (14)$$

and since C must clearly be positive we have a case of equation (8), viz. the further branch of a hyperbola. Q.E.D.

Comparing (14) and (8) we get

$$\frac{h^2}{b^2} = \frac{C}{1} = \frac{2\mu}{2a} \quad . \quad . \quad . \quad . \quad (15)$$

Hence, writing $C = \mu/a$ in (14), we get

$$v^2 = \mu\left\{\frac{1}{a} - \frac{2}{r}\right\} \quad . \quad . \quad . \quad . \quad (16)$$

As $r \to \infty$, $v \to V$ and (14) gives $C = V^2$. Then (15) gives

$$a = \frac{\mu}{V^2}, \quad b = \frac{h}{V} = \frac{cV}{V} = c$$

The angle between the asymptotes is 2α where $\tan \alpha = b/a$ and the angle between the initial and final directions of motion will be

$$\begin{aligned}\theta &= \pi - 2\alpha \\ &= 2\left(\frac{\pi}{2} - \alpha\right) \\ &= 2\cot^{-1} b/a = 2\tan^{-1} a/b\end{aligned}$$

giving $$\theta = 2\tan^{-1}\left(\frac{\mu}{cV^2}\right)$$ Q.E.D.

Example 3. A particle moves under an attraction $\dfrac{\mu}{r^2}$ per unit mass to a centre of force O. It is projected from a point K at distance c from O with speed $\sqrt{\dfrac{\mu}{c}}$ in a direction making an acute angle α with KO. Prove the orbit is an ellipse with one focus at O and its major axis parallel to the direction of projection. Prove that the particle first reaches the perihelion at time $\left(\dfrac{1}{4} - \dfrac{\cos\alpha}{2\pi}\right)\sigma$ after projection, where σ is the period of the motion. (M.T.)

Using (3), with $h = \sqrt{\dfrac{\mu}{c}}\,.\,c\sin\alpha$ and $C = -\dfrac{\mu}{c}$ we get the orbit

$$\frac{c^2\sin^2\alpha}{p^2} = \frac{2c}{r} - 1$$

which is an ellipse, O at a focus, $a = c$ and $b = c\sin\alpha$. These values mean that the major axis is parallel to the direction of projection, that is to say, K is at one end of the minor axis (v. Fig. 59).

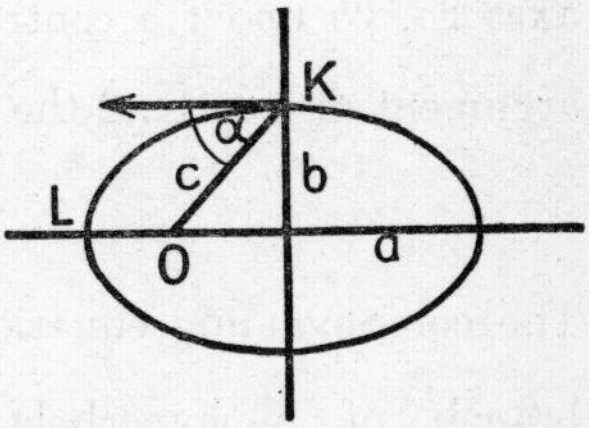

FIG. 59.

Now the point of *nearest approach* to O is called *perihelion*; the point furthest from O is called *aphelion*. Hence the time from K to L (perihelion) will be (v. Ex. 1, equations (14) and (15) of 6.1)

$$\begin{aligned}t &= \frac{\text{area of sector } OKL}{\frac{1}{2}h} \\ &= \frac{\frac{1}{4}\pi ab - \frac{1}{2}bc\cos\alpha}{\frac{1}{2}h}\end{aligned}$$

Writing $\sigma = \dfrac{\pi ab}{\frac{1}{2}h}$ this becomes

$$t = \tfrac{1}{4}\sigma - \frac{bc\cos\alpha}{2\pi ab}\,.\,\sigma$$

i.e. $$t = \left(\tfrac{1}{4} - \frac{\cos\alpha}{2\pi}\right)\sigma$$ Q.E.D.

Example 4. Consider the central force $-\mu r$ per unit mass (direct distance law).

Then the potential function is $\frac{1}{2}\mu r^2$ and (3) gives

$$\frac{h^2}{p^2} = C - \mu r^2$$

Equation (9) shows this to be an ellipse with pole at centre, whatever the conditions of projection.

If we make the force one of repulsion, viz., $+\mu r$, we get

$$\frac{h^2}{p^2} = C + \mu r^2$$

which is a hyperbola by (10).

6.3 Disturbed central orbits

Here we consider those problems in which a particle, describing a central orbit, suffers a sudden change in the law of force, the position of the centre of force, or the magnitude and direction of its velocity. In particular we shall be chiefly concerned with disturbances in the orbits described under the laws of force $\pm \frac{\mu}{r^2}$ and $\pm \mu r$.

Suppose, for example, that a particle P is describing an ellipse of axes $2a$, $2b$ under a central force $-\frac{\mu}{r^2}$ per unit mass. Then by the argument of 6.2 Ex. 2 the velocity v at any point of the orbit satisfies

$$v^2 = \mu\left\{\frac{2}{r} - \frac{1}{a}\right\} \quad . \quad . \quad . \quad . \quad (1)$$

The corresponding equations when the orbit is a parabola or either branch of a hyperbola will be $v^2 = \frac{2\mu}{r}$, $v^2 = \mu\left\{\frac{2}{r} + \frac{1}{a}\right\}$ and $v^2 = \mu\left\{\frac{1}{a} - \frac{2}{r}\right\}$ respectively. Now suppose that for a given value of r the velocity suddenly changes from v_1 to v_2 and the direction of motion turns through an angle α (v. Fig. 60). Let this produce a change in a from a_1 to a_2. Applying (1) to the two orbits we get

$$v_1^2 = \mu\left\{\frac{2}{r} - \frac{1}{a_1}\right\} \quad \text{and} \quad v_2^2 = \mu\left\{\frac{2}{r} - \frac{1}{a_2}\right\}$$

Hence

$$v_1^2 - v_2^2 = \mu\left\{\frac{1}{a_2} - \frac{1}{a_1}\right\} \quad . \quad . \quad . \quad (2)$$

which gives the value of a_2, and the new orbit is an ellipse, parabola or hyperbola according as $\frac{1}{a_2} >, =, < 0$. The change in the angular momentum about the centre of force S will be from h_1 to h_2, where

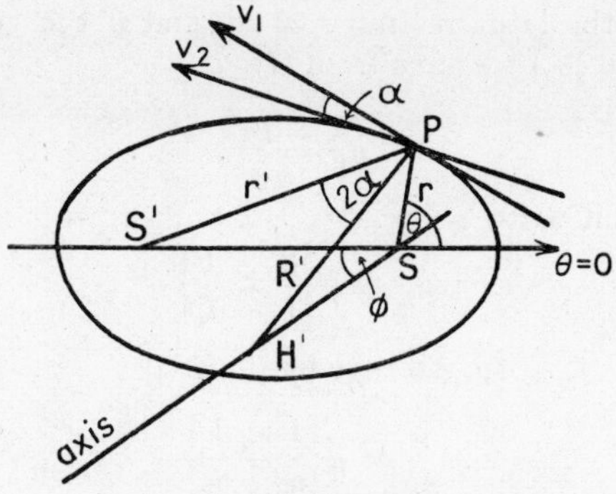

FIG. 60.

$h_1 = p_1 v_1$ and $h_2 = p_2 v_2$. Since a tangent to an ellipse is equally inclined to the two focal radii it is easy to see that

$$p_2 = p_1 \cos \alpha - \sqrt{r^2 - p_1^2} \sin \alpha \quad . \quad . \quad (3)$$

so that we can find h_2. Since $h^2 = \mu l = \mu \frac{b^2}{a} = \mu a(1 - e^2)$ we can find the new eccentricity e_2 from the equation

$$h_2^2 = p_2^2 v_2^2 = \mu a_2 (1 \sim e_2^2) \quad . \quad . \quad . \quad (4)$$

If the axis is rotated through ϕ we can find its position by using the fact that PS' is rotated through 2α and that $PH' + PS = R' + r = 2a_2$. These facts fix the position of H', the new second focus. Also ϕ follows from the polar equation

$$\frac{l_2}{r} = 1 + e_2 \cos (\theta - \phi) \quad . \quad . \quad . \quad (5)$$

since we are given θ, r for P and $l_2 = \mu a_2 (1 - e_2^2)$.

In the special case when the direction of motion of P remains unaltered we have $\alpha = 0$, $p_2 = p_1$ and

$$\frac{h_2}{h_1} = \frac{v_2}{v_1} \quad . \quad . \quad . \quad . \quad . \quad (6)$$

Example 1. A particle is describing a parabola about a centre of force which attracts according to the inverse square of the distance. If the speed of the particle is halved without change of direction of motion when the particle is at one end of the latus rectum, prove that the new path will be an ellipse whose eccentricity is $(5/8)^{\frac{1}{2}}$. (L.U.)

In the first orbit we have

$$v^2 = \frac{h_1^2}{p^2} = \frac{2\mu}{r} \quad . \quad . \quad . \quad . \quad (7)$$

where the orbit is

$$\frac{a}{p^2} = \frac{1}{r} \quad . \quad . \quad . \quad . \quad . \quad (8)$$

At one end of the latus rectum $r = 2a$, and if the velocity changes from v_1 to v_2 $(= \frac{1}{2}v_1)$ we have from (7),

$$v_1^2 = \frac{\mu}{a} \quad . \quad . \quad . \quad . \quad . \quad (9)$$

For the new orbit write

$$v_2^2 = \mu\left\{\frac{2}{r} - \frac{1}{a_2}\right\}$$

and put $r = 2a$, $v_2 = \frac{1}{2}v_1$, so that by (9) we get

$$\frac{\mu}{4a} = \mu\left\{\frac{1}{a} - \frac{1}{a_2}\right\}$$

giving $a_2 = \dfrac{4a}{3} > 0$. The new orbit is therefore an ellipse. Let its eccentricity be e_2 and angular momentum be h_2. Then

$$h_2 = \frac{v_2}{v_1}.h = \tfrac{1}{2}h_1$$

so that $\quad h_2^2 = \frac{1}{4}h_1^2 = \frac{1}{4}\cdot\dfrac{2\mu}{2a}\cdot(a \times 2a)$ by (7) and (8)

Hence $\quad \mu a_2(1 - e_2^2) = h_2^2 = \dfrac{a\mu}{2} = \dfrac{4a}{3}\mu(1 - e_2^2)$

giving $\quad e_2 = (\frac{5}{8})^{\frac{1}{2}}$ Q.E.D.

Example 2. A planet, of mass M and periodic time T, when at aphelion comes into collision with a meteor of mass m, moving in the same orbit in the opposite direction with velocity v. If $\dfrac{m}{M}$ be small, show that the major axis of the planet's path is reduced by

$$\frac{2m}{M}\cdot\frac{vT}{\pi}\sqrt{\frac{1-e}{1+e}} \qquad \text{(L.U.)}$$

Aphelion is the point of the orbit furthest away from the centre of force, that is at one end of the major axis with $r = a(1 + e)$. The law of force for a planet of mass M will be $-\dfrac{\mu M}{r^2}$ and the velocity at any point will be V where

$$V^2 = \mu\left\{\frac{2}{r} - \frac{1}{a}\right\} \quad . \quad . \quad . \quad . \quad (10)$$

For *small changes* in velocity we may proceed by differentials, whence (10) gives

$$2V\,dV = \frac{\mu}{a^2}\,da$$

The increase in the major axis will therefore be

$$2da = \frac{4a^2V}{\mu} dV \quad . \quad . \quad . \quad . \quad (11)$$

Since momentum is conserved on impact (v. 1.5) the new velocity V' is given by

$$(M + m)V' = MV - mv$$

so that $V' = V - \frac{m}{M}v$, if $\frac{m}{M}$ is sufficiently small. Hence $V' - V = dV = -\frac{m}{M}v$ and (11) shows that the axis *decreases*. (11) now gives the decrease in the axis as

$$|\,2da\,| = \frac{4m}{\mu M}.v.a^2.V \quad . \quad . \quad . \quad (12)$$

Also V is the velocity in the original orbit when $r = a(1 + e)$, so that

$$V^2 = \frac{\mu}{a}\left\{\frac{2}{1+e} - 1\right\} = \frac{\mu}{a}\left(\frac{1-e}{1+e}\right)$$

Also the periodic time will be $T = \frac{2\pi a^{3/2}}{\sqrt{\mu}}$ (v. 6.1(15)) and so (12) becomes

$$|\,2da\,| = \frac{4m}{\mu M}.\frac{\sqrt{\mu}}{\sqrt{a}}\sqrt{\frac{1-e}{1+e}}.a^2.v$$

or

$$|\,2da\,| = \frac{2m}{M}.\frac{vT}{\pi}.\sqrt{\frac{1-e}{1+e}}$$

Example 3. A particle of unit mass is describing an elliptic orbit of axes $2a$ and $2b$ under an attraction μr to the centre C when it is at a distance r from C. Prove that its speed v is given by

$$v^2 = \mu(a^2 + b^2 - r^2)$$

and that the angular momentum about C is $ab\sqrt{\mu}$.

If, in the above orbit, $a = 2b$ and the intensity of attraction is suddenly increased in the ratio $1 : 4$ when $r = \frac{3b}{2}$, prove that the axes of the new orbit are $(\sqrt{79} \pm \sqrt{15})b/4$. (L.U.)

Comparing the equation

$$v^2 = \frac{h^2}{p^2} = C - \mu r^2$$

with

$$\frac{a^2b^2}{p^2} = a^2 + b^2 - r^2$$

we get

$$C = \mu(a^2 + b^2) \quad \text{and} \quad h = ab\sqrt{\mu}$$

Hence

$$v^2 = \mu(a^2 + b^2 - r^2)$$

Now μ changes to $\mu' = 4\mu$ without change of r or of v. Suppose a, b become A, B respectively. Then we get, with $a = 2b$ and $r = \frac{3b}{2}$

$$5b^2 - \frac{9b^2}{4} = 4\left\{A^2 + B^2 - \frac{9b^2}{4}\right\}$$

giving
$$A^2 + B^2 = \frac{47}{16}b^2 \quad . \quad . \quad . \quad . \quad . \quad (13)$$

Since h remains unaltered we have

$$2b^2\sqrt{\mu} = AB\sqrt{4\mu}$$

or
$$AB = b^2 \quad . \quad . \quad . \quad . \quad . \quad . \quad (14)$$

(13) and (14) give
$$(A + B)^2 = \frac{79}{16}b^2$$

and
$$(A - B)^2 = \frac{15}{16}b^2$$

Hence
$$2A,\ 2B = \{\sqrt{79} \pm \sqrt{15}\}\frac{b}{4} \qquad \text{Q.E.D.}$$

Example 4. A particle of unit mass is describing an ellipse with angular momentum h, and when at one end of the minor axis receives a very small impulse u along the radius vector to the focus. Show that the major axis is altered by $\frac{4abeu}{h}$, that the eccentricity is altered by $\frac{ua}{h}(1 - e^2)^{3/2}$, and that the major axis is turned through the angle $\frac{3au(1 - e^2)}{h}$, where a, b are the semi-axes and e the eccentricity of the ellipse.

Fig. 61 shows the particle at K when it receives a small additional

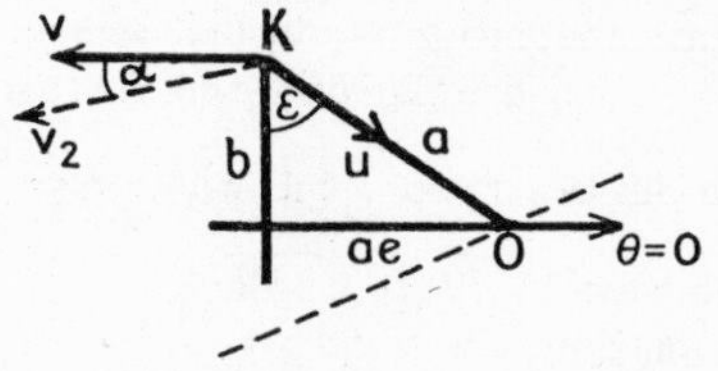

Fig. 61.

velocity u along KO. Since O is a focus we have $OK = r = a$ and $\sin \epsilon = e$. Using (3) we can write

$$\tan \alpha = \alpha = \frac{u \cos \epsilon}{v - u \sin \epsilon} = \frac{u \cos \epsilon}{v} + O(u^2) = \frac{u}{v}\sqrt{1 - e^2} \qquad (15)$$

and so $$p_2 = p_1 - \sqrt{a^2 - p_1^2}.\frac{u}{v}\sqrt{1 - e^2}$$

Since $p_1 = b = a\sqrt{1 - e^2}$ we get

$$p_2 = p_1 + \Delta p_1 = b - \frac{eub}{v}$$

and so $$\Delta p_1 = -\frac{eb}{v}.u \quad . \quad . \quad . \quad . \quad (16)$$

Now, using increments, (1) implies

$$2v\Delta v = \frac{\mu}{a^2}\Delta a \quad . \quad . \quad . \quad . \quad (17)$$

and, with $r = a$, $$v^2 = \frac{\mu}{a} \quad . \quad . \quad . \quad . \quad . \quad (18)$$

If v_2 = new velocity, we have

$$v_2^2 = u^2 \cos^2 \alpha + (v - u \sin \alpha)^2 = v^2 - 2uv \sin \alpha + u^2$$

and so $$v_2 = v + \Delta v = v - eu + O(u^2)$$

Writing $\Delta v = -eu$ in (17) therefore gives

$$\Delta a = -2\sqrt{\frac{\mu}{a}}.\frac{a^2}{\mu}.eu$$

Since we have $h^2 = \mu\frac{b^2}{a} = \mu a(1 - e^2)$, we therefore get

$$\Delta a = -\frac{2euab}{h} \quad . \quad . \quad . \quad . \quad (19)$$

and the change in the major axis is twice this. **Q.E.D.**

Since $h = pv$ we also get

$$\Delta h = p\Delta v + v\Delta p$$
$$= -eub - eub = -2eub \quad . \quad . \quad . \quad (20)$$

and from $$h^2 = \mu a(1 - e^2)$$
we get $$2h\Delta h = \mu\Delta a(1 - e^2) - 2\mu ae\Delta e$$

This gives, by (19) and (20),

$$\Delta e = \frac{ua(1 - e^2)^{3/2}}{h} = \frac{ub^3}{a^2h} \quad . \quad . \quad . \quad . \quad (21)$$

Finally, (5) shows that the axis turns through a small angle ϕ which may be regarded as $-\Delta\theta$. Hence writing

$$\frac{l}{r} = 1 + e \cos \theta$$

we get, since $r = a$ before and after the impulse,

$$\frac{\Delta l}{a} = \Delta e.\cos \theta - e \sin \theta.\Delta\theta$$

Writing $\mu l = h^2$ we get $\Delta l = 2h\Delta h/\mu$, and using (20) and (21) gives

$$\Delta\theta = \frac{3au(1 - e^2)}{h}$$

since $\cos\theta = -e$, $\sin\theta = \sqrt{1 - e^2}$.

Exercise VI

1. A particle P, of mass m, moves under an attractive force $m\lambda u^3$ towards a fixed centre of force S, where λ is constant and u is the reciprocal of SP. If θ is the angle turned through by SP from its initial position, find from the equations of motion the differential equation connecting u and θ.

If P is projected with velocity $5\lambda^{\frac{1}{2}}/4l$ at right angles to SP when SP equals l, show that when P has receded to infinity the radius vector will have turned through an angle $\frac{5}{6}\pi$. (M.T.)

2. A particle moves in a plane under an attraction n^2r per unit mass towards a fixed centre O in the plane, where r denotes distance from O. Show that in general the orbit is an ellipse.

Show that the region of the plane which is accessible by projection from a given point A with given velocity w is bounded by an ellipse having O as centre and A as focus. (M.T.)

3. Establish the formulae

$$\frac{d^2u}{d\theta^2} + u = \frac{P}{h^2u^2}, \quad \dot{\theta} = hu^2, \quad (u = 1/r)$$

for the motion of a particle describing a central orbit under an attraction P per unit mass to the origin of polar co-ordinates (r, θ).

If $P = \mu u^5$, find the speed v with which the particle can describe the circle $r = a$.

If the particle moves under this attraction, with the same areal constant as in the circular path, and $\dot{r} = -3v/4\sqrt{2}$ when $r = 2a$, $\theta = 0$, find the equation of the spiral path of the particle and show that as θ tends to infinity the path is asymptotic to the circle $r = a$. (L.U.)

4. A particle P of unit mass moves on a smooth horizontal plane and is repelled by a force equal to μ/OP^3, where μ is a constant, acting away from a fixed point O at a height a above the plane. The particle is projected from infinity along a line at a distance $b(< a)$ from O', the orthogonal projection of O on the plane. If the speed of projection is $\sqrt{\mu}/\sqrt{(a^2 - b^2)}$, show that the particle will approach to within a distance $\sqrt{ab}$ of O' before receding to infinity again along the plane. Show also that the direction of motion of the particle is eventually turned through an angle

$$\pi - b\int_{ab}^{\infty}\sqrt{\frac{w + a^2}{w^2 - a^2b^2}}\,\frac{dw}{w} \qquad \text{(L.U.)}$$

5. A particle describes a central orbit with acceleration $\mu(r^{-5} - \frac{1}{8}a^2r^{-7})$, starting from a point where $r = a$ with velocity $\frac{5}{4}\sqrt{(2\mu)}/a^2$ at an inclination $\sin^{-1}\frac{4}{5}$ to the radius vector. Prove that its path is

$$1 - \theta = a\sqrt{3}/\sqrt{(4r^2 - a^2)} \qquad \text{(C.)}$$

6. A particle describes a central orbit with acceleration $\mu/(r-a)^2$ towards the origin, starting with the velocity from infinity at a distance c (which is greater than a and less than $2a$) at an angle $2\cos^{-1}\sqrt{(a/c)}$. Prove that the path is given by the equation

$$\tfrac{1}{2}\theta = \tanh^{-1}\sqrt{\{(r-a/a\}} - \tan^{-1}\sqrt{\{(r-a)/a\}} \qquad \text{(C.)}$$

7. A particle moving with a central acceleration

$$4\kappa^2(2r^{-3} - 3ra^{-4} - 2r^3a^{-6})$$

starts from a point distant $\frac{4}{3}a$ from the origin in direction making an angle $\tan^{-1} 27/125$ with the radius vector with such velocity that the rate of description of areas is κ. Show that the equation of the orbit is

$$1 + \frac{r^2}{a^2} = \coth^2\left(\frac{a}{\sqrt{(a^2+r^2)}} + \theta + \tanh^{-1}\tfrac{3}{5} - \tfrac{3}{5}\right) \qquad \text{(C.)}$$

8. A particle is projected with velocity less than that from infinity under a force tending to a fixed point and varying inversely as the nth power of the distance. Prove that if n is not < 3 the particle will ultimately fall into the centre of force. (C.)

9. A particle moves under a central force varying inversely as the nth power of the distance ($n > 1$), the velocity of projection is that due to a fall from rest at infinity, and the direction of projection makes an angle β with the radius vector of length R. Prove that the maximum distance is $R\operatorname{cosec}^{\frac{2}{n-3}}\beta$ when $n > 3$, and that the particle goes to infinity if $n =$ or < 3. (C.)

10. Prove that the time of describing any part of a central orbit is

$$\int \frac{r\,dr}{\sqrt{\{2r^2(C+V) - h^2\}}},$$

taken between appropriate limits, where V is the potential, and C and h are constants depending on the initial conditions. (C).

11. Prove that, if a possible orbit under a central force $\phi(r)$ is known, a possible orbit under a central force $\phi(r) + \lambda r^{-3}$ can be found. In particular prove that a particle projected from an apse at distance a with velocity $\sqrt{(\lambda+\mu)}/a$, under an attraction

$$\tfrac{1}{2}\mu(n-1)a^{n-3}r^{-n} + \lambda r^{-3}, \quad (n > 3),$$

will arrive at the centre in time

$$\frac{a^2}{2}\left(\frac{\pi}{\mu}\right)^{\frac{1}{2}} \Gamma\left(\frac{n+1}{2n-6}\right) \Big/ \Gamma\left(\frac{2}{n-3}\right) \qquad \text{(C.)}$$

12. A particle moves in a plane under an attraction $f(r)$ per unit mass towards a fixed centre of attraction O in the plane. If the particle moves in a circle of radius a with O as centre, prove that its velocity is $\sqrt{\{af(a)\}}$.

The particle is projected from a point A, at distance a from O, with a velocity whose component perpendicular to OA is $\sqrt{\{af(a)\}}$, and whose component along OA is λa, where λ is small. Show that the orbit is nearly circular if

$$3f(a) + af'(a) > 0$$

and that, if this condition is satisfied, the apsidal distances are $a(1 \pm \lambda/n)$, where

$$an^2 = 3f(a) + af'(a) \qquad \text{(M.T.)}$$

13. A comet approaches the sun with velocity v from a great distance in such a manner that it would miss the sun by a distance b were it not deflected. Let the actual orbit be given by $u(\theta)$, where $1/u$ is the distance from the sun and θ is the angle measured relative to the point of closest approach. Show that conservation of angular momentum yields $\dot{\theta} = vbu^2$ and that conservation of energy yields

$$\dot{u}^2/u^4 + v^2b^2u^2 - 2\gamma Mu = v^2$$

where γ is the gravitational constant and M the mass of the sun. Hence obtain $u(\theta)$ in the form

$$u = (\sin\phi + \cos\theta)/b\cos\phi$$

where ϕ is a constant angle whose tangent is $\gamma M/v^2b$.

Show also that the comet will eventually recede to infinity having its direction of motion turned through an angle 2ϕ. (M.T.)

14. A comet describes about the Sun an ellipse of eccentricity e nearly equal to unity. At a point where the radius vector makes an angle θ with the apse line, the comet is instantaneously affected by a planet so that its velocity is increased in the ratio $n + 1 : n$, where n is great, without altering its direction. Show that, if the new orbit is a parabola,

$$e = 1 - \frac{4}{n}\cos^2 \tfrac{1}{2}\theta \quad \text{nearly} \qquad \text{(C.)}$$

15. Prove that the central orbit described with acceleration $\mu/(\text{distance})^2$, by a particle projected with velocity V from a point where the distance is R, is a rectangular hyperbola if the angle of projection is

$$\operatorname{cosec}^{-1}\{V\sqrt{(V^2R^2 - 2\mu R)}/\mu\} \qquad \text{(C.)}$$

16. A particle is describing an elliptic orbit about a centre of force at a focus. With the usual notation, prove that

$$v^2 = \mu\left(\frac{2}{r} - \frac{1}{a}\right), \qquad h^2 = \mu l$$

Prove also that the time average of the kinetic energy per unit mass taken over a period is $\mu/2a$. (L.U.)

17. Discuss the stability of the motion of a particle describing a circular orbit of radius a under an attractive force $f(r)$ per unit mass acting to the centre of the circle.

If
$$f(r) = \mu\left\{\frac{1}{r} - \frac{2a}{r^2} + \frac{\beta^2}{r^3}\right\}$$

where μ, a and β ($a > \beta$) are positive, prove that there can be no circular orbit lying in the region between two concentric circles, and discuss the stability of possible orbits. (L.U.)

18. A particle describes an elliptic orbit about a focus and, when at the end of the minor axis, it receives a small impulse towards the centre equal to $\frac{1}{n}$th of its momentum. Show that the eccentricity e is increased or diminished by $\frac{1}{n}\sqrt{(1 - e^2)}$ according to the direction of motion at the instant. (C.)

19. An ellipse of eccentricity e and latus rectum $2l$ is described freely about a focus, with moment of momentum equal to h. When the particle is at the nearer apse it receives a small radial impulse μ. Prove that the apse line is turned through the angle $l\mu/eh$. (C.)

20. A particle is describing an ellipse about a centre of force in one focus S, and when it is at the end E of the further latus rectum it receives a blow in direction SE which makes it move at right angles to SE. Find the momentum generated by the blow, and prove that the particle will proceed to describe an ellipse of eccentricity $\{2e^2/(1 + e^2)\}$. (C.)

21. A particle is describing an ellipse about a focus S, and when it is at one end of the latus rectum it receives a blow which makes it describe a confocal hyperbola. Prove that the direction of the blow makes with the tangent to the ellipse an angle $\cot^{-1} e$, where e is the eccentricity of the ellipse. (C.)

CHAPTER VII

KINETICS OF PARTICLE MOTION (III)

7.1 Motion on a fixed plane curve

Using the results of 4.3 we can write down the equations of motion for a particle moving under given forces on a fixed plane curve (v. Fig. 62). If the resultant normal force (the normal being in the sense of ψ increasing) is N and the resultant tangential force (in the sense of s increasing) is T, then the equations are

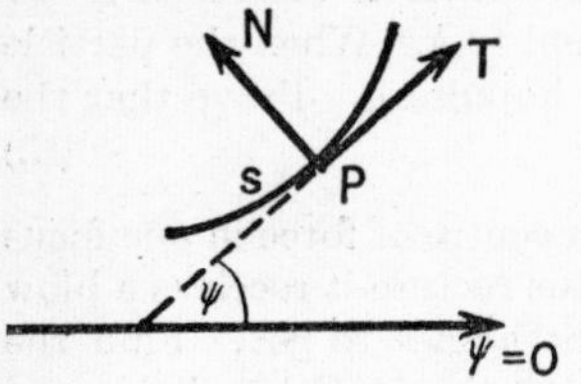

FIG. 62.

$$m\frac{dv}{dt} = mv\frac{dv}{ds} = m\frac{d^2s}{dt^2} = T \quad . \qquad (1)$$

and

$$m\frac{v^2}{\rho} = mv^2\frac{d\psi}{ds} = N \quad . \quad . \quad . \quad . \qquad (2)$$

In (2) the algebraic value of ρ $\left(\text{or } \frac{ds}{d\psi}\right)$ must be taken.

Example 1. The simple pendulum. This is a simple case of a particle (the bob of the pendulum) being constrained to move on the arc of a circle, in a vertical plane under gravity (v. Fig. 63 (i)). If the length of the string is l and the tension in the string T when OP is inclined to the downward vertical at an angle θ we have (v. 4.3, Ex. 1)

$$m\ddot{\theta} = -mg\sin\theta$$

i.e.

$$\ddot{\theta} = -\left(\frac{g}{l}\right)\sin\theta \quad . \quad . \quad . \quad . \qquad (3)$$

and

$$m\dot{\theta}^2 = T - mg\cos\theta \; . \quad . \quad . \quad . \qquad (4)$$

Equation (4) gives the tension for any θ, and equation (3) shows that, provided θ is *sufficiently small*, the bob moves with S.H.M. (v. 5.2(6)) whose equation is

$$\ddot{\theta} = -\left(\frac{g}{l}\right)\theta \, . \quad . \quad . \quad . \quad . \quad . \qquad (5)$$

The well-known periodic time follows as $\tau = 2\pi\sqrt{\frac{l}{g}}$.

If the bob is allowed to swing out of the vertical plane of Fig. 63 we analyse the motion vectorially as follows (v. Fig. 63 (ii)). We have

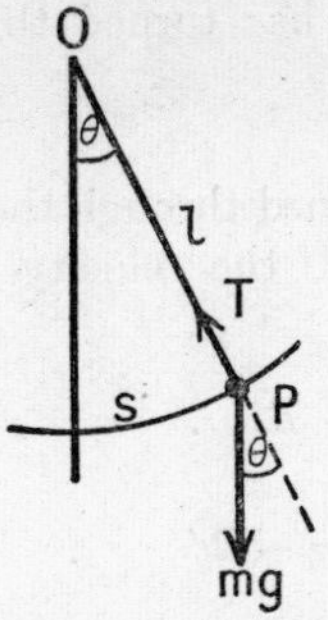

FIG. 63 (i).

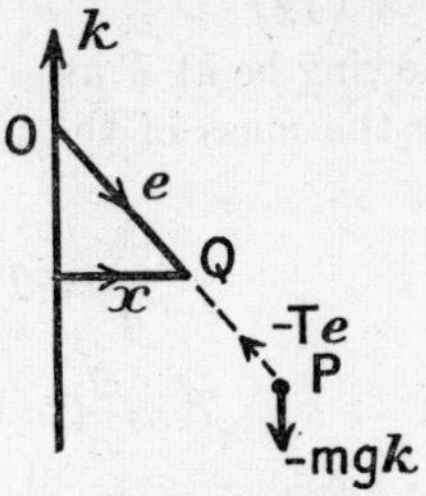

FIG. 63 (ii).

$\overline{OP} = \boldsymbol{r} = l\,\boldsymbol{e}$, where $\boldsymbol{e}$ is a unit vector along the string, and so

$$ml\,\ddot{\boldsymbol{e}} = -\,T\,\boldsymbol{e} - mg\,\boldsymbol{k}$$

Hence
$$l\,\boldsymbol{e} \times \ddot{\boldsymbol{e}} = -\,g\,\boldsymbol{e} \times \boldsymbol{k} \quad . \quad . \quad . \quad . \quad (6)$$

If the bob swings only through small distances we can put $\boldsymbol{e} = -\,\boldsymbol{k} + \boldsymbol{x}$ and neglect the products x^2 and $x \times \ddot{x}$. Then (6) reduces to

$$l(\boldsymbol{k} \times \ddot{\boldsymbol{x}}) = -\,g(\boldsymbol{k} \times \boldsymbol{x}) . \quad . \quad . \quad . \quad (7)$$

Now $\quad 1 = \boldsymbol{e}^2 = \boldsymbol{k}^2 - 2\boldsymbol{x}.\boldsymbol{k} + \boldsymbol{x}^2 = \boldsymbol{k}^2 - 2\boldsymbol{x}.\boldsymbol{k} = 1 - 2\boldsymbol{x}.\boldsymbol{k}$

and so $\quad \boldsymbol{k}.\boldsymbol{x} = 0,\quad$ and therefore $\quad \boldsymbol{k}.\dot{\boldsymbol{x}} = \boldsymbol{k}.\ddot{\boldsymbol{x}} = 0$

Multiplying (7) vectorially by $\boldsymbol{k}$ and using 2.12(1), we get

$$\ddot{\boldsymbol{x}} = -\left(\frac{g}{l}\right)\boldsymbol{x} \quad . \quad . \quad . \quad . \quad (8)$$

The vector $\boldsymbol{x}$ lies entirely in the plane perpendicular to $\boldsymbol{k}$ and (8) shows that the point Q (and therefore P) moves under a central force of attraction of the form $-\,\mu r$. This has been analysed in 6.2, Ex. 4 showing that Q (and P) describes ellipses in the plane.

The reader will also be able to prove this by using rectangular Cartesian co-ordinates (x, y) in the plane, since the equations

$$\ddot{x} = -\,\omega^2 x\,; \quad \ddot{y} = -\,\omega^2 y$$

give solutions

$$x = A\cos\omega t + B\sin\omega t\,; \quad y = C\cos\omega t + D\sin\omega t$$

Eliminating t shows that (x, y) lies on an ellipse.

Example 2. A small ring can slide on a thin smooth wire which is in the form of a circle of radius a. The wire is fixed in a vertical plane, the ring being attached to the lowest point of the wire by a light elastic string of natural length a and modulus equal to the weight of the ring. The ring is projected from the highest point of the wire with speed $\sqrt{\tfrac{1}{2}ga}$. Find its speed when it reaches the lowest point. Show that the reaction of the wire on the ring at first acts outwards and begins to act inwards when the string has turned through an angle $\cos^{-1}\left(\frac{11}{12}\right)$. (L.U.)

Let the ring be at P after the string has turned through the angle ϕ, and take the mass of the ring to be unity. If the velocity at P is v we have

$$\frac{v^2}{a} = T\cos\phi - g\cos\theta - R \quad . \quad . \quad . \quad (9)$$

where

$$T = \frac{g}{a}(2a\cos\phi - a), \quad \theta = \pi - 2\phi \quad . \quad . \quad (10)$$

The *energy equation* gives

$$\tfrac{1}{2}v^2 - ag(1 + \cos\theta) + \tfrac{1}{2}.\frac{g}{a}(2a\cos\phi - a)^2 = \tfrac{1}{2}.\tfrac{1}{2}ga + \tfrac{1}{2}.\frac{g}{a}.a^2$$

giving

$$\frac{v^2}{a} = \tfrac{1}{2}g\,(5 + 4\cos\theta + 8\cos\phi - \cos^2\phi)\ (. \quad . \quad (11)$$

The speed at A follows from (11) by writing $\theta = 0$, $\phi = \pi/2$. Now (9), (10) and (11) imply

$$\frac{2R}{g} = 24\cos^2\phi - 10\cos\phi - 11$$
$$= (12\cos\phi - 11)(2\cos\phi + 1) \quad . \quad . \quad (12)$$

At $\phi = 0$, $R = \frac{3}{2}g > 0$ and acts outwards.

At $\phi = \pi/2$, R $= -\frac{11}{2}g < 0$ and acts inwards.

R changes sign when $\phi = \cos^{-1}\left(\frac{11}{12}\right)$.

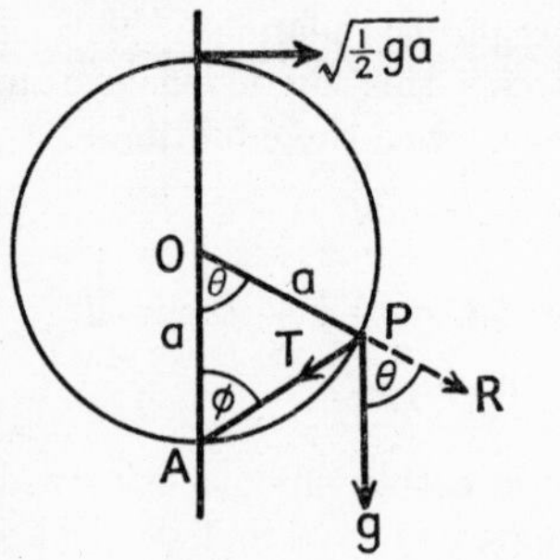

FIG. 64.

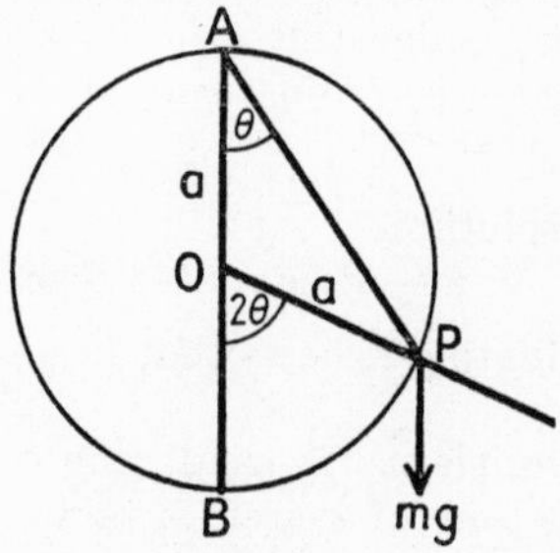

FIG. 65.

Example 3. A bead of mass m slides on a smooth circular wire of radius a fixed in a vertical plane. The bead is joined to the highest point A of the circle by a light elastic string of natural length a and modulus $3mg$. Prove that if the bead is let go from rest with the string just taut, the length of the string after a time t is

$$2a.\frac{1 + 3\cosh nt}{5 + 3\cosh nt} \qquad \text{(M.T.)}$$

The general position of the bead is shown at P in Fig. 65. The initial position corresponds to $\theta = \pi/3$. The energy equation gives

$$4a^2\dot{\theta}^2 + 3ag(2\cos\theta - 1)^2 - 4ag\cos^2\theta = \text{constant} = -ag$$

reducing to $$a\dot{\theta}^2 = g(2\cos\theta - 1)(1 - \cos\theta) \quad . \quad . \quad . \quad (13)$$

Put $s = \cos\theta$, so that $AP = 2as$, and (13) gives

$$a\dot{s}^2 = g(2s - 1)(1 - s)(1 - s^2)$$

or $$\dot{s}^2 = n^2(1 + s)(1 - s)^2(s - \tfrac{1}{2}) \quad \text{with } n^2 = \frac{2g}{a}$$

We now have $$\int_{\frac{1}{2}}^{s} \frac{ds}{(1 - s)\sqrt{(1 + s)(s - \frac{1}{2})}} = nt$$

and substituting $1 - s = \dfrac{1}{x}$, we get

$$nt = \sqrt{2}\int_2^x \frac{dx}{\sqrt{2x^2 - 5x + 2}}$$

$$= \int_2^x \frac{dx}{\sqrt{\left(x - \frac{5}{4}\right)^2 - \frac{9}{16}}}$$

$$= \cosh^{-1}\left(\frac{4x - 5}{3}\right) - \cosh^{-1} 1$$

Hence $4x - 5 = 3\cosh nt$ gives

$$s = \frac{1 + 3\cosh nt}{5 + 3\cosh nt} \qquad \text{Q.E.D.}$$

We notice that $s \to 1$ as $t \to \infty$ so that the bead takes an "infinite time" to reach B.

Example 4. A heavy particle is projected horizontally with speed U on a fixed rough plane inclined at an angle α to the horizontal. If subsequently the direction of motion makes an angle θ with the downward direction of a line of greatest slope, prove that the speed is then

$$U \operatorname{cosec}\theta\,(\tan\tfrac{1}{2}\theta)^{\mu\cot\alpha}$$

where μ is the coefficient of friction (L.U.)

In Fig. 66 we have $\theta = \dfrac{\pi}{2} - \psi$, and equations of motion

$$m\frac{dv}{dt} = mg\sin\alpha\cos\theta - \mu mg\cos\alpha \quad . \quad . \quad (14)$$

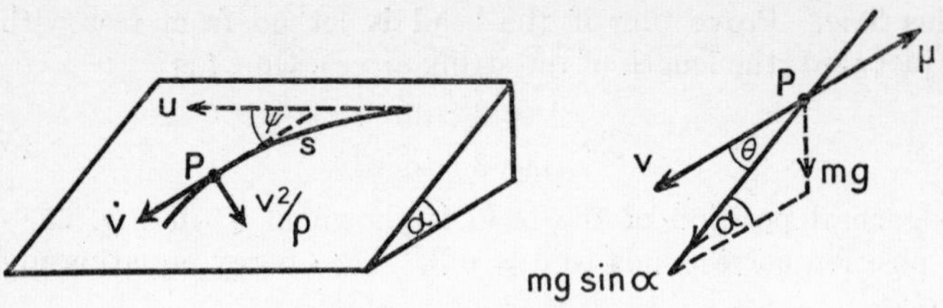

FIG. 66.

$$m\frac{v^2}{\rho} = mg \sin \alpha \sin \theta \quad . \quad . \quad . \quad . \quad . \quad (15)$$

These become $$v\frac{dv}{ds} = g \sin \alpha \cos \theta - \mu g \cos \alpha \quad . \quad . \quad . \quad (16)$$

and, since $d\theta = -d\psi$,

$$v^2\frac{d\theta}{ds} = -g \sin \alpha \sin \theta \quad . \quad . \quad . \quad . \quad (17)$$

Dividing (16) by (17), gives

$$\frac{1}{v}\frac{dv}{d\theta} = \mu \cot \alpha \operatorname{cosec} \theta - \cot \theta$$

giving $$\log Av = (\mu \cot \alpha) \log (\tan \tfrac{1}{2}\theta) - \log (\sin \theta)$$

where A is a constant of integration.

Hence $$Av = \operatorname{cosec} \theta (\tan \tfrac{1}{2}\theta)^{\mu \cot \alpha}$$

and since $v = U$ when $\theta = \pi/2$ we get $A^{-1} = U$. Q.E.D.

Example 5. A rough cycloidal tube is fixed with its axis vertical and vertex uppermost. A particle is projected within the tube from the vertex with a velocity $\sqrt{4ag}.\sin \alpha$, where a is the radius of the generating circle of the cycloid and $\tan \alpha$ is the coefficient of friction. Prove that the particle will reach the cusp with velocity V, where

$$V^2 = 4ag \cos^2 \alpha \quad \text{(L.U.)}$$

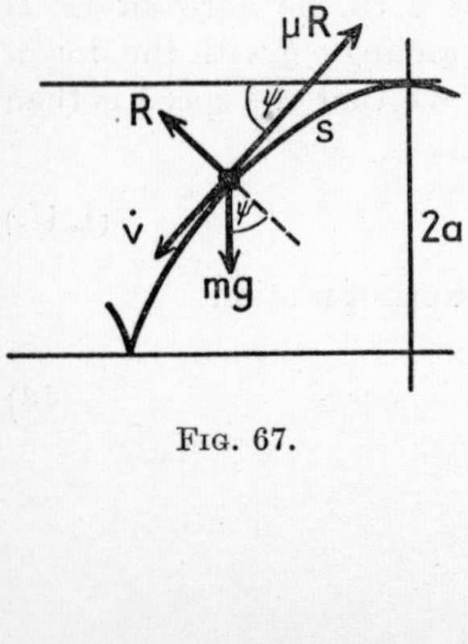

FIG. 67.

The equations of motion will be (v. Fig. 67)

$$m\frac{dv}{dt} = mg \sin \psi - \mu R \quad . \quad (18)$$

$$m\frac{v^2}{\rho} = mg \cos \psi - R \quad . \quad (19)$$

Eliminating R between (18) and (19) gives

$$\frac{dv}{dt} - \mu\frac{v^2}{\rho} = g (\sin \psi - \mu \cos \psi)$$

From 4.3(5) we have $v = \dot{s} = 4a \cos\psi\,\dot{\psi} = \rho\dot{\psi}$, and so

$$\frac{dv}{dt} - \mu v \frac{d\psi}{dt} = g\,(\sin\psi - \mu\cos\psi)$$

which is
$$\frac{d}{dt}\{ve^{-\mu\psi}\} = ge^{-\mu\psi}\,(\sin\psi - \mu\cos\psi) \quad . \quad . \quad (20)$$

Writing
$$z = e^{-\mu\psi}\,(\sin\psi - \mu\cos\psi)$$

we get
$$\frac{dz}{dt} = (1+\mu^2)e^{-\mu\psi}\cos\psi\,.\,\dot{\psi} = \frac{(1+\mu^2)}{4a}\,.\,ve^{-\mu\psi}$$

Hence (20) can be written

$$\frac{d^2z}{dt^2} = \left(\frac{g}{4a}\right)(1+\mu^2)z$$

giving an integral
$$\left(\frac{dz}{dt}\right)^2 = \left(\frac{g}{4a}\right)(1+\mu^2)z^2 + C$$

that is,
$$(1+\mu^2)v^2 = 4ag(\sin\psi - \mu\cos\psi)^2 + Ae^{2\mu\psi} \quad . \quad (21)$$

with A an arbitrary constant.

Since $v^2 = 4ag\sin^2\alpha$ when $\psi = 0$ (and $\mu = \tan\alpha$) (21) gives $A = 0$, and so

$$v^2\sec^2\alpha = 4ag\,(\sin\psi - \mu\cos\psi)^2$$

When the particle reaches the cusp we have $\psi = \pi/2$.

Hence
$$v^2 = V^2 = 4ag\cos^2\alpha$$
Q.E.D.

7.2 Plane motion in a resisting medium

Let us consider the motion of a particle in a vertical plane under gravity, when the medium offers a resistance of the form kv^p per unit mass ; k, p being constants and v the velocity of the particle. We find that the use of the results of 4.3 gives us many interesting solutions.

From Fig. 68 we find the equations of motion,

$$\frac{dv}{dt} = v\frac{dv}{ds} = -g\sin\psi = kv^p \qquad (1)$$

$$\frac{v^2}{\rho} = v^2\frac{d\psi}{ds} = -g\cos\psi \quad . \qquad (2)$$

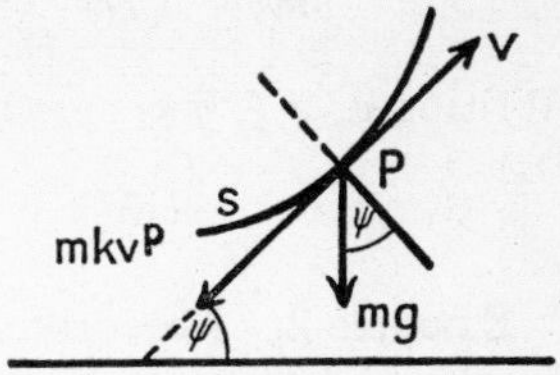

FIG. 68.

Since the particle is not constrained to move on a specific curve there is no normal reaction R comparable to the examples of 7.1. Now write the horizontal velocity $u = v\cos\psi$,

whence
$$\frac{du}{d\psi} = -v\sin\psi + \cos\psi\frac{dv}{d\psi} \quad . \quad . \quad . \quad (3)$$

(1) and (2) give

$$v\frac{dv}{ds} = \frac{v}{\rho}.\frac{dv}{d\psi} = -\frac{g\cos\psi}{v}.\frac{dv}{d\psi}$$

$$= -g\sin\psi - kv^p$$

that is,

$$g\cos\psi\frac{dv}{d\psi} = vg\sin\psi + kv^{p+1} \qquad (4)$$

(3) and (4) now give

$$g\frac{du}{d\psi} = kv^{p+1}$$

which is

$$\frac{d\psi}{du} = \left(\frac{k}{g}\right)u^{p+1}\sec^{p+1}\psi \qquad (5)$$

This possesses an elementary solution when p is integral.

Example 1. Take the case of $p = 5$, and prove that the hodograph of the trajectory is

$$y(15x^4 + 10x^2y^2 + 3y^4) = Cx^5 + 3g/k$$

where C is a constant, and the y-axis is drawn vertically downwards. (L.U.)

First, we notice that if a particle P with position vector $\boldsymbol{r}$ describes a plane curve $f(\boldsymbol{r}) = 0$ we define the hodograph of the motion as the curve $g(\dot{\boldsymbol{r}}) = 0$ described by the point Q whose position vector is $\boldsymbol{s} = \dot{\boldsymbol{r}}$. Thus if the co-ordinates of P are x, y where $x = f_1(t)$, $y = f_2(t)$, the co-ordinates of Q will be ξ, η where $\xi = f_1'(t)$, $\eta = f_2'(t)$.

In this problem, using (5), we have

$$\int\frac{du}{u^6} = \frac{k}{g}\int\sec^6\psi\,d\psi + C'$$

giving

$$-\frac{1}{5u^5} = \left(\frac{k}{g}\right)\{\tan\psi + \tfrac{2}{3}\tan^3\psi + \tfrac{1}{5}\tan^5\psi\} + C'$$

Writing $u = \xi$, $\dot{y} = -\eta$ and $\tan\psi = \frac{\dot{y}}{\dot{x}} = -\frac{\eta}{\xi}$, we get

$$\eta(15\xi^4 + 10\xi^2\eta^2 + 3\eta^4) = C\xi^5 + 3g/k \qquad \text{Q.E.D.}$$

Example 2. The driving force of a self-propelled rocket is related to the resistance it encounters in such a way that it travels at a constant speed u. Prove that, when projected at an angle α, the equation of its path is

$$y = \frac{u^2}{g}\log\left\{\frac{\cos\alpha}{\cos\left(\alpha + \frac{gx}{u^2}\right)}\right\} \qquad \text{(L.U.)}$$

The motion of the rocket, under gravity, will be such that s will increase as ψ decreases, i.e. in (2) we must take $\rho = -\dfrac{ds}{d\psi}$. Then we have

$$u^2 \frac{d\psi}{ds} = g \cos \psi \quad . \quad . \quad . \quad . \quad (6)$$

together with the general equations

$$\cos \psi = \frac{dx}{ds}; \quad \tan \psi = \frac{dy}{dx} \quad . \quad . \quad . \quad (7)$$

Now (6) and (7) give $$\frac{d\psi}{dx} = \left(\frac{g}{u^2}\right)$$

so that $$\psi = a + \frac{gx}{u^2} \quad (\psi = a \text{ when } x = 0)$$

and (7) implies $$\frac{dy}{dx} = \tan\left(a + \frac{gx}{u^2}\right)$$

Since $y = 0$ when $x = 0$, this gives

$$y = \frac{u^2}{g} \log \left| \frac{\cos a}{\cos\left(a + \dfrac{gx}{u^2}\right)} \right| \qquad \text{Q.E.D.}$$

We also notice that $y = 0$ when $\dfrac{gx}{u^2} = 0$ or $\pi - 2a$ and so the *horizontal range* is $\dfrac{u^2}{g}(\pi - 2a)$.

Example 3. A particle of mass m moves under equal constant forces mf along the tangent and normal to its path, and the resistance is $mf.\dfrac{v^2}{k^2}$ when the velocity is v. Prove that the intrinsic equation of the path is $$k^2\{e^{2fs/k^2} - 1\} = u^2\{e^{2\psi} - 1\}$$
where u is the velocity of projection.

The equations of motion are

$$v\frac{dv}{ds} = f - f.\frac{v^2}{k^2} \quad . \quad . \quad . \quad . \quad (8)$$

and $$v^2 \frac{d\psi}{ds} = f \quad . \quad . \quad . \quad . \quad . \quad (9)$$

(8) gives $$v\frac{dv}{ds} = \frac{k^2}{f}(k^2 - v^2)$$

so that $$\int_u^v \frac{v\, dv}{k^2 - v^2} = \frac{f}{k^2}\int_0^s ds$$

i.e. $$-\tfrac{1}{2} \log \frac{(k^2 - v^2)}{(k^2 - u^2)} = \frac{fs}{k^2}$$

Hence we have $$(k^2 - v^2)e^{2fs/k^2} = k^2 - u^2 \quad . \quad . \quad . \quad . \quad (10)$$

But (8) and (9) also give

$$\frac{1}{v}.\frac{dv}{d\psi} = \frac{1}{k^2}(k^2 - v^2)$$

giving
$$\int_u^v \frac{dv}{v(k^2 - v^2)} = \frac{1}{k^2}\int_0^\psi d\psi$$

i.e.
$$\int_u^u \left\{\frac{1}{v} + \frac{1}{2}.\frac{1}{k - v} - \frac{1}{2}.\frac{1}{k + v}\right\}dv = \psi$$

Hence
$$\frac{v}{\sqrt{k^2 - v^2}} = e^\psi.\frac{u}{\sqrt{k^2 - u^2}}$$

which gives
$$\frac{v^2}{k^2 - v^2} = \frac{u^2}{k^2 - u^2}.e^{2\psi} \quad . \quad . \quad . \quad (11)$$

Now (10) and (11) give $\quad v^2e^{2fs/k^2} = u^2e^{2\psi}$

whence (10) gives

$$k^2e^{2fs/k^2} - u^2e^{2\psi} = k^2 - u^2$$

i.e.
$$k^2\{e^{2fs/k^2} - 1\} = u^2\{e^{2\psi} - 1\}$$
Q.E.D.

7.3 Particle on a rotating surface

Let the particle P of mass m be constrained to move on a *smooth* surface (which includes a smooth curve) which is made to rotate with constant angular velocity ω about a fixed axis through O defined by the unit vector $\boldsymbol{k}$, as shown in Fig. 69. Let the resultant force acting on P be $\boldsymbol{F}$ per unit mass. The equation of motion will be

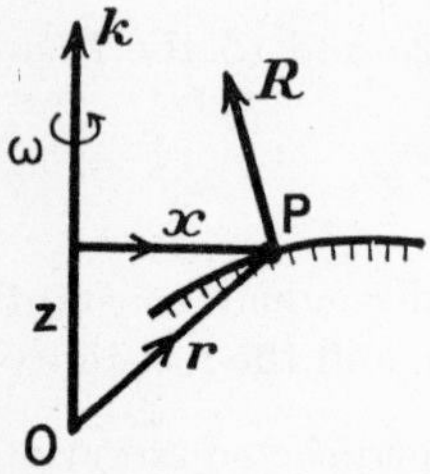

FIG. 69.

$$\frac{d^2\boldsymbol{r}}{dt^2} = \boldsymbol{F}$$

Taking a frame of reference at O which moves with the surface with angular velocity $\boldsymbol{\omega} = \omega\boldsymbol{k}$ we get (v. 3.6(5))

$$\frac{\partial^2\boldsymbol{r}}{\partial t^2} + 2\omega\boldsymbol{k} \times \frac{\partial\boldsymbol{r}}{\partial t} + \omega^2\boldsymbol{k} \times (\boldsymbol{k} \times \boldsymbol{r}) = \boldsymbol{F} \quad . \quad . \quad (1)$$

In this equation $\frac{\partial\boldsymbol{r}}{\partial t}$ is the velocity of P relative to the surface. Writing $\boldsymbol{r} = z\,\boldsymbol{k} + \boldsymbol{x}$, where $\boldsymbol{x}.\boldsymbol{k} = 0$, (1) becomes

$$\frac{\partial^2\boldsymbol{r}}{\partial t^2} + 2\omega\,\boldsymbol{k} \times \frac{\partial\boldsymbol{r}}{\partial t} - \omega^2\,\boldsymbol{x} = \boldsymbol{F} \quad . \quad . \quad . \quad (2)$$

Multiplying (2) in scalar multiplication by $\frac{\partial\boldsymbol{r}}{\partial t}$ gives

$$\frac{\partial\boldsymbol{r}}{\partial t}.\frac{\partial^2\boldsymbol{r}}{\partial t^2} - \omega^2\,\boldsymbol{x}.\frac{\partial\boldsymbol{x}}{\partial t} = \boldsymbol{F}.\frac{\partial\boldsymbol{r}}{\partial t} \quad . \quad . \quad . \quad (3)$$

Now write $\boldsymbol{F} = \boldsymbol{F}_0 + \boldsymbol{R}$, where $\boldsymbol{R}$ is the reaction of the surface and let us consider the case where $\boldsymbol{F}_0$ is a conservative field of force with potential function V. Then since P must move on the surface $\boldsymbol{R}.\dfrac{\partial \boldsymbol{r}}{\partial t} = 0$ and so the rhs of (3) reduces to $\boldsymbol{F}_0.\dfrac{\partial \boldsymbol{r}}{\partial t}$. Integrating (3) w.r.t. time, we get

$$\tfrac{1}{2}\left(\frac{\partial \boldsymbol{r}}{\partial t}\right)^2 + \int - \boldsymbol{F}_0.\boldsymbol{dr} - \tfrac{1}{2}\omega^2\boldsymbol{x}^2 = \text{constant}$$

which is the *energy equation*

$$T + V' = K \qquad . \quad . \quad . \quad . \quad (4)$$

where T = kinetic energy relative to the surface, and

$$V' = V - \tfrac{1}{2}\omega^2 x^2 \quad \text{per unit mass} \qquad . \quad . \quad (5)$$

This function V' is called the **modified potential energy** (function). Equation (4) will give the motion of P relative to the surface.

If we are interested in the actual forces acting on P, such as the reaction of the surface, then we can find them directly from (1). As an example, consider the surface to be a **plane wire rotating about a point O in its plane** (*v.* Fig. 70).

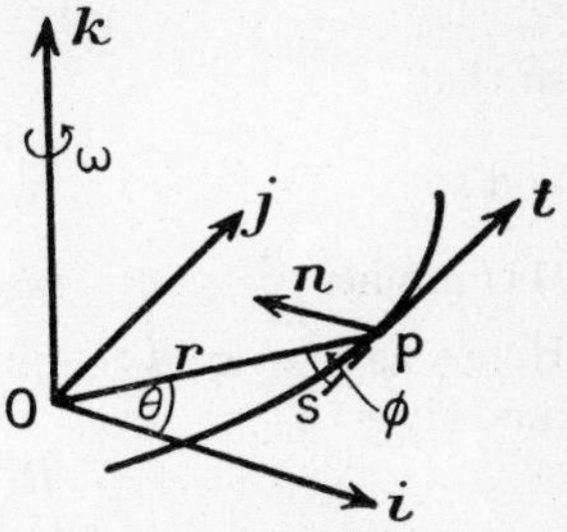

FIG. 70.

Let the applied force be $\boldsymbol{F}_0 = T\,\boldsymbol{t} + N\,\boldsymbol{n} + S\,\boldsymbol{k}$, $\boldsymbol{t}$ being a unit vector along the tangent at P and $\boldsymbol{n}$ along the normal. Since $\boldsymbol{R} = R\,\boldsymbol{n} + M\,\boldsymbol{k}$ we get, from (1), for the equations per unit mass,

$$\frac{\partial^2 \boldsymbol{r}}{\partial t^2} + 2\omega\,\boldsymbol{k} \times \frac{\partial \boldsymbol{r}}{\partial t} - \omega^2\,\boldsymbol{r} = T\,\boldsymbol{t} + (R + N)\boldsymbol{n} + (S + M)\boldsymbol{k} \qquad (6)$$

But if v is the velocity of P we can write

$$\frac{\partial \boldsymbol{r}}{\partial t} = v\,\boldsymbol{t} \quad \text{and} \quad \frac{\partial^2 \boldsymbol{r}}{\partial t^2} = v\frac{dv}{ds}\boldsymbol{t} + \frac{v^2}{\rho}\boldsymbol{n} \quad (\text{v. } 4.3(3)\,)$$

and also

$$\boldsymbol{r} = r\cos\phi\,\boldsymbol{t} - r\sin\phi\,\boldsymbol{n}$$
$$= r\frac{dr}{ds}\boldsymbol{t} - r^2\frac{d\theta}{ds}\boldsymbol{n}$$

Then (6) gives, since $\boldsymbol{k} \times \boldsymbol{t} = \boldsymbol{n}$,

$$v\frac{dv}{ds} - \omega^2 r\frac{dr}{ds} = T \qquad . \quad . \quad . \quad . \quad (7)$$

$$\frac{v^2}{\rho} + 2\omega v + \omega^2 r^2\frac{d\theta}{ds} = N + R \qquad . \quad . \quad . \quad (8)$$

and

$$S + M = 0$$

Example 1. A particle P of mass m moves on a circular wire of radius a which rotates in a horizontal plane about a point O of itself. The point A is the extremity of the diameter through O and at time t OP makes an angle θ with OA. Initially P is projected with velocity $2a\omega$ relative to the wire from A. Prove that, as $t \to \infty$, $v \to 0$ and $\theta \to \pi/2$, and that the reaction of the wire is given by

$$R = m\left\{\frac{3v^2}{2a} + 2\omega v\right\} \qquad \text{(L.U.)}$$

Writing $\rho = a$, $T = N = 0$ and $S = 2a\theta$, $r = 2a\cos\theta$ in (7) and (8), gives

$$v\,dv + 2a^2\omega^2 \sin 2\theta\,d\theta = 0 \quad . \quad . \quad . \quad (9)$$

and
$$\frac{R}{m} = \frac{v^2}{a} + 2\omega v + 2a\omega^2\cos^2\theta \quad . \quad . \quad (10)$$

Hence (9) implies

$$\tfrac{1}{2}v^2 - a^2\omega^2\cos 2\theta = C = a^2\omega^2$$

so that
$$v^2 = 4a^2\omega^2\cos^2\theta$$

and so
$$v = 2a\frac{d\theta}{dt} = 2a\omega\cos\theta \quad . \quad . \quad . \quad (11)$$

(11) implies
$$\omega t = \log(\sec\theta + \tan\theta)$$

Hence as $t \to \infty$, $\theta \to \pi/2$ and (11) shows that $v \to 0$. Equation (10) now gives

$$\frac{R}{m} = \frac{v^2}{a} + 2\omega v + \frac{v^2}{2a} \quad \text{by (11)}$$

which is
$$R = m\left\{\frac{3v^2}{2a} + 2\omega v\right\} \qquad \text{Q.E.D.}$$

Example 2. Suppose, in the problem of Ex. 1, the initial velocity is $2b\omega$ at the point A and that $b \gg a$. Then show that the particle describes a quadrant of the circle in time

$$\frac{\pi a}{4b\omega}\left\{1 + \frac{1}{4}\cdot\frac{a^2}{b^2}\cdot\left(1 - \frac{2}{\pi}\right)\right\}$$

Writing $v = 2a\dot\theta$, (9) becomes

$$2\ddot\theta + \omega^2\sin 2\theta = 0$$

or
$$\ddot\phi + \omega^2\sin\phi = 0 \quad . \quad . \quad . \quad . \quad (12)$$

where $\phi = 2\theta =$ the angle between CP and CA, C being the centre of the circle. Integration of (12) gives

$$\dot\phi^2 - 2\omega^2\cos\phi = \kappa, \quad \text{a constant}$$

This equation is also immediately deducible from (4) and (5). When $\phi = 0$, $\dot\phi = \dfrac{a}{2b\omega}$ and so $\kappa = 2\omega^2\left\{\dfrac{2b^2}{a^2} - 1\right\}$.

Hence $$\dot\phi = \frac{2b\omega}{a}\left\{1 + \frac{a^2}{2b^2}(\cos\phi - 1\right\}^{\frac{1}{2}}$$

$$= \frac{2b\omega}{a}\left\{1 + \frac{a^2}{4b^2}(\cos\phi - 1)\right\} \quad \text{since } \frac{a}{b} \text{ is small.}$$

Hence $$\frac{2b\omega}{a}t = \int_0^{\pi/2}\left\{1 + \frac{a^2}{4b^2}(\cos\phi - 1)\right\}^{-1} d\phi$$

$$= \int_0^{\pi/2}\left\{1 - \frac{a^2}{4b^2}(\cos\phi - 1)\right\} d\phi$$

$$= \frac{\pi}{2} - \frac{a^2}{4b^2}\left(1 - \frac{\pi}{2}\right)$$

giving $$t = \frac{\pi a}{4b\omega}\left\{1 + \frac{1}{4}\cdot\frac{a^2}{b^2}\left(1 - \frac{2}{\pi}\right)\right\}$$ Q.E.D.

Example 3. A smooth, thin, horizontal straight tube whose equations are $x = a$, $z = 0$, contains a particle of unit mass connected to a point $A(a, 0, 0)$ in the tube by means of an elastic string of natural length a and modulus of elasticity λ. The particle is at rest at a distance a from A. The tube is made to rotate with constant angular velocity ω about the vertical axis Oz in the sense which causes the string to extend. If $\lambda > a\omega^2$, prove that the string will slacken again after a time

$$\frac{2}{n}\left\{\pi - \tan^{-1}\left(\frac{n}{\omega}\right)\right\}$$

where $n^2 = \frac{\lambda}{a} - \omega^2$. (L.U.)

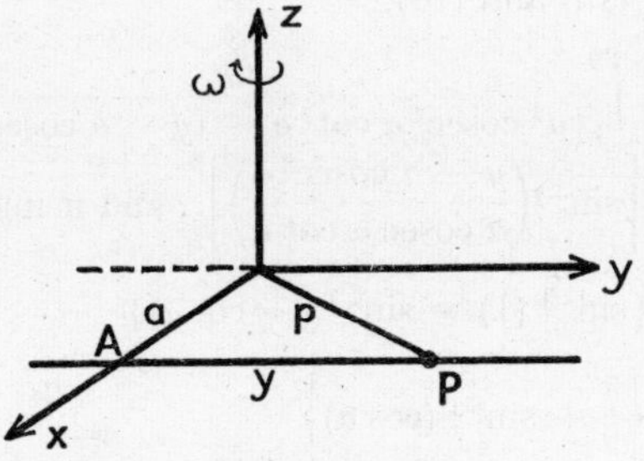

FIG. 71.

Let the particle be at P, at time t as shown in Fig. 71. Using the modified potential we have

$$V' = \tfrac{1}{2}\cdot\frac{\lambda}{a}(y - a)^2 - \tfrac{1}{2}\omega^2 p^2 = \tfrac{1}{2}\cdot\frac{\lambda}{a}(y - a)^2 - \tfrac{1}{2}\omega^2(a^2 + y^2)$$

The energy equation becomes

$$\dot{y}^2 + \frac{\lambda}{a}(y - a)^2 - \omega^2(a^2 + y^2) = \dot{y}^2 + n^2y^2 - 2\lambda y + n^2a^2$$
$$= C, \text{ a constant}$$

Since $\dot{y}$ = relative velocity of $P = a\omega$ at $t = 0$ and $y = a$, we get $C = -a^2\omega^2$, and so

$$\dot{y}^2 + n^2y^2 - 2\lambda y + a^2(n^2 + \omega^2) = 0 \quad . \quad . \quad (13)$$

Define α by the equations $\tan \alpha = \frac{n}{\omega}$, $0 < \alpha < \pi/2$.

Then $\sqrt{\frac{\lambda}{a}} . \sin \alpha = n$ and (13) can be written

$$\dot{y}^2 + n^2\{y^2 - 2ay \operatorname{cosec}^2 \alpha + a^2 \operatorname{cosec}^2 \alpha\} = 0 \quad . \quad (14)$$

which gives

$$\dot{y}^2 = n^2\{a^2 \operatorname{cosec}^2 \alpha \cot^2 \alpha - (y - a \operatorname{cosec}^2 \alpha)^2\} \quad . \quad (15)$$
$$= Y(y), \quad \text{say.}$$

Now suppose the maximum length of the string during the motion is b, then the required time will be be t, where

$$\int_a^b \frac{dy}{Y^{\frac{1}{2}}} + \int_b^a \frac{dy}{-Y^{\frac{1}{2}}} = t$$

that is,

$$t = 2\int_a^b \frac{dy}{Y^{\frac{1}{2}}} \quad . \quad . \quad . \quad . \quad (16)$$

The value of b follows by writing $\dot{y} = 0$ in (14), whence

$$b^2 - 2a \operatorname{cosec}^2 \alpha . b + a^2 \operatorname{cosec}^2 \alpha = 0$$

giving

$$b = a \operatorname{cosec}^2 \alpha + a \operatorname{cosec} \alpha . \cot \alpha \quad . \quad . \quad (17)$$

We now have by (15) and (16),

$$t = \frac{2}{n}\int_a^b \frac{dy}{\{a^2 \operatorname{cosec}^2 \alpha \cot^2 \alpha - (y - a \operatorname{cosec}^2 \alpha)^2\}^{\frac{1}{2}}}$$
$$= \frac{2}{n}\left[\sin^{-1}\left(\frac{y - a \operatorname{cosec}^2 \alpha}{a \operatorname{cosec} \alpha \cot \alpha}\right)\right]_a^b, \text{ and using (17)}$$
$$t = \frac{2}{n}\{\sin^{-1}(1) - \sin^{-1}(-\cos \alpha)\}$$
$$= \frac{2}{n}\left\{\frac{\pi}{2} + \sin^{-1}(\cos \alpha)\right\}$$
$$= \frac{2}{n}\left\{\frac{\pi}{2} + \frac{\pi}{2} - \alpha\right\}$$

or

$$t = \frac{2}{n}\left\{\pi - \tan^{-1}\left(\frac{n}{\omega}\right)\right\} \quad \text{Q.E.D.}$$

Example 4. A particle moves in a smooth circular tube of radius a which rotates about a fixed vertical diameter with constant angular velocity ω. Prove that, if θ is the angular distance of the particle from the lowest point, and if initially it is at rest relative to the tube with the value α for θ, where $\omega \cos(\frac{1}{2}\alpha) = \sqrt{\frac{g}{a}}$, then at any subsequent time t

$$\cot(\tfrac{1}{2}\theta) = \cot(\tfrac{1}{2}\alpha)\cosh(\omega t \sin \tfrac{1}{2}\alpha)$$

Let O be the centre of the circle and let OP, where P is the particle, be inclined at θ to the downward vertical. The modified potential will be, per unit mass,

$$V' = -ag\cos\theta - \tfrac{1}{2}\omega^2(a^2\sin^2\theta)$$

and the energy equation becomes

$$\begin{aligned}\tfrac{1}{2}a^2\dot{\theta}^2 - ag\cos\theta - \tfrac{1}{2}a^2\omega^2\sin^2\theta &= C\\ &= -ag\cos\alpha - \tfrac{1}{2}a^2\omega^2\sin^2\alpha\end{aligned}$$

Writing $g = a\omega^2\cos^2(\frac{1}{2}\alpha)$ we get

$$\frac{\dot{\theta}^2}{\omega^2} = 2\cos^2(\tfrac{1}{2}\alpha)(\cos\theta - \cos\alpha) + (\sin^2\theta - \sin^2\alpha) \quad . \quad (18)$$

Now write $x = \cot(\frac{1}{2}\theta)$, $\dot{x} = -\frac{1}{2}\operatorname{cosec}^2(\frac{1}{2}\theta)\dot{\theta}$ and $\phi = \frac{1}{2}\theta$, $\beta = \frac{1}{2}\alpha$, whence (18) gives

$$\begin{aligned}\frac{4\dot{x}^2}{\omega^2}\sin^4\phi &= 2\cos^2\beta\,(\cos 2\phi - \cos 2\beta) + (\sin^2 2\phi - \sin^2 2\beta)\\ &= 4\cos^2\beta\,(\cos^2\phi - \cos^2\beta) + (\cos 2\beta - \cos 2\phi)(\cos 2\beta + \cos 2\phi)\\ &= (\cos^2\phi - \cos^2\beta)\{4\cos^2\beta - 2(\cos 2\beta + \cos 2\phi)\}\\ &= 4(\cos^2\phi - \cos^2\beta)(1 - \cos^2\phi)\end{aligned}$$

whence

$$\begin{aligned}\dot{x}^2 &= \omega^2\{x^2 - (1 + x^2)\cos^2\beta\}\\ &= \omega^2\sin^2\beta(x^2 - \cot^2\beta)\end{aligned}$$

Hence
$$\int_{\cot\beta}^{x}\frac{dx}{\sqrt{x^2 - \cot^2\beta}} = \omega t\sin\beta$$

giving
$$x = \cot\beta\cosh(\omega t\sin\beta)$$
Q.E.D.

Example 5. Stability on a rotating curve. A smooth wire in the form of the curve

$$y = b\cosh\left(\frac{x}{a}\right) \quad (a, b > 0)$$

rotates with constant angular velocity ω about the y-axis which is vertically upwards. If a bead slides on the wire, and if $a^2\omega^2 > bg$, show that there are three positions of relative equilibrium, and that the symmetrical pair are each stable, and the other is unstable. (M.T.)

First, a general word about *stability*.

Suppose a particle P moves in a general field of force with equation of motion $m\ddot{\boldsymbol{r}} = \boldsymbol{F}$. Then there might well be some positions (say, $\boldsymbol{r} = \boldsymbol{r}_1, \boldsymbol{r}_2, \ldots \boldsymbol{r}_n$) in which P may be at rest, i.e. $\dot{\boldsymbol{r}} = \ddot{\boldsymbol{r}} = \boldsymbol{0}$. These are positions of equilibrium. Consider now a very small disturbance of P from one such position, that is to say, suppose we can write $\boldsymbol{r} = \boldsymbol{r}_k + \boldsymbol{\varepsilon}$, where $\boldsymbol{\varepsilon}$, $\dot{\boldsymbol{\varepsilon}}$, $\ddot{\boldsymbol{\varepsilon}}$ are vectors of infinitesimal moduli. The equation of motion will now become

$$m\,\ddot{\boldsymbol{\varepsilon}} = \boldsymbol{F}(\boldsymbol{r}_k + \boldsymbol{\varepsilon}) \qquad . \quad . \quad . \quad . \quad (19)$$

If (19) reduces to an equation of the form

$$m\,\ddot{\boldsymbol{\varepsilon}} = \lambda\,\boldsymbol{\varepsilon} + O(\boldsymbol{\varepsilon}^2) \qquad . \quad . \quad . \quad . \quad (20)$$

we say that the position $\boldsymbol{r} = \boldsymbol{r}_k$ is a *stable* position when $\lambda < 0$ and *unstable* when $\lambda > 0$. It is clear from (20) that (e.g.) with $\lambda < 0$ the motion is S.H.M. and so $|\,\boldsymbol{\varepsilon}\,|$ is bounded (v. 5.2, Ex. 2) ; hence P must return to the equilibrium position $\boldsymbol{r} = \boldsymbol{r}_k$. Conversely, when $\lambda > 0$ (20) gives $|\,\boldsymbol{\varepsilon}\,| \propto e^{at}$, $a > 0$, and so P continues to move away from the equilibrium position.

Discussion of the stability of a position of equilibrium depends upon some such technique as the above ; the following solution of the above example should suffice to illustrate this technique.

Since P lies on the curve $y = b\cosh\left(\dfrac{x}{a}\right)$ we have $\dot{y} = \dfrac{b}{a}\sinh\left(\dfrac{x}{a}\right)\dot{x}$, and since the curve is rotating about the vertical y-axis we get the modified potential

$$V' = +\,gy - \tfrac{1}{2}\omega^2x^2$$

The energy equation is therefore

$$\dot{x}^2 + \dot{y}^2 + 2gy - \omega^2x^2 = K,\ \text{a constant}$$

i.e.
$$\dot{x}^2\left\{1 + \frac{b^2}{a^2}\sinh^2\left(\frac{x}{a}\right)\right\} + 2gb\cosh\left(\frac{x}{a}\right) - \omega^2x^2 = K$$

Differentiating this w.r.t. the time t, gives

$$\ddot{x}\left\{1 + \frac{b^2}{a^2}\sinh^2\left(\frac{x}{a}\right)\right\} + \frac{b^2}{2a^3}\dot{x}^2\sinh\left(\frac{2x}{a}\right) + \frac{gb}{a}\sinh\left(\frac{x}{a}\right) - \omega^2x = 0 \quad (21)$$

This gives the motion of P relative to the wire—which is why, in this case, we speak of positions of *relative equilibrium*. Writing $\dot{x} = \ddot{x} = 0$, (21) gives

$$\frac{gb}{a}\sinh\left(\frac{x}{a}\right) = \omega^2x \qquad . \quad . \quad . \quad . \quad (22)$$

solutions of which give the positions of relative equilibrium. These are $x = 0$ and $x = \pm\,x_1$ provided the line $y = \dfrac{\omega^2ax}{gb}$ intersects the curve $y = \sinh\left(\dfrac{x}{a}\right)$: this will be so if the gradient of $y = \sinh\left(\dfrac{x}{a}\right)$ at $x = 0$ is less than $\dfrac{a\omega^2}{gb}$. Hence there are three positions of relative equilibrium provided $a^2\omega^2 > gb$.

(i) For the position $x = 0$, put $x = \epsilon$ (small) in (21). This gives, to the first order,

$$\ddot{\epsilon} + \epsilon\left(\frac{gb}{a^2} - \omega^2\right) = 0$$

which gives an unstable position, since $a^2\omega^2 > gb$.

(ii) For the positions $x = \pm x_1$, put $x = \pm x_1 + \epsilon$, $\dot{x} = \dot{\epsilon}$ and $\ddot{x} = \ddot{\epsilon}$ in (21). Furthermore it is often convenient to use the first mean value theorem, $f(x_0 + \epsilon) = f(x_0) + \epsilon f'(x_0)$, when handling such terms as $\sinh\left(\dfrac{\pm x_1 + \epsilon}{a}\right)$, We now get, to the first order,

$$\ddot{\epsilon}\left\{1 + \frac{b^2}{a^2}\sinh^2\left(\pm\frac{x_1}{a}\right)\right\} + \frac{gb}{a}\left\{\sinh\left(\pm\frac{x_1}{a}\right) + \frac{\epsilon}{a}.\cosh\left(\pm\frac{x_1}{a}\right)\right\} - \omega^2(\pm x_1 + \epsilon) = 0$$

Using (22) with $x = \pm x_1$, this reduces to

$$\ddot{\epsilon}\left(1 + \frac{{x_1}^2\omega^4}{g^2}\right) + \left\{\frac{a^2}{gb}\cosh\left(\frac{x_1}{a}\right) - \omega^2\right\}\epsilon = 0$$

giving stability at $x = \pm x_1$, provided

$$\frac{gb}{a^2}\cosh\left(\frac{x_1}{a}\right) - \omega^2 > 0$$

that is, provided
$$\frac{gb}{a^2\omega^2}\cosh\left(\frac{x_1}{a}\right) > 1$$

Since the curve $y = \sinh\left(\dfrac{x}{a}\right)$ crosses the line $y = \dfrac{a\omega^2}{gb}.x$ (from below) at $x = x_1$, its gradient must be greater than $\dfrac{a\omega^2}{gb}$. Hence $\dfrac{1}{a}\cosh\left(\dfrac{x_1}{a}\right) > \dfrac{a\omega^2}{gb}$. Thus the positions of equilibrium at $x = \pm x_1$ are both stable. Q.E.D.

Exercise VII

1. A railway train runs smoothly along a curved track of radius 1,200 yd. at 60 m.p.h. Show that the period of oscillation of a pendulum carried in the train is less by about one-tenth of 1 per cent. than the period of the same pendulum when the train is at rest. (C.)

2. Find the tangential and normal components of the acceleration of a particle describing a plane curve.

A smooth wire bent into the form of a catenary of parameter c is fixed with its axis vertical and vertex upwards. A smooth bead which is threaded on the wire is projected from the vertex along the wire with velocity $\sqrt{(2gc)}$. Prove that, when the bead reaches the point at a depth h below the vertex, it has a velocity $\sqrt{\{2g(h + c)\}}$ and find the reaction of the wire on the bead at this instant. (L.U.)

3. A bead slides on a smooth parabolic wire held in a vertical plane with axis vertical and vertex downwards. Prove that the square of the normal reaction at any point is inversely proportional to the cube of the height of the point above the directrix. (M.T.)

4. A cycloidal wire in a vertical plane, with its axis vertical and vertex upwards is completely occupied by equal small smooth rings. Prove that, if the constraint at the cusps is removed, then in time t the length of the arc cleared of rings will be

$$2l \sinh^2 \sqrt{(gt^2/4l)}$$

where l is the length of the cycloid. (C.)

5. A particle moves on the outside of a smooth cylinder whose generators are horizontal, starting from rest on the highest generator, which passes through extremities of major axes of the normal sections. Prove that it will leave the cylinder at a point whose eccentric angle ϕ is given by the equation

$$e^2 \cos^3 \phi = 3 \cos \phi - 2$$

where e is the eccentricity of the normal sections. (C.)

6. A series of vertical circles touch at their highest points, and smooth particles slide down the arcs with the velocity due to falling from the highest point ; prove that the foci of the free paths lie on a straight line whose inclination to the vertical is $\tan^{-1}(\frac{5}{8}\sqrt{5})$. (C.)

7. A particle slides down a smooth cycloidal tube with its axis vertical and vertex downwards, starting from rest at an arc-distance s_1 from the vertex. After a time t, and before the first particle has reached the vertex, a second particle slides down the tube starting from rest at an arc-distance s_2 from the vertex. Prove that the arc-distance from the vertex of the point where the particles meet is

$$\sin \frac{2\pi t}{T} \Big/ \sqrt{\left(\frac{1}{s_1^2} + \frac{1}{s_2^2} - \frac{2}{s_1 s_2} \cos \frac{2\pi t}{T}\right)}$$

where T is the time of a complete oscillation in the tube. (L.U.)

8. Show that the time a train, if unresisted, takes to pass through a tunnel under a river in the form of an arc of an inverted cycloid of length $2s$ and height h cut off by a horizontal line is

$$\frac{s}{\sqrt{2gh}} \cos^{-1}\left(\frac{v^2 - 2gh}{v^2 + 2gh}\right)$$

where v is the velocity with which the train enters and leaves the tunnel. (C.)

9. A particle slides down the arc of a rough circle ($\mu = \frac{1}{2}$) fixed in a vertical plane, and the particle starts from rest at an end of the horizontal diameter. Prove that, if θ is the angle which the radius vector through the particle makes with the horizontal when the velocity is a maximum, then

$$\sin \theta = \tfrac{1}{3} \cos \theta + e^{-\theta}$$

(C.)

10. A particle of unit mass moves in a rough straight tube AB under the action of a central repulsive force from a point C of magnitude λ/r at a distance r from C. The point A is the foot of the perpendicular from C on the tube, and the particle is projected from A along the tube with velocity v. Prove that it comes to rest when the radius vector from C makes with CA an angle θ satisfying the equation

$$\mu\theta - \log \sec \theta = \tfrac{1}{2}v^2/\lambda$$

where μ is the coefficient of friction. (C.)

11. A particle starts from rest at a point close to that point of a rough cycloidal arc (vertex uppermost) at which it could rest in limiting equilibrium. Show that the velocity at a point at which the tangent makes an angle ϕ with the horizon is $2\sqrt{(ag)}\sin(\phi - \varepsilon)$, and that the particle leaves the cycloid when the velocity is $\sqrt{(2ag)}(\sin \frac{1}{2}\varepsilon + \cos \frac{1}{2}\varepsilon)$, where ε is the angle of friction. (C.)

12. A particle slides down a rough cycloid whose axis is vertical and vertex downwards. Prove that the time of reaching a certain point on the cycloid is independent of the starting point.

Prove also that, if λ is the angle of friction, and if the tangent at the starting point makes with the horizontal an angle greater than α, where α is the least positive angle which satisfies the equation

$$\sin(\alpha - \lambda) = e^{(\alpha + \lambda)\tan\lambda} \sin 2\lambda$$

the particle will oscillate. (C.)

13. Derive for a particle moving in a plane curve the expressions $v\dfrac{d\psi}{dt}, \dfrac{dv}{dt}$ for the normal and tangential components respectively of the acceleration.

A particle moving under gravity in a medium offering a constant resistance to its motion is projected with velocity u inclined at an angle $\dfrac{\pi}{2} - \alpha$ to the upward vertical. Prove that when its velocity is v the angle which the direction of motion makes with the upward vertical is $\dfrac{\pi}{2} - \psi$, where

$$v(1 + \sin\alpha)^n \cos^{n+1}\psi = u(1 + \sin\psi)^n \cos^n \cos^{n+1}\alpha$$

and n is the ratio of the constant resistance to the weight of the particle. (M.T.)

14. A particle is projected at an angle α to the horizontal and moves in a uniform gravitational field in a medium whose resistance per unit mass is kv where v is the speed and k is constant. Prove that if the particle meets the horizontal plane again after time t and at an acute angle β to the horizontal, then

$$\tan\beta = \frac{e^{kt} - 1 - kt}{e^{-kt} - 1 + kt}\tan\alpha$$

Prove also that when the range is a maximum for a given speed of projection α and β are complementary. (L.U.)

15. A particle P is projected under gravity in a medium whose resistance per unit mass is kv^n where v is the speed. If ψ is the angle between the direction of motion of P and the horizontal, show (i) that the horizontal velocity u of P is determined by the equation

$$u^{-n} = u_0^{-n} - \frac{nk}{g}\int_{\psi_0}^{\psi} \sec^{n+1}\psi\, d\psi$$

where u_0, ψ_0 are the values of u, ψ at a point P_0 of the curve and (ii) that $d^2y/dx^2 = -g/u^2$, where x and y are the horizontal and vertical co-ordinates of P, positive y being taken upwards.

If $n = 4$, show that

$$\frac{d^3y}{dx^3} = -2gk\left\{1 + \left(\frac{dy}{dx}\right)^2\right\}^{3/2} \qquad \text{(L.U.)}$$

16. A particle is projected vertically upwards in a medium in which the resistance is kg (velocity)^2. Prove that it returns to the point of projection with kinetic energy diminished in the ratio $1 : 1 + kV^2$, where V is the velocity of projection.

Prove that in the same medium the angle θ between the asymptotes of the complete trajectory of a projectile is given by the equation

$$U^2/w^2 = \cot\theta \operatorname{cosec}\theta + \sinh^{-1}\cot\theta$$

where U is the terminal velocity and w the velocity when the projectile moves horizontally. (C.)

17. A particle moves under gravity in a medium whose resistance is proportional to the velocity. Prove that the range on a horizontal plane is a maximum, for given velocity of projection, when the angle of elevation at first and the angle of descent at last are complementary. (C.)

18. A particle is projected up a plane of inclination α under gravity and a resistance proportional to the velocity. The direction of projection makes an angle β with the vertical, the range R is a maximum and t is the time of flight. Prove that, if U is the terminal velocity and V the velocity of projection, then

(i) $1 + (V/U)\sec\beta = \exp.(gtU)$,
(ii) $UV(U + V\cos\beta)/(V + U\cos\beta) = g(R\sin\alpha + Ut)$,
(iii) $UV^2\sin\beta/(V + U\cos\beta) = gR\cos\alpha$. (C.)

19. A smooth cycloidal tube rotates with uniform angular velocity about its base which is vertical. Prove that a particle cannot rest in the tube anywhere except at the lowest point unless the angular velocity ω of the tube exceeds $\sqrt{(g/a)}$, where a is the radius of the generating circle, and that, when ω exceeds this value, there are two positions of relative equilibrium, the arc-distances of which from the vertex of the cycloid are

$$2\omega^{-1}\sqrt{[2a^2\omega^2 \pm 2a\sqrt{(a^2\omega^4 - g^2)}]} \qquad \text{(C.)}$$

20. A particle is placed at rest on the smooth inner surface of a vertical circular cylinder, which rotates with uniform angular velocity ω about the generator which is initially furthest from the particle. Prove that the pressure vanishes when the particle has descended a distance

$$\frac{1}{2}\frac{g}{\omega^2}\left(\log\frac{2}{3-\sqrt{5}}\right)^2 \qquad \text{(C.)}$$

21. A bead of mass m is threaded on a smooth circular wire of radius a which is made to rotate about a fixed vertical diameter with constant angular velocity ω. At time t the bead is at an angular distance θ from the lowest point of the wire, and $\theta = \frac{1}{2}\pi$, $d\theta/dt = 0$ when $t = 0$. Express $d\theta/dt$ as a function of $\cos\theta$.

If $a\omega^2 = 4g$, describe the motion of the bead, and show that the couple required to rotate the wire is

$$2ma^2\omega^2 \sin\theta\cos\theta\,[\cos\theta(\tfrac{1}{2} - \cos\theta)]^{1/2} \qquad \text{(L.U.)}$$

22. A bead moves on a smooth wire in the form of the curve $y = f(x)$ which is made to rotate with constant angular velocity ω about the y axis, which is vertical. Prove that the x co-ordinate of the bead is such that

$$\dot{x}^2\{1 + f'^2(x)\} - \omega^2x^2 + 2gf(x) \text{ is constant}$$

If the wire is in the form of a circle of radius a and rotates about a vertical diameter with angular velocity $\sqrt{(2g/a)}$ and the bead is initially at rest, relative to the wire, on the level of the centre of the circle, prove that it describes an arc of $\frac{1}{3}\pi$ radians in time

$$\sqrt{\left(\frac{a}{g}\right)}\cosh^{-1}(2 + \sqrt{3}) \qquad \text{(L.U.)}$$

23. A small bead m moves on a smooth wire circle a which rotates about its vertical diameter with constant angular velocity ω. The bead experiences, apart from gravity, an attractive force towards a point A of the wire at the same level as the centre O. The magnitude of the force is mk times the distance AP. Establish the equation

$$ak\sin\theta + a\omega 2\sin\theta\cos\theta = g\cos\theta$$

for the positions of equilibrium of the bead (at P) where θ is the angle AOP. (M.T.)

24. A thin circular wire rotates with uniform angular velocity about one of its vertical tangents. A smooth bead can slide freely along the wire. Show that there are two positions of relative equilibrium of which only the lower is stable. (M.T.)

25. A long smooth straight wire is inclined at an acute angle α to the upward vertical and is rotated about the upward vertical through one end O with constant angular velocity ω. A small bead of unit mass is free to slide on the wire and is initially at rest relative to the wire and at a distance l from O. Show that the bead will move continuously outwards from the axis of rotation if

$$l > (g/\omega^2)\cot\alpha\,\mathrm{cosec}\,\alpha$$

If $l = (2g/\omega^2)\cot\alpha\,\mathrm{cosec}\,\alpha$, show that the system of forces required to maintain the system at constant angular velocity has, after time t, a moment

$$(8g^2/\omega^2) \cot \alpha \cos \alpha \cosh^3 (\tfrac{1}{2}\omega t \sin \alpha) \sinh (\tfrac{1}{2}\omega t \sin \alpha)$$

about the axis of rotation. (M.T.)

26. A particle of unit mass moves on a smooth plane which is inclined at an angle α to the horizontal and which rotates with uniform angular velocity ω about the vertical through a point O of the plane. The particle is pulled towards O by a force equal to k times its distance from O. Prove that the particle can rest on the plane without relative motion at a point A at distance $\dfrac{g \sin \alpha}{k - \omega^2 \cos^2 \alpha}$ from O down the line of greatest slope.

Show that, when $k > \omega^2$, the particle if disturbed from A will remain in the neighbourhood of A, its motion being compounded of two periodic oscillations, and that in the particular case $\alpha = 45°$, $k = \frac{11}{4}\omega^2$ these periods are $\dfrac{4\pi}{\omega\sqrt{3}}$ and $\dfrac{4\pi}{\omega\sqrt{21}}$. (M.T.)

27. A particle slides on a smooth helix of angle α and radius a under a force to a fixed point on the axis equal to μ (distance). Show that the pressure cannot vanish unless the greatest velocity of the particle is $a\sqrt{\mu} \sec \alpha$. (C.)

28. A particle moves on a helical wire whose axis is vertical. Prove that the velocity v after describing an arc s is given by the equations

$$v^2 = ag \sec \alpha \sinh \phi, \quad \frac{ds}{d\phi} = \tfrac{1}{2}a \frac{\sec^2 \alpha \cosh \phi}{\tan \alpha - \mu \cosh \phi}$$

where a is the radius of the cylinder on which the helix lies, α the inclination of the helix to the horizon, and μ the coefficient of friction. (C.)

29. A small smooth groove is cut on the surface of a right circular cone whose axis is vertical and vertex upwards in such a manner that the tangent is always inclined to the vertical at the same angle β. A particle slides down the groove from rest at the vertex; show that the time of descending through a vertical height h is equal to the time of falling freely through a height $h \sec^2 \beta$. Show also that the pressure is constant and makes with the principal normal to the path a constant angle

$$\tan^{-1} \{\tfrac{1}{2} \sin \alpha/\sqrt{(\cos^2 \alpha - \cos^2 \beta)}\}$$

where 2α is the angle of the cone. (C.)

CHAPTER VIII

KINETICS OF PARTICLE MOTION (IV)

8.1 Particle on a fixed surface

In this section we shall examine some problems which can be solved by using the results of 4.4.

Example 1. A particle of mass m is moving, under gravity, on the inside of a smooth spherical bowl of radius a. Using the equations of energy and of angular momentum, prove that, when the particle is at a depth z below the centre of the sphere,

$$ma^2\dot{z}^2 - 2(h + mgz)(a^2 - z^2)$$

is constant, where h is also a constant. If the particle is initially moving horizontally with speed u on the surface at $z = 0$, prove that the projection of the radius vector on the plane $z = 0$ turns through an angle ϕ in time t, where

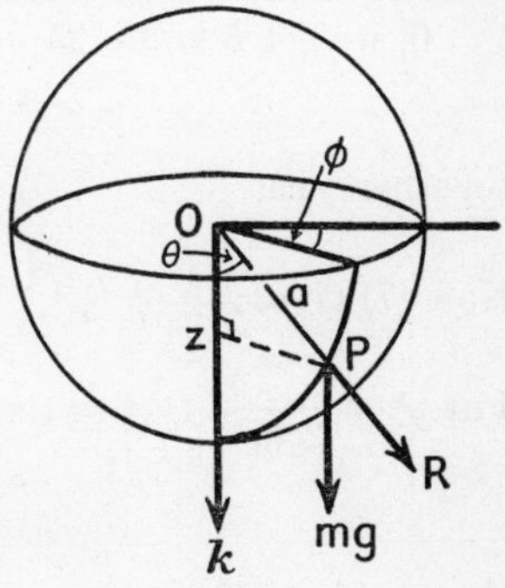

FIG. 72.

$$\phi = \frac{ut}{2a} + \sin^{-1}\left\{\frac{u^2z}{2g(a^2 - z^2)}\right\}^{\frac{1}{2}} \quad \text{(L.U.)}$$

We can use either spherical polar co-ordinates (a, θ, ϕ) (v. Fig. 72) or cylindrical polar co-ordinates r, ϕ, z, with z measured downwards and $r = a \sin\theta = \sqrt{a^2 - z^2}$. Since the forces are the weight mg parallel to the vertical and the reaction R which passes through O, there is zero moment about the axis $\theta = 0$; that is, by 5.3(4),

$$0 = \boldsymbol{k}.\boldsymbol{\Gamma}(O) = \boldsymbol{k}.\frac{d}{dt}\boldsymbol{H}(O) = \frac{d}{dt}\{\boldsymbol{k}.\boldsymbol{H}(O)\}$$

so that $$\boldsymbol{k}.\boldsymbol{H}(O) = \text{a constant} \quad . \quad . \quad . \quad (1)$$

This equation (1) expresses the *conservation of angular momentum* (cf. 6.1(2)). But the angular momentum of the particle at P about the vertical diameter is simply $m \times$ (horizontal velocity) $\times\, a \sin\theta$. We now get :

(i) Using co-ordinates θ, ϕ (v. 4.4(9)),

$$(ma \sin\theta\dot{\phi})\, a \sin\theta = \text{constant} = mk \quad \text{(say)} \quad . \quad (2)$$

this being the conservation of angular momentum of (1). The energy equation is now

$$ma^2\dot{\theta}^2 + ma^2 \sin^2 \theta\dot{\phi}^2 - 2mga \cos \theta = 2h \quad \text{(say)} \quad . \quad (3)$$

(2) and (3) give

$$ma^2\dot{\theta}^2 + \frac{mk^2}{a^2 \sin^2 \theta} - 2(h + mga \cos \theta) = 0$$

Writing $z = a \cos \theta$, $\dot{z} = - a \sin \theta\dot{\theta}$, we get

$$ma^2\dot{z}^2 - 2(h + mgz)(a^2 - z^2) = - mk^2, \quad \text{a constant} \quad . \quad (4)$$

(ii) Using co-ordinates r, ϕ, z (v. 4.4.(3)),

$$mr^2\dot{\phi} = mk \quad . \quad . \quad . \quad . \quad (5)$$

and the energy equation is

$$m(\dot{z}^2 + \dot{r}^2 + r^2\dot{\phi}^2) - 2mgz = 2h$$

so that

$$m(\dot{z}^2 + \dot{r}^2) + m\frac{k^2}{r^2} + 2(h + mgz) = 0$$

and since $z^2 + r^2 = a^2$, we have $\dot{r}^2 = \dot{z}^2.z^2/r^2$.

Hence $\quad .ma^2\dot{z}^2 - 2(h + mgz)(a^2 - z^2) = - mk^2$

as before.

Using equation (4) with the initial conditions $z = 0$, $a\dot{\phi} = u$ at $t = 0$, we get $k = au$, $2h = u^2m$, and

$$a^2\dot{z}^2 = 2gz(a^2 - z^2) - u^2z^2 \quad . \quad . \quad . \quad (6)$$

together with
$$\dot{\phi} = \frac{au}{a^2 - z^2} \quad . \quad . \quad . \quad . \quad . \quad (7)$$

Now (7) gives
$$\dot{\phi} - \frac{u}{2a} = \frac{u(a^2 + z^2)}{2a(a^2 - z^2)} \quad . \quad . \quad . \quad . \quad (8)$$

Put $y^2 = \dfrac{u^2z}{2g(a^2 - z^2)}$ so that

$$2y\dot{y} = \frac{u^2}{2g}.\frac{(a^2 + z^2)}{(a^2 - z^2)^2}.\dot{z} \quad . \quad . \quad . \quad . \quad (9)$$

Hence (8) implies

$$\begin{aligned}\phi - \frac{ut}{2a} &= \frac{u}{2a}\int_0^y \left(\frac{a^2 + z^2}{a^2 - z^2}\right).\frac{dt}{dy}.dy \\ &= \frac{u}{2a}\int_0^y \frac{4g}{u^2}.\frac{a^2 - z^2}{\dot{z}}.y\,dy, \quad \text{by (9)} \\ &= \frac{2g}{u}\int_0^y \frac{(a^2 - z^2)y\,dy}{\sqrt{2gz(a^2 - z^2) - u^2z^2}} \quad \text{by (6)} \\ &= \frac{2g}{u}\int_0^y \frac{(a^2 - z^2)y\,dy}{\sqrt{2gz(a^2 - z^2)}.\sqrt{1 - y^2}} \\ &= \frac{2g}{u}\int_0^y \frac{1}{\sqrt{2g}}.\sqrt{\frac{a^2 - z^2}{z}}.\frac{y\,dy}{\sqrt{1 - y^2}}\end{aligned}$$

$$= \frac{2g}{u}\int_0^y \frac{u}{2g}\cdot\frac{dy}{\sqrt{1-y^2}}$$

that is $$\phi - \frac{ut}{2a} = \sin^{-1} y = \sin^{-1}\left\{\frac{u^2 z}{2g(a^2, - z^2)}\right\} \qquad \text{Q.E.D.}$$

We might also obtain equations (2), (3) and (4) by using vectors in the following way.

Let $\boldsymbol{e}$ be a unit vector along $\overline{OP}$, so that $\overline{OP} = a\,\boldsymbol{e}$. The equation of motion of the particle at P will be

$$ma\,\ddot{\boldsymbol{e}} = mg\,\boldsymbol{k} + R\,\boldsymbol{e} \quad . \quad . \quad . \quad . \quad (10)$$

Hence $$a\,\boldsymbol{e}\times\ddot{\boldsymbol{e}} = g\,\boldsymbol{e}\times\boldsymbol{k}$$

and so $$\boldsymbol{k}.(\boldsymbol{e}\times\ddot{\boldsymbol{e}}) = \boldsymbol{k}.(\boldsymbol{e}\times\boldsymbol{k}) = 0 \quad \text{(v. 2.9(i))}$$

i.e. $$\boldsymbol{k}.(\boldsymbol{e}\times\dot{\boldsymbol{e}}) = \dot{\boldsymbol{e}}.(\boldsymbol{k}\times\boldsymbol{e}) = A \text{ a constant} \quad . \quad (11)$$

Since $\boldsymbol{e}^2 = 1$ we have $\boldsymbol{e}.\dot{\boldsymbol{e}} = 0$ and so (10) also gives

$$ma\,\dot{\boldsymbol{e}}.\ddot{\boldsymbol{e}} = mg\,\boldsymbol{k}.\dot{\boldsymbol{e}}$$

giving the energy integral,

$$ma\,\dot{\boldsymbol{e}}^2 = 2mg\,\boldsymbol{k}.\boldsymbol{e} + B \quad . \quad . \quad . \quad . \quad (12)$$

where B is a constant.

Now clearly we can write (v. 3.4(3)) $\dot{\boldsymbol{e}} = \boldsymbol{\omega}\times\boldsymbol{e}$, where

$$\boldsymbol{\omega} = \dot{\phi}\,\boldsymbol{k} + \dot{\theta}\frac{\boldsymbol{k}\times\boldsymbol{e}}{|\boldsymbol{k}\times\boldsymbol{e}|}$$

i.e. $$\boldsymbol{\omega} = \dot{\phi}\,\boldsymbol{k} + \frac{\dot{\theta}}{\sin\theta}(\boldsymbol{k}\times\boldsymbol{e})$$

Hence $$\dot{\boldsymbol{e}} = \dot{\phi}(\boldsymbol{k}\times\boldsymbol{e}) - \frac{\dot{\theta}}{\sin\theta}(\boldsymbol{k} - \cos\theta\,\boldsymbol{e}) \qquad \text{(v.2.12 (1))}$$

whence (11) gives

$$A = \dot{\phi}(\boldsymbol{k}\times\boldsymbol{e})^2 = \dot{\phi}\sin^2\theta \quad \text{(cf. (2))}$$

and since $\dot{\boldsymbol{e}}^2 = \dot{\phi}^2\sin^2\theta + \dot{\theta}^2$, (12) becomes equation (3).

Furthermore, the *reaction* R can be found from (10) as follows. Multiplying (10) by $\boldsymbol{e}.$ gives

$$R = ma\,\boldsymbol{e}.\ddot{\boldsymbol{e}} - mg\,\boldsymbol{e}.\boldsymbol{k} \quad . \quad . \quad . \quad (13)$$

But
$$\begin{aligned}\ddot{\boldsymbol{e}} &= \dot{\boldsymbol{\omega}}\times\boldsymbol{e} + \boldsymbol{\omega}\times\dot{\boldsymbol{e}}\\ &= \dot{\boldsymbol{\omega}}\times\boldsymbol{e} + \boldsymbol{\omega}\times(\boldsymbol{\omega}\times\boldsymbol{e})\\ &= \dot{\boldsymbol{\omega}}\times\boldsymbol{e} + (\boldsymbol{\omega}.\boldsymbol{e})\boldsymbol{\omega} - \boldsymbol{\omega}^2\boldsymbol{e}\end{aligned}$$

so that
$$\begin{aligned}\boldsymbol{e}.\ddot{\boldsymbol{e}} &= (\boldsymbol{\omega}.\boldsymbol{e})^2 - \boldsymbol{\omega}^2\\ &= (\dot{\phi}\cos\theta)^2 - \dot{\phi}^2 - \dot{\theta}^2\\ &= -(\dot{\theta}^2 + \dot{\phi}^2\sin^2\theta)\end{aligned}$$

Then (13) gives $$R = -ma(\dot{\theta}^2 + \dot{\phi}^2\sin^2\theta) - mg\cos\theta \qquad (14)$$

By using (2) and (3) we can express R as a function of θ only.

We also notice that using 4.4(10) we get (14) immediately by equating the acceleration along OP to $g\cos\theta + R/m$.

Example 2. A particle moves on the inner surface of a smooth right circular cone with axis vertical and vertex downwards, being projected horizontally from a height k above the vertex with velocity $\sqrt{8gk/3}$. Show that the orbit touches alternately the two horizontal circles at heights k, $2k$ above the vertex.

Prove also that, if the cone be developed into a plane, the trace of the path is the same as if the particle moved in a plane under the action of a constant central force. (L.U.)

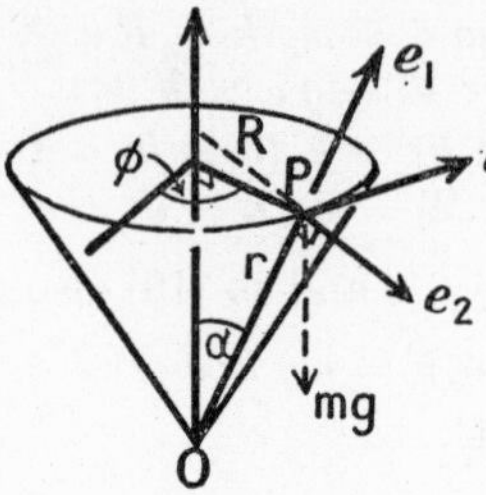

FIG. 73.

Consider the particle at P, as shown in Fig. 73, and use the results of 4.4(12). The equations of motion become

$$\ddot{r} - r\dot{\phi}^2 \sin^2 \alpha = -g \cos \alpha \quad . \quad . \quad . \quad (15)$$

$$\frac{\sin \alpha}{r} \frac{d}{dt}(r^2\dot{\phi}) = 0 \quad . \quad . \quad . \quad . \quad (16)$$

$$-r\dot{\phi}^2 \sin \alpha \cos \alpha = g \sin \alpha - \frac{R}{m}. \quad . \quad . \quad (17)$$

(16) implies that $r^2\dot{\phi}$ is constant, and therefore

$$(r \cos \alpha)(r \sin \alpha \dot{\phi}) = \text{constant} = k\sqrt{\frac{8gk}{3}} \quad . \quad . \quad (18)$$

Then (15) and (18) give

$$\ddot{r} - \frac{8gk^3}{3r^3}.\sec^2 \alpha = -g \cos \alpha$$

so that
$$\tfrac{1}{2}\dot{r}^2 = -gr\cos\alpha - \frac{4gk^3}{3r^2\cos^2\alpha} + C$$

Writing $\dot{r} = 0$ when $r \cos \alpha = k$, we get $C = \dfrac{7gk}{3}$.

Hence
$$\tfrac{1}{2}.\frac{\dot{r}^2}{kg} = \frac{7}{3} - \frac{4}{3y^2} - y, \quad \text{where } y = \frac{r\cos\alpha}{k},$$

giving
$$\tfrac{1}{2}.\frac{\dot{r}^2}{kg} = \frac{1}{3y^2}(1-y)(y-2)(3y+2)$$

Hence
$$\dot{r}^2 \geqslant 0 \quad \text{for} \quad 1 \leqslant y \leqslant 2$$
Q.E.D.

When $\dot{r} = 0$ ($r \cos \alpha = k$ or $2k$) (18) shows that the particle is moving horizontally with speeds $\sqrt{\dfrac{8gk}{3}}$ and $\tfrac{1}{2}\sqrt{\dfrac{8gk}{3}}$. Thus the orbit touches the horizontal circles.

Now the cone is a developable surface * since successive tangent planes can be rotated into coincidence with one another. In the resultant plane so produced the radius vector $\boldsymbol{r}$ will rotate through $d\theta$ whilst ϕ increases by $d\phi$ (v. Fig. 74). Thus $\dot{\theta}$ measures the angular velocity in this plane. But we see that

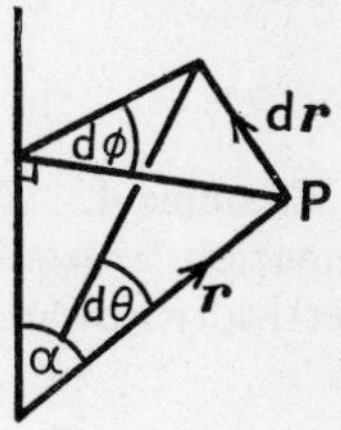

FIG. 74.

$$|\,d\boldsymbol{r}\,| = r\,d\theta = r \sin \alpha\, d\phi$$

which gives $\quad d\theta = \sin \alpha\, d\phi$

Hence (15) becomes $\quad \ddot{r} - r\dot{\theta}^2 = -\,g \cos \alpha$

and (16) gives $\quad r^2\dot{\theta} = \text{constant}$

These are the equations appropriate to motion under a constant central force.

Example 3. A hollow circular cone, internally smooth, of angle 2α, is fixed with its axis vertical and vertex downwards. A particle of mass m hangs at rest by an inextensible string which passes through a hole at the vertex, and a particle of equal mass m attached to the other end of the string describes a horizontal circle on the inner surface of the cone in time T per revolution. Find the period of a small oscillation if this steady motion is slightly disturbed. (L.U.)

Let the tension in the string be mF and let the lower particle be a distance x beneath the vertex. Then in a general motion the equations will be (v. Ex. 2):

$$\ddot{r} - r\dot{\phi}^2 \sin^2 \alpha = -\,F - g \cos \alpha \quad . \quad . \quad . \quad (19)$$

$$r^2\dot{\phi} = h, \text{ a constant} \quad . \quad . \quad . \quad (20)$$

and $\quad \ddot{x} = g - F \quad . \quad . \quad . \quad . \quad (21)$

together with $\quad x + r = l$, a constant $\quad . \quad . \quad . \quad (22)$

Hence (19), (21) and (22) give

$$2\ddot{r} - r\dot{\phi}^2 \sin^2 \alpha = -\,g(1 + \cos \alpha) \quad . \quad . \quad . \quad (23)$$

In the steady motion we have $r = a$, $\dot{r} = \ddot{r} = 0$, $\dot{\phi} = \omega$ where $T = \dfrac{2\pi}{\omega}$.

Hence (20) gives $h = a^2\omega$ and (23) gives

$$a\omega^2 \sin^2 \alpha = g(1 + \cos \alpha)$$

In a slight disturbance, put $r = a + \epsilon$, whence (23) can be written

$$2\ddot{\epsilon} - \frac{h^2 \sin^2 \alpha}{(a + \epsilon)^3} = -\,a\omega^2 \sin^2 \alpha$$

* See, *e.g.*, R. J. T. Bell. *Co-ordinate Geometry of Three Dimensions*, § 213.

which is $$2\ddot{\epsilon} - a^4\omega^2 \sin^2 \alpha . \frac{1}{a^3}\left\{1 - \frac{3\epsilon}{a}\right\} = - a\omega^2 \sin^2 \alpha$$
if ϵ is sufficiently small. This reduces to
$$\ddot{\epsilon} + (\tfrac{3}{2} . \omega^2 \sin^2 \alpha)\, \epsilon = 0$$
which is S.H.M., and the periodic time is
$$\tau = T\sqrt{\frac{2}{3 \sin^2 \alpha}}$$

Example 4. The inner surface of a smooth funnel is given by the equation $z^3 = x^2 + y^2$, the positive direction of the z-axis being vertically upwards. A particle is projected on the inner surface along a horizontal tangent at height h above the origin, with speed $\sqrt{2kgh}$. Find the value of k when

(i) the motion is bounded by the planes $z = h$, $z = 2h$;

(ii) the motion is in a horizontal circle. (L.U.)

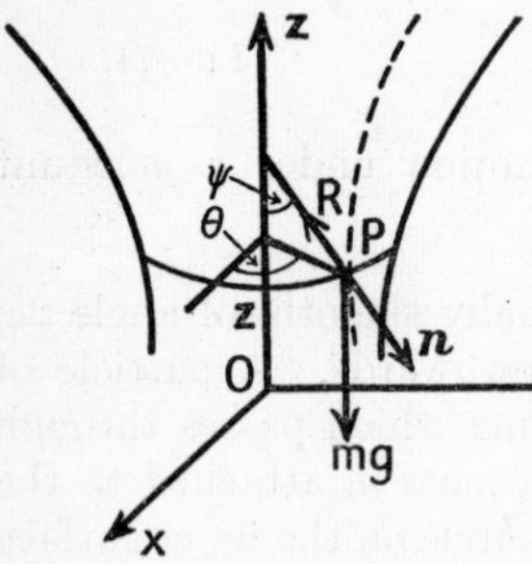

FIG. 75.

This problem illustrates the motion of a particle on a *surface of revolution* (v. Fig. 75).

Defining P by cylindrical polar co-ordinates (r, θ, z) we can write down the equations expressing the conservation of energy and of angular momentum about the z-axis (v. Ex. 1).

These are $$\dot{z}^2 + \dot{r}^2 + r^2\dot{\theta}^2 + 2gz = A \qquad (24)$$
and $$r^2\dot{\theta} = B \qquad (25)$$
with A, B arbitrary constants. The equation of the surface will be of the form $f(z, r) = 0$, where $r^2 = x^2 + y^2$, and so (24) and (25) will give an equation for $\dot{z}$ (or $\dot{r}$). The reaction R will act along the normal at P, a line which always intersects the axis. We can find R by the equation
$$R - mg \cos \psi = - m(\ddot{r} - r\dot{\theta}^2) \sin \psi + \ddot{z} \cos \psi \qquad (26)$$
and ψ will be given by
$$\cot \psi = \frac{dr}{dz} \qquad (27)$$

In this particular case we have $r^2 = z^3$ and Fig. 76 shows a cross- section of the curve through P. Using the initial conditions we get $r^2\dot{\theta} = h^2\sqrt{2kg} = B$, whence (24) gives

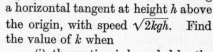

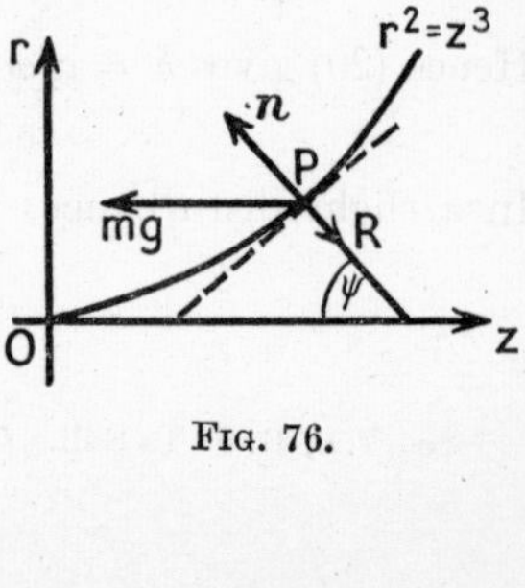

FIG. 76.

$$\dot{z}^2 + \dot{r}^2 + \frac{2kgh^4}{r^2} + 2gz = 2gh(1 + k) \quad . \quad . \quad (28)$$

Writing $\dot{r} = \frac{3}{2}.\frac{z^2\dot{z}}{r}$ and $\dot{r}^2 = \frac{9}{4}.z\dot{z}^2$, (28) becomes

$$\frac{\dot{z}^2}{8g}(4z^3 + 9z^4) = f(z)\text{, (say),}$$

$$= -z^4 + hz^3(1 + k) - kh^4 \quad . \quad . \quad (29)$$

(i) For motion bounded by the planes $z = h$, $z = 2h$, we need to choose k so that $f(h) = f(2h) = 0$ and $f(z) > 0$ only when $h < z < 2h$. But $f(h) = 0$ already, and (29) gives

$$0 = f(2h) = h^4\{-16 - k + 8(1 + k)\}$$

Hence a *necessary* condition is $k = 8/7$. Putting this value in (29) gives

$$f(z) = \frac{1}{7}(2h - z)(z - h)(7z^2 + 6zh + 4h^2)$$

Since $7z^2 + 6zh + 4h^2 > 0$ for all z it follows that $f(z) \geqslant 0$ if, and only if, $h \leqslant z \leqslant 2h$. Hence $k = 8/7$ is also *sufficient*.

(ii) For motion in a horizontal circle, i.e. the circle $z = h$, we must have $f(z) = (z - h)^2X(z)$, where $X(z) < 0$ for all z. This ensures that $\dot{z} = 0$ when $z = h$ and $\dot{z}^2 < 0$ for all other $z > 0$; hence only the one circular motion is real. Hence $(z - h)$ must be a factor of $f'(z)$, i.e. $f'(h) = 0$. This gives $-4h^3 + 3h^3(1 + k) = 0$, and so a necessary condition is $k = \frac{1}{3}$. Putting this value in (29) gives

$$f(z) = -\tfrac{1}{3}(3z^2 + 2zh + h^2)(z - h)^2$$

which is of the required form. Hence $k = \frac{1}{3}$ is also sufficient.

Q.E.D.

8.2 Motion of a particle relative to the rotating earth

Let the unit vector $\boldsymbol{k}$ denote the direction of the earth's axis about which the earth rotates with constant angular velocity ω, where

$$\omega = \frac{2\pi}{24 \times 3600} = 0{\cdot}73 \times 10^{-5} \text{ radians per second}$$

Suppose $\boldsymbol{r} = \overline{OP}$ is the position vector of the particle w.r.t. an origin O on the surface of the earth, as shown in Fig. 77. Taking C as the earth's centre and the vector $\overline{CO} = \boldsymbol{a}$, the velocity of P will be $\boldsymbol{v}$ where, by 3.6(4),

$$\boldsymbol{v} = \frac{\partial}{\partial t}(\boldsymbol{a} + \boldsymbol{r}) + \omega\,\boldsymbol{k} \times (\boldsymbol{a} + \boldsymbol{r})$$

and since $\overline{CO}$ is a constant vector in the

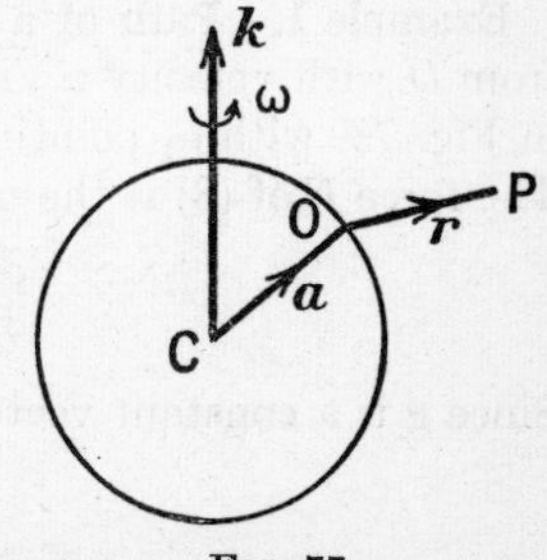

FIG. 77

moving frame of reference, this becomes

$$\boldsymbol{v} = \omega\, \boldsymbol{k} \times \boldsymbol{a} + \frac{\partial \boldsymbol{r}}{\partial t} + \omega\, \boldsymbol{k} \times \boldsymbol{r} \quad . \quad . \quad . \qquad (1)$$

The acceleration of P will therefore be $\boldsymbol{f}$ (v. 3.6(5)) where

$$\boldsymbol{f} = \omega^2\, \boldsymbol{k} \times (\boldsymbol{k} \times \boldsymbol{a}) + \frac{\partial^2 \boldsymbol{r}}{\partial t^2} + 2\omega\, \boldsymbol{k} \times \frac{\partial \boldsymbol{r}}{\partial t} + \omega^2\, \boldsymbol{k} \times (\boldsymbol{k} \times \boldsymbol{r}) \qquad (2)$$

Now the acceleration due to gravity, commonly denoted by g, does not take the earth's rotation into account ; it is only the *apparent acceleration* at O. We therefore distinguish between this apparent acceleration, denoted by the vector $\boldsymbol{g}$, and the actual acceleration, denoted by γ. These are the accelerations, relative to the moving and fixed frames respectively, of a particle at rest at O. Thus we have

$$\boldsymbol{g} = \frac{\partial^2 \boldsymbol{r}}{\partial t^2} \quad \text{at} \quad \boldsymbol{r} = \frac{\partial \boldsymbol{r}}{\partial t} = \boldsymbol{0} \quad . \quad . \quad . \qquad (3)$$

and (2) gives

$$\gamma = \boldsymbol{f} \quad \text{at} \quad \boldsymbol{r} = \frac{\partial \boldsymbol{r}}{\partial t} = \boldsymbol{0} \quad . \quad . \quad . \qquad (4)$$

Hence

$$\gamma = \omega^2\, \boldsymbol{k} \times (\boldsymbol{k} \times \boldsymbol{a}) + \boldsymbol{g} \quad . \quad . \quad . \qquad (5)$$

so that

$$\boldsymbol{f} = \gamma - \boldsymbol{g} + \frac{\partial^2 \boldsymbol{r}}{\partial t^2} + 2\omega\, \boldsymbol{k} \times \frac{\partial \boldsymbol{r}}{\partial t} + \omega^2\, \boldsymbol{k} \times (\boldsymbol{k} \times \boldsymbol{r}) \quad . \qquad (6)$$

Now suppose that the total force acting on the particle at P is $\boldsymbol{F} + m\,\gamma$, then using (6) we get

$$m\boldsymbol{f} = \boldsymbol{F} + m\,\gamma$$

giving

$$m\, \frac{\partial^2 \boldsymbol{r}}{\partial t} + 2m\omega\, \boldsymbol{k} \times \frac{\partial \boldsymbol{r}}{\partial t} + m\omega^2\, \boldsymbol{k} \times (\boldsymbol{k} \times \boldsymbol{r}) = \boldsymbol{F} + m\,\boldsymbol{g} \quad . \qquad (7)$$

If we agree to neglect terms in (7) involving ω^2 we can write the simpler equation,

$$m\, \frac{\partial^2 \boldsymbol{r}}{\partial t^2} + 2m\omega\, \boldsymbol{k} \times \frac{\partial \boldsymbol{r}}{\partial t} = \boldsymbol{F} + m\boldsymbol{g} \quad . \quad . \qquad (8)$$

Example 1. Path of a projectile. Let the particle P be projected from O with velocity $\boldsymbol{u}$ and take an orthonormal triad at O, as shown in Fig. 78, with $\boldsymbol{e}_1$ pointing East, $\boldsymbol{e}_2$ North and $\boldsymbol{e}_3$ vertically upwards. The force $\boldsymbol{F}$ of (8) is the nul vector $\boldsymbol{0}$ and so (8) becomes

$$\frac{\partial^2 \boldsymbol{r}}{\partial t^2} + 2\omega\, \boldsymbol{k} \times \frac{\partial \boldsymbol{r}}{\partial t} = \boldsymbol{g} . \quad . \quad . \quad . \qquad (9)$$

Since $\boldsymbol{g}$ is a constant vector we can integrate (9) to give

$$\frac{\partial \boldsymbol{r}}{\partial t} + 2\omega\, \boldsymbol{k} \times \boldsymbol{r} = \boldsymbol{g}t + \boldsymbol{u}$$

Substituting for $\frac{\partial \boldsymbol{r}}{\partial t}$ in (9) and neglecting the term in ω^2 we get

$$\frac{\partial^2 \boldsymbol{r}}{\partial t^2} + 2\omega\, \boldsymbol{k} \times \{\boldsymbol{g}t + \boldsymbol{u}\} = \boldsymbol{g}$$

Integrating twice w.r.t. time we now have

$$\boldsymbol{r} + \omega\, \boldsymbol{k} \times \{\tfrac{1}{3}t^3\, \boldsymbol{g} + t^2\, \boldsymbol{u}\} = \tfrac{1}{2}t^2\, \boldsymbol{g} + t\, \boldsymbol{u} \quad . \quad . \quad (10)$$

whereas the solution for the " ordinary " projectile is simply

$$\boldsymbol{r} = \tfrac{1}{2}t^2\, \boldsymbol{g} + t\, \boldsymbol{u}$$

If the latitude of the point O is λ, we have

$$\boldsymbol{k} = \cos\lambda\, \boldsymbol{e}_2 + \sin\lambda\, \boldsymbol{e}_3$$

and writing

$$\boldsymbol{r} = x\, \boldsymbol{e}_1 + y\, \boldsymbol{e}_2 + z\, \boldsymbol{e}_3$$
$$\boldsymbol{u} = u_1\, \boldsymbol{e}_1 + u_2\, \boldsymbol{e}_2 + u_3\, \boldsymbol{e}_3$$
$$\boldsymbol{g} = -\, g\, \boldsymbol{e}_3$$

equation (10) gives

$$x = u_1 t + \omega\{\tfrac{1}{3}gt^3 \cos\lambda + u_2 t^2 \sin\lambda - u_3 t^2 \cos\lambda\}$$
$$y = u_2 t - \omega\{u_1 t^2 \sin\lambda\}$$
$$z = u_3 t - \tfrac{1}{2}gt^2 + \omega\{u_1 t^2 \cos\lambda\}$$

These show the deviation, due to ω, from the elementary treatment : they are applicable in the northern hemisphere. In the southern hemisphere we replace λ by $-\lambda$ and $\boldsymbol{e}_2$ by $-\boldsymbol{e}_2$, $\boldsymbol{e}_1$ by $-\boldsymbol{e}_1$.

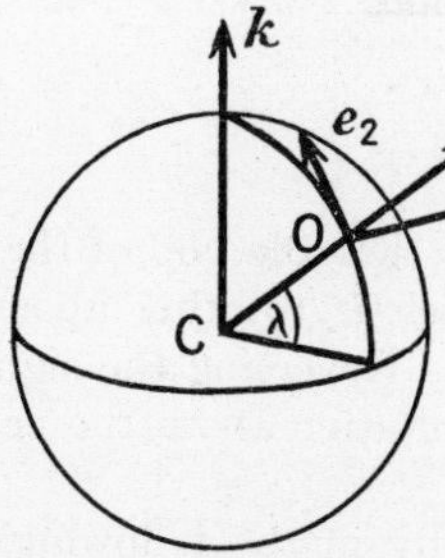

FIG. 78.

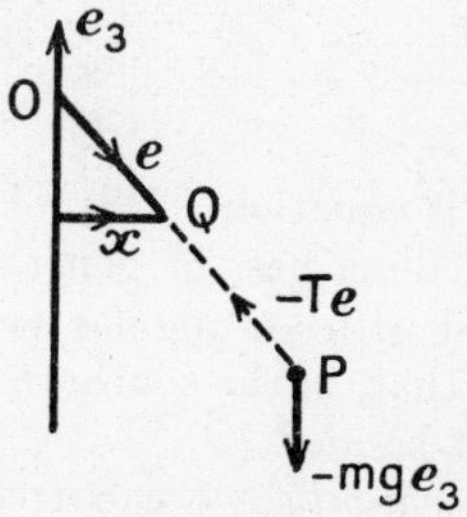

FIG. 79.

Example 2. Foucault's pendulum. This is a discussion of the motion of a simple pendulum, allowing for the earth's rotation, and the reader might do well to first read 7.1, Ex. 1. Let the bob be at P, as shown in Fig. 79, and let $\boldsymbol{e}$ be a unit vector along the string whose tension is T. The equation of motion, (8), becomes

$$l\,\frac{\partial^2 \boldsymbol{e}}{\partial t^2} + 2\omega l\, \boldsymbol{k} \times \frac{\partial \boldsymbol{e}}{dt} = -\frac{T}{m}\boldsymbol{e} - g\,\boldsymbol{e}_3 \quad . \quad . \quad (11)$$

Multiplying by $\times\, \boldsymbol{e}$ gives

$$\frac{\partial^2 \boldsymbol{e}}{\partial t^2} \times \boldsymbol{e} + 2\omega(\boldsymbol{e}\,.\,\boldsymbol{k})\,\frac{\partial \boldsymbol{e}}{\partial t} = -\left(\frac{g}{l}\right)\boldsymbol{e}_3 \times \boldsymbol{e} \quad . \quad (12)$$

by using 2.12(1) and remembering that $\boldsymbol{e}.\frac{\partial \boldsymbol{e}}{\partial t} = 0$ (v. 2.7). Now write $\boldsymbol{e} = -\boldsymbol{e}_3 + \boldsymbol{x}$, where $|\boldsymbol{x}|$ is sufficiently small for us to neglect $\boldsymbol{x}^2$. If we also agree to neglect the products $\frac{\partial^2 \boldsymbol{x}}{\partial t^2} \times \boldsymbol{x}$ and $(\boldsymbol{x}.\boldsymbol{k}) \frac{\partial \boldsymbol{x}}{\partial t}$ equation (12) reduces to

$$-\frac{\partial^2 \boldsymbol{x}}{\partial t^2} \times \boldsymbol{e}_3 - 2\omega\,(\boldsymbol{e}_3.\boldsymbol{k}) \frac{\partial \boldsymbol{x}}{\partial t} = -\left(\frac{g}{l}\right) \boldsymbol{e}_3 \times \boldsymbol{x} \quad . \quad (13)$$

Writing $\boldsymbol{e}_3.\boldsymbol{k} = \sin\lambda$, (13) becomes

$$\frac{\partial^2 \boldsymbol{x}}{\partial t^2} \times \boldsymbol{e}_3 + 2\omega \sin\lambda \frac{\partial \boldsymbol{x}}{\partial t} = -\left(\frac{g}{l}\right) \boldsymbol{x} \times \boldsymbol{e}_3 \quad . \quad (14)$$

Since $|\boldsymbol{x}|$ is small $\boldsymbol{x}.\boldsymbol{e}_3 = 0$ and so, multiplying (14) by $\boldsymbol{e}_3\times$, we get

$$\frac{\partial^2 \boldsymbol{x}}{\partial t^2} + 2\omega \sin\lambda\, \boldsymbol{e}_3 \times \frac{\partial \boldsymbol{x}}{\partial t} = -\left(\frac{g}{l}\right) \boldsymbol{x} \quad . \quad . \quad (15)$$

Now let us refer the motion of $\boldsymbol{x}$ to another rotating frame of reference, rotating about the vertical with angular velocity $-\omega \sin\lambda\, \boldsymbol{e}_3$. Hence we replace $\frac{\partial \boldsymbol{x}}{\partial t}$ by $\frac{\partial' \boldsymbol{x}}{\partial' t} - \omega \sin\lambda\, \boldsymbol{e}_3 \times \boldsymbol{x}$ and $\frac{\partial^2 \boldsymbol{x}}{\partial t^2}$ by $\frac{\partial' \boldsymbol{x}}{\partial' t^2} - 2\omega \sin\lambda\, \boldsymbol{e}_3 \times \frac{\partial' \boldsymbol{x}}{\partial' t}$. Neglecting the term in ω^2 equation (15) becomes

$$\frac{\partial'^2 \boldsymbol{x}}{\partial' t^2} = -\left(\frac{g}{l}\right) \boldsymbol{x}$$

which is equation 7.1(8). Hence (15) proves that the bob of the pendulum describes, in general, an ellipse which is rotating about the vertical with an angular velocity $-\omega \sin\lambda$. Reversing the sign of λ shows that, in the southern hemisphere the rotation about the vertical is right-handed.

Alternatively, we can treat (15) analytically in the following way. Put $\boldsymbol{x} = x\,\boldsymbol{e}_1 + y\,\boldsymbol{e}_2$, $x \neq |\boldsymbol{x}|$, whence we get

$$\left.\begin{aligned} \ddot{x} - 2\omega \sin\lambda \dot{y} + \mu^2 x = 0 \\ \ddot{y} + 2\omega \sin\lambda \dot{x} + \mu^2 y = 0 \end{aligned}\right\} \quad . \quad . \quad . \quad (16)$$

with $\mu^2 = \left(\frac{g}{l}\right)$. Now write $s = x + iy$ so that (16) give

$$\ddot{s} + 2i\dot{s}\omega \sin\lambda + \mu^2 s = 0$$

giving the solution

$$s = e^{-i\omega t \sin\lambda}(Ae^{i\mu t} + Be^{-i\mu t}) \quad . \quad . \quad . \quad (17)$$

If we take rotating axes $O\xi$, $O\eta$ with angular velocity $-\omega \sin\lambda$ about the vertical we have

$$\xi = se^{+i\omega t \sin\lambda} = \xi + i\eta$$

Hence (17) gives $\xi = C\cos\mu t$, $\eta = D\sin\mu t$, where C, D are constants. Thus the locus of (ξ, η) is an ellipse. Therefore (x, y) describes an ellipse which is rotating in its own plane about the vertical with a left-handed angular velocity of $\omega\sin\lambda$.

8.3 The analytical method of Lagrange *

In considering the motion of a particle in space we can obtain its equations of motion in a very general form, using an elegant method first discovered by Lagrange.

First, suppose the position of the particle P to be defined by three independent co-ordinates q_1, q_2, q_3—which will include all possible co-ordinate systems. It follows that the Cartesian co-ordinates will be functions of the q's, that is to say, $x \equiv x(q_1, q_2, q_3)$; $y \equiv y(q_1, q_2, q_3)$; $z \equiv z(q_1, q_2, q_3)$. Now the underlying assumption of dynamics is that these q's must be determinate functions of the time, t. The most general relation between the q's and x, y, z will therefore allow for the presence of t explicitly as we change from one set to the other. We therefore write

$$x \equiv x(q_1, q_2, q_3, t)\ ;\ y \equiv y(q_1, q_2, q_3, t)\ ;\ z \equiv z(q_1, q_2, q_3, t) \qquad (1)$$

Hence (e.g.)

$$\frac{dx}{dt} = \dot{x} = \frac{\partial x}{\partial q_1}\dot{q}_1 + \frac{\partial x}{\partial q_2}\dot{q}_2 + \frac{\partial x}{\partial q_3}\dot{q}_3 + \frac{\partial x}{\partial t} \quad . \quad . \quad (2)$$

so that

$$\frac{\partial \dot{x}}{\partial \dot{q}_r} = \frac{\partial x}{\partial q_r} \quad (r = 1, 2, 3) \quad . \quad . \quad . \quad (3)$$

(2) also implies

$$\frac{\partial \dot{x}}{\partial q_r} = \frac{\partial^2 x}{\partial q_r\,\partial q_1}\cdot\dot{q}_1 + \frac{\partial^2 x}{\partial q_r\,\partial q_2}\cdot\dot{q}_2 + \frac{\partial^2 x}{\partial q_r\,\partial q_3}\cdot\dot{q}_3 + \frac{\partial^2 x}{\partial q_r\,\partial t} \quad (r = 1, 2, 3)$$

$$= \frac{d}{dt}\left(\frac{\partial x}{\partial q_r}\right) \quad (r = 1, 2, 3) \quad . \quad . \quad . \quad (4)$$

Suppose the resultant force acting on P has components (X, Y, Z) parallel to the Cartesian axes, then the equations of motion are

$$m\ddot{x} = X\ ;\ \ m\ddot{y} = Y\ ;\ \ m\ddot{z} = Z \quad . \quad . \quad (5)$$

Multiplying these by $\dfrac{\partial x}{\partial q_r}, \dfrac{\partial y}{\partial q_r}, \dfrac{\partial z}{\partial q_r}$ respectively and adding, we get

$$m\left\{\ddot{x}\frac{\partial x}{\partial q_r} + \ddot{y}\frac{\partial y}{\partial q_r} + \ddot{z}\frac{\partial z}{\partial q_r}\right\} = X\frac{\partial x}{\partial q_r} + Y\frac{\partial y}{\partial q_r} + Z\frac{\partial z}{\partial q_r} \qquad (6)$$

$$(r = 1, 2, 3)$$

* French mathematician, 1736–1813. His great work on applied mathematics, *La Mécanique Analytique,* was published in 1788.

But
$$\ddot{x}\frac{\partial x}{\partial q_r} = \ddot{x}\frac{\partial \dot{x}}{\partial \dot{q}_r}, \quad \text{by (3)}$$
$$= \frac{d}{dt}\left\{\dot{x}\frac{\partial \dot{x}}{\partial \dot{q}_r}\right\} - \dot{x}\frac{d}{dt}\left(\frac{\partial \dot{x}}{\partial \dot{q}_r}\right)$$
$$= \frac{d}{dt}\left\{\dot{x}\frac{\partial \dot{x}}{\partial \dot{q}_r}\right\} - \dot{x}\frac{\partial \dot{x}}{\partial q_r}, \quad \text{by (3) and (4)}$$
$$= \frac{d}{dt}\left\{\frac{\partial}{\partial \dot{q}_r}(\tfrac{1}{2}\dot{x}^2)\right\} - \frac{\partial}{\partial q_r}(\tfrac{1}{2}\dot{x}^2) \quad . \quad . \quad . \quad (7)$$

Writing $T = \frac{1}{2}m(\dot{x}^2 + \dot{y}^2 + \dot{z}^2)$ for the kinetic energy of the particle, equation (6) can be written
$$\frac{d}{dt}\left(\frac{\partial T}{\partial \dot{q}_r}\right) - \frac{\partial T}{\partial q_r} = X\frac{\partial x}{\partial q_r} + Y\frac{\partial y}{\partial q_r} + Z\frac{\partial z}{\partial q_r} \quad . \quad . \quad (8)$$
$$(r = 1, 2, 3)$$

Now the Work Done by the force (X, Y, Z) in a general displacement of P defined by dq_1, dq_2, dq_3 will be
$$\delta W = X\,dx + Y\,dy + Z\,dz$$
$$= X\left\{\frac{\partial x}{\partial q_1}dq_1 + \frac{\partial x}{\partial q_2}dq_2 + \frac{\partial x}{\partial q_3}dq_3\right\} + \text{etc.}$$
$$= \sum_{r=1}^{3}\left\{X\frac{\partial x}{\partial q_r} + Y\frac{\partial y}{\partial q_r} + Z\frac{\partial z}{\partial q_r}\right\}dq_r$$

i.e.
$$\delta W = \sum_{r=1}^{3} Q_r\,dq_r \quad \text{(say)} \quad . \quad . \quad . \quad . \quad . \quad (9)$$

Thus (8) and (9) give
$$\frac{d}{dt}\left(\frac{\partial T}{\partial \dot{q}_r}\right) - \frac{\partial T}{\partial q_r} = Q_r \quad . \quad . \quad . \quad (10)$$
$$(r = 1, 2, 3)$$

which are called the *Lagrange equations*. The Q_r are *generalised components of force*: the difference between these and force components proper can be brought out as follows:

The q's, being general, will form a set of axes at P of the kind discussed in 2.15. For the sake of simplicity let us suppose the system at P to be orthogonal with axis defined by an orthonormal triad $(\boldsymbol{e}_1, \boldsymbol{e}_2. \boldsymbol{e}_3)$. The metric is given by 2.15(4), viz.,
$$ds^2 = h_1^2\,dq_1^2 + h_2^2\,dq_2^2 + h_3^2\,dq_3^2$$
$$= ds_1^2 + ds_2^2 + ds_3^2 \quad . \quad . \quad . \quad . \quad (11)$$

where ds_1, ds_2 ,ds_3 are the lengths of infinitesimal displacements at P along $\boldsymbol{e}_1$, $\boldsymbol{e}_2$, $\boldsymbol{e}_3$ respectively. Now the force $\boldsymbol{F} = (X, Y, Z)$ can be resolved into components (F_1, F_2, F_3) along these axes at P. The work done in a small displacement will be

$$\begin{aligned}\delta W &= F_1\,ds_1 + F_2\,ds_2 + F_3\,ds_3\\ &= h_1F_1\,dq_1 + h_2F_2\,dq_2 + h_3F_3\,dq_3\\ &= Q_1\,dq_1 + Q_2\,dq_2 + Q_3\,dq_3\end{aligned}$$

Thus $Q_r = h_rF_r \quad (r = 1, 2, 3)$. In the simple case of rectangular Cartesian co-ordinates $(x = q_1, y = q_2, z = q_3)$ we have $h_1=h_2=h_3=1$ so that the Q's and the F's are identical. Examples 2 and 3 of 2.15 illustrate other and different cases.

Example 1. To find the components of acceleration of a particle defined by spherical polar co-ordinates (r, θ, ϕ).

Since

$$T = \tfrac{1}{2}\{\dot{r}^2 + r^2\dot{\theta}^2 + r^2\sin^2\theta\,\dot{\phi}^2\} \qquad (\text{v. 2.15, Ex. and 4.4(7)})$$

we have, e.g. $$\frac{d}{dt}\left(\frac{\partial T}{\partial\dot{r}}\right) - \frac{\partial T}{\partial r} = Q_1 = h_1f_1 \quad (q_1 \equiv r)$$

which gives $$h_1f_1 = f_1 = \frac{d}{dt}(\dot{r}) - (r\dot{\theta}^2 + r\sin^2\theta\dot{\phi}^2)$$

Similarly $$\begin{aligned}h_2f_2 = rf_2 &= \frac{d}{dt}\left(\frac{\partial T}{\partial\dot{\theta}}\right) - \frac{\partial T}{\partial\theta}\\ &= \frac{d}{dt}(r^2\dot{\theta}) - r^2\sin\theta\cos\theta\dot{\phi}^2\end{aligned}$$

and $$h_3f_3 = r\sin\theta f_3 = \frac{d}{dt}\left(\frac{\partial T}{\partial\dot{\phi}}\right) = \frac{d}{dt}(r^2\sin^2\theta\dot{\phi})$$

These give f_1, f_2, f_3, as found in 4.4(8).

The reader should verify the result of 4.4(4) by taking $q_1 = r$, $q_2 = \theta$, $q_3 = z$, $h_1 = 1$, $h_2 = r$, $h_3 = 1$ and $T = \frac{1}{2}(\dot{r}^2 + r^2\dot{\theta}^2 + \dot{z}^2)$.

When the particle is restricted to move only on a *surface* its position is defined by two co-ordinates only, say, q_1 and q_2. Equation (10) is still applicable with $r = 1, 2$. In this way the results 4.4(5), 4.4(10) and 4.4(12) easily follow by using the appropriate expression for T.

Of course, equations (10) are primarily kinetic results as the following examples show.

Example 2. The equations of motion for Galileo's projectile. The motion takes place in the vertical plane Ox, Oy. Hence $T = \frac{1}{2}m(\dot{x}^2 + \dot{y}^2)$ and, since the force is conservative, we have $\delta W = -\,dV = -\,d(mgy) = -\,mg\,dy = Q_2\,dy$. Then (10) gives

$$m\ddot{x} = 0\,; \quad m\ddot{y} = -\,mg$$

Example 3. A particle moves on a plane which is rotating about its normal through a point O of itself with constant angular velocity ω: to find the equations of motion.

To find the kinetic energy T we must use the velocity

$$\boldsymbol{v} = \frac{\partial \boldsymbol{r}}{\partial t} + \boldsymbol{\omega} \times \boldsymbol{r}$$

so that
$$\boldsymbol{v}^2 = \left(\frac{\partial \boldsymbol{r}}{\partial t}\right)^2 + 2(\boldsymbol{\omega} \times \boldsymbol{r}) \cdot \frac{\partial \boldsymbol{r}}{\partial t} + (\boldsymbol{\omega} \times \boldsymbol{r})^2 \quad . \quad . \quad (12)$$

By 2.12, Ex.1 we have

$$(\boldsymbol{\omega} \times \boldsymbol{r})^2 = -(\boldsymbol{\omega} . \boldsymbol{r})^2 + \boldsymbol{\omega}^2 \boldsymbol{r}^2$$

Writing $\boldsymbol{r} = x\,\boldsymbol{i} + y\,\boldsymbol{j}$ and $\boldsymbol{\omega} = \omega\,\boldsymbol{k}$, (12) gives

$$T = \tfrac{1}{2}m\{\dot{x}^2 + \dot{y}^2 + 2\omega(x\dot{y} - y\dot{x}) + \omega^2(x^2 + y^2)\}$$

If the forces acting on the particle have components (X, Y) equation (10) gives

$$m(\ddot{x} - 2\dot{y}\omega - \omega^2 x) = X$$
$$m(\ddot{y} + 2\dot{x}\omega - \omega^2 y) = Y$$

which should be compared with 4.2(3).

Example 4. *The conservation of energy.* If the field of force is conservative there exists a function $V(q_1, q_2, q_3)$ such that

$$\delta W = -dV = -\sum_{r=1}^{3} \frac{\partial V}{q_r} dq_r$$

Hence (10) becomes

$$\frac{d}{dt}\left(\frac{\partial T}{\partial \dot{q}_r}\right) - \frac{\partial T}{\partial q_r} = -\frac{\partial V}{\partial q_r} \quad (r = 1, 2, 3) \quad . \quad . \quad (13)$$

Now suppose that T does *not contain t explicitly*. Then it will be of the form $T = \frac{1}{2}g_{rs}\dot{q}_r\dot{q}_s$ (summation convention), where the g_{rs} are functions of the q's. Thus T is a quadratic function of the $\dot{q}$'s.

Now

$$\frac{d}{dt}(T + V) = \sum_{r=1}^{3}\left\{\frac{\partial T}{\partial \dot{q}_r}\ddot{q}_r + \frac{\partial T}{\partial q_r}\dot{q}_r + \frac{\partial V}{\partial q_r}\dot{q}_r\right\}$$
$$= \sum_{r=1}^{3}\left\{\frac{\partial T}{\partial q_r}\ddot{q}_r + \frac{d}{dt}\left(\frac{\partial T}{\partial \dot{q}_r}\right)\dot{q}_r + 2\frac{\partial V}{\partial q_r}\right\}\dot{q}_r \quad \text{by (13)}$$
$$= \sum_{r=1}^{3}\left\{\frac{d}{dt}\left(\frac{\partial T}{\partial \dot{q}_r}\dot{q}_r\right) + 2\frac{\partial V}{\partial q_r}\dot{q}_r\right\}$$

But
$$2T = \sum_{r=1}^{3}\frac{\partial T}{\partial \dot{q}_r}\dot{q}_r$$

by Euler's theorem on homogeneous functions. Hence we get

$$\frac{d}{dt}(T + V) = \frac{d}{dt}(2T + 2V)$$

giving $\quad T + V = \text{constant} = H \quad$ (say)

Exercise VIII

1. A particle is projected horizontally with velocity $\sqrt{7ag/2}$ inside a smooth hollow sphere of radius a. If the particle starts from the lowest point of the sphere find its velocity when it leaves the sphere, and show that it will subsequently strike the sphere again at the point from which it started. (M.T.)

2. A heavy particle is projected horizontally with speed v_0 from the lowest point of the inner surface of a fixed sphere of radius a. The coefficient of friction between the particle and the sphere is $1/\sqrt{2}$. Show that, under certain conditions which should be stated, the velocity of the particle when at an angular distance θ from the lowest point is v, where

$$v^2 = v_0^2\, e^{-\theta\sqrt{2}} - ag\sqrt{2}\sin\theta \qquad \text{(L.U.)}$$

3. Obtain expressions for the components of the acceleration of a particle in spherical polar co-ordinates (r, θ, ϕ).

A particle, of mass m, is projected horizontally along the surface with velocity v from a point on the inner surface of a smooth sphere, of radius a, at an angular distance α from the lowest point. Prove that the reaction of the surface, when the particle is at an angular distance θ from the lowest point, is

$$m(3g\cos\theta - 2g\cos\alpha + v^2/a) \qquad \text{(L.U.)}$$

4. A particle of mass m is contrained to remain on the surface of a sphere of radius a, and is attached to a fixed point of the sphere by a slightly extensible thread of natural length $a\alpha$ and modulus λ. Prove that, if the particle is projected at right angles to the unstretched thread with velocity v the greatest subsequent elongation is $2a\lambda^{-1}mv^2 \cot\alpha$. (C.)

5. A particle is projected horizontally on the interior surface of a smooth cone whose axis is vertical and vertex downwards. Prove that its path when the cone is developed into a plane is the same as the path of a particle under the action of a constant force to a fixed point. (C.)

6. A particle moves on a smooth cone under a force to the vertex varying inversely as the square of the distance. Prove that, if the cone is developed into a plane, the path will be a conic having one focus at the vertex of the cone. (C.)

7. A particle moves under gravity on a right circular cone with a vertical axis. Show that, if the equations of motion can be integrated without elliptic functions, the particle must be below the vertex, and that its distance r from the vertex at time t is given by an equation of the form

$$(r\dot{r})^2 = 2g\cos\alpha(r - r_0)(r + 2r_0)^2$$

where 2α is the vertical angle of the cone. (C.)

8. A fixed smooth circular cone of angle 2α has its axis vertical and its vertex downwards. A particle of mass M hangs below the cone by a long string that passes through a small hole at the vertex, the upper end of the string being attached to a particle of mass m that is held on the inner surface of the cone at a distance d from the vertex. The system is set in motion by projecting m horizontally along the cone with velocity V. Show that, provided

$$mV^2 > gd(M + m \cos \alpha)$$

the particle m never approaches nearer than d to the vertex. Show also, in this case, that the greatest distance of the particle m from the vertex is a solution of the equation

$$2g(M + m \cos \alpha)\, x^2 - mV^2(d + x) = 0$$

Determine the tension in the string at the moment when m is at the greatest distance from the vertex. (M.T.)

9. Obtain the formulae for the components of acceleration of a particle moving in three dimensional space referred to spherical polar co-ordinates.

A particle moving on the outer surface of a smooth cone, of vertical angle 2α, fixed with its axis vertical and vertex uppermost, is observed to be moving horizontally with speed u when passing through the highest point of its path distant d from the vertex. Prove that if

$$u^2 \cos \alpha < gd \sin^2 \alpha$$

the particle never leaves the surface of the cone. (L.U.)

10. A heavy particle of unit mass moves on the outside of a smooth right circular cone, of semi-angle 30°, whose axis is vertical and vertex uppermost. The particle is attached to the vertex by a light elastic string of natural length a, the tension of the string for unit extension being k/a. The particle describes a horizontal circle of radius b on the cone, with constant speed ωb, the length of the string being greater than a. Prove that

$$b = \frac{\sqrt{3g} + 2k}{4k - a\omega^2}\, a$$

provided that $4k > a\omega^2$.

Show also that the motion of the particle is stable for small disturbances, assuming that the particle remains in contact with the cone. (L.U.)

11. A particle moves on the inside of a smooth conical cup whose generators make an angle α ($< \pi/2$) with the upward vertical. It is projected horizontally along the surface from a point at height h above the vertex O with speed u, where $u^2 = 9gh/2$. If y is the height of the particle above O at time t, establish the equation

$$\dot{y}^2 = \frac{g \cos^2 \alpha}{2} \frac{(3h - y)(y - h)(4y + 3h)}{y^2}$$

and prove that the path of the particle touches alternately the horizontal circles at heights h and $3h$ above O.

Express the vertical component of acceleration as a function of y, and prove that it vanishes when $2y^3 = 9h^3$. (M.T.)

12. A particle moves on the inside of a smooth circular cone of vertical angle 2α under a force to the vertex varying inversely as the square of the distance. It is projected from an apse at a distance c from the axis with velocity $\frac{1}{2}\sqrt{6}$ of that requisite for circular motion. Prove that the polar equation of the projection of the path on a plane perpendicular to the axis is

$$3c/r = 2 + \cos(\theta \sin \alpha)$$

that the time from one apse to the next is $\pi\,(2c \operatorname{cosec} \alpha)^{\frac{3}{2}}/\sqrt{\mu}$, and that the pressure is inversely proportional to the cube of the distance from the vertex. (C.)

13. A particle is projected horizontally along the smooth inner surface of a right circular cone, whose axis is vertical and vertex downwards, the initial velocity being $\sqrt{\{2gh/(n^2 + n)\}}$, where h is the initial height above the vertex. Prove that the lowest point of its path is at a height h/n above the vertex. (C.)

14. A right circular cone of vertical angle 2α is placed with one generator vertical and vertex upwards. From a point on the generator of least slope a particle is projected horizontally and at right angles to the generator with velocity v. Prove that it will just skim the surface of the cone without pressure if the distance of the point of projection from the vertex is

$$\tfrac{1}{2}v^2 \operatorname{cosec}^2 \alpha/g \qquad \text{(C.)}$$

15. A particle is projected horizontally from a fixed point on the interior surface of a smooth paraboloid of revolution whose axis is vertical and vertex downwards. Prove that when it is again moving horizontally its velocity is independent of the velocity of projection. (C.)

16. Give the mathematical theory of the Foucault pendulum, stating any approximations that are introduced. (M.T.)

17. The position vector of a particle relative to a point on the Earth's surface is $\boldsymbol{r}$; the velocity and acceleration of the particle relative to the Earth are $\dot{\boldsymbol{r}}$ and $\ddot{\boldsymbol{r}}$. If the particle moves under the Earth's attraction and a force $\boldsymbol{F}$ per unit mass, prove that

$$\ddot{\boldsymbol{r}} + 2\boldsymbol{\omega}\times\dot{\boldsymbol{r}} = \mathbf{g}(\boldsymbol{r}) + \boldsymbol{F}$$

where $\boldsymbol{\omega}$ is the Earth's angular velocity, and $\boldsymbol{g}(\boldsymbol{r})$ is the acceleration (relative to the Earth) of a freely falling particle instantaneously at rest relative to the Earth. How accurate is this equation?

A particle is projected due East with speed V along a smooth horizontal table. Prove that the initial curvature of the path on the table due to the rotation of the Earth is $2\,|\,\omega\,|\,V^{-1}\sin\lambda$, λ being the north latitude. (M.T.)

18. A shot is fired from a point on the earth's surface so that the horizontal component of the initial velocity points due north. Show that, when the shot again reaches the earth's surface, its deviation from the northerly direction due to the earth's rotation is to the east or to the west according as $3\tan\lambda - \tan\alpha$ is positive or negative. Here λ is the latitude, and α is the angle of projection above the horizontal. The earth's curvature and variations in gravity may be neglected; it is also assumed that the time of flight is short compared with the length of a day. (M.T.)

19. A smooth plane is inclined at an angle α to the horizontal in such a way that the direction of steepest descent is south. A particle is projected eastwards along the plane with velocity V. Show that the initial curvature of the path relative to the plane is

$$\frac{g \sin \alpha}{V^2} + \frac{2\omega \sin (\lambda - \alpha)}{V}$$

where λ is the north latitude and ω is the angular velocity of the earth. It may be assumed that the particle remains in contact with the plane.

(M.T.)

CHAPTER IX

SYSTEMS OF MANY PARTICLES

9.1 The general motion of n particles

Let the particles have masses m_i ($i = 1, 2 \ldots n$) and be situated at the points P_i whose position vectors are $\boldsymbol{r}_i$ w.r.t. a fixed origin O in space.

We define the **centre of mass** as the point G with position vector $\overline{OG} = \bar{\boldsymbol{r}}$, where, writing $M = \sum_{i=1}^{n} m_i$,

$$M\,\bar{\boldsymbol{r}} = \sum_{i=1}^{n} m_i \boldsymbol{r}_i \quad . \quad . \quad . \quad . \quad (1)$$

We define the **linear momentum** of the system by

$$\boldsymbol{L} = \sum_{i=1}^{n} m_i \dot{\boldsymbol{r}}_i = \sum_{i=1}^{n} m_i \boldsymbol{v}_i \,. \quad . \quad . \quad . \quad . \quad (2)$$

We define the **angular momentum about a fixed point** A(**a**) by

$$\boldsymbol{H}(A) = \sum_{i=1}^{n} \overline{AP}_i \times m_i \dot{\boldsymbol{r}}_i = \sum_{i=1}^{n} (\boldsymbol{r}_i - \boldsymbol{a}) \times m_i \boldsymbol{v}_i \quad . \quad (3)$$

In particular

$$\boldsymbol{H}(O) = \sum_{i=1}^{n} \boldsymbol{r}_i \times m_i \boldsymbol{v}_i \quad . \quad . \quad . \quad . \quad . \quad . \quad (4)$$

We define the **kinetic energy** of the system by

$$T = \tfrac{1}{2} \sum_{i=1}^{n} m_i \dot{r}_i^2 = \tfrac{1}{2} \sum_{i=1}^{n} m_i v_i^2 \quad . \quad . \quad . \quad . \quad (5)$$

If we write the velocity of the centre of mass as $\bar{\boldsymbol{v}}$, (1) and (2) show that

$\boldsymbol{L} = M\,\bar{\boldsymbol{v}} =$ linear momentum of a particle of mass M situated at G . . . . (6)

Now suppose that the forces acting at P_i have a resultant represented by the line vector $\boldsymbol{F}_i$. The Newtonian equations of motion will therefore be

$$m_i \ddot{\boldsymbol{r}}_i = \boldsymbol{F}_i \quad (i = 1, 2, \ldots n) \quad . \quad . \quad . \quad (7)$$

These forces $\boldsymbol{F}_i$ may be regarded as being derived from two sources :

(i) forces acting on P_i which are due to the presence of all the other particles P_j $(j \neq i)$; and

(ii) forces due to agents which are independent of the P_j $(j \neq i)$.

Under the heading (i) we shall have forces of *universal gravitation* and forces acting in any joining *strings* and/or *light rods*. These forces will therefore act in the lines of P_iP_j $(j \neq i)$. For a given mass m_i at P_i denote the force due to the particle m_j at P_j (under this heading (i)) by $\boldsymbol{S}_{ij}$ $(j = 1, 2, \ldots n)$, and let us use the convention that $\boldsymbol{S}_{ii} = \boldsymbol{0}$ (all i). The law of action-reaction also gives us $\boldsymbol{S}_{ij} = -\boldsymbol{S}_{ji}$ $(i, j = 1, 2, \ldots n)$.

If the forces acting on m_i at P_i, and under the heading (ii), have a resultant $\boldsymbol{R}_i$, then (7) becomes

$$m_i \ddot{\boldsymbol{r}}_i = \boldsymbol{R}_i + \sum_{j=1}^{n} \boldsymbol{S}_{ij} \quad . \quad . \quad . \quad (8)$$

Since $\boldsymbol{S}_{ij} + \boldsymbol{S}_{ji} = \boldsymbol{0}$ (all i, j) we have

$$\sum_i \sum_j \boldsymbol{S}_{ij} = \sum_{i<j} (\boldsymbol{S}_{ij} + \boldsymbol{S}_{ji}) = \boldsymbol{0} \quad . \quad . \quad . \quad (9)$$

and since $\boldsymbol{S}_{ij}$ acts in the line P_iP_j it is parallel to the vector $(\boldsymbol{r}_i - \boldsymbol{r}_j)$: hence

$$\sum_{i=1}^{n} \left\{ \boldsymbol{r}_i \times \sum_{j=i}^{n} \boldsymbol{S}_{ij} \right\} = \sum_{i<j} (\boldsymbol{r}_i - \boldsymbol{r}_j) \times \boldsymbol{S}_{ij} = \boldsymbol{0} \quad . \quad . \quad (10)$$

Using (8) and (9) we have

$$\sum_{i=1}^{n} m_i \ddot{\boldsymbol{r}}_i = \sum_{i=1}^{n} \boldsymbol{R}_i$$

and writing $\boldsymbol{R} = \sum_{i=1}^{n} \boldsymbol{R}_i$ and using (1), this becomes

$$M \ddot{\bar{\boldsymbol{r}}} = \boldsymbol{R} \quad . \quad . \quad . \quad . \quad . \quad (11)$$

The forces under (i) we shall call *internal forces* of the system, and those under (ii), *external forces*. Equation (11) shows that *the centre of mass, G, moves as if it were a particle of mass $M = \sum_i m_i$ and as if all the external forces acted at it.*

Using (8) and (10) we also get

$$\sum_{i=1}^{n} \boldsymbol{r} \times m_i \ddot{\boldsymbol{r}}_i = \sum_{i=1}^{n} \boldsymbol{r}_i \times \boldsymbol{R}_i \quad . \quad . \quad . \quad (12)$$

Since O is a fixed point the lhs of (12) becomes

$$\frac{d}{dt}\left\{\sum_i (\boldsymbol{r}_i \times m_i \dot{\boldsymbol{r}}_i)\right\} = \frac{d}{dt}\boldsymbol{H}(O)$$

and since the rhs of (12) is the *torque about* O (v. 3.2) *of the external forces,* say $\boldsymbol{\Gamma}(O)$, we can write (12) as

$$\frac{d}{dt}\boldsymbol{H}(O) = \boldsymbol{\Gamma}(O) \quad . \quad . \quad . \quad . \quad (13)$$

Although the $\boldsymbol{R}$ of (11) and the $\boldsymbol{\Gamma}(O)$ of (13) involve only external forces it must not be supposed that the internal forces play no significant rôle in the motion of the system. This is clear from considerations of energy. Thus suppose all the forces $\boldsymbol{F}_i$ are conservative (and this includes the internal forces). Then (7) gives

$$m_i \dot{\boldsymbol{r}}_i . \ddot{\boldsymbol{r}}_i = \left\{\boldsymbol{R}_i + \sum_{j=1}^{n} \boldsymbol{S}_{ij}\right\} . \dot{\boldsymbol{r}}_i$$

whence, summing over i and integrating w.r.t. t, we get

$$T = \sum_{i=1}^{n} \int \boldsymbol{R}_i . d\boldsymbol{r}_i + \sum_{i=1}^{n}\sum_{j=1}^{n} \int \boldsymbol{S}_{ij} . d\boldsymbol{r}_i + C \quad . \quad . \quad (14)$$

The contribution to the work done of the internal forces $\boldsymbol{S}_{ij}$ can be written

$$\sum_{i=1}^{n}\sum_{j=1}^{n} \int \boldsymbol{S}_{ij} . d\boldsymbol{r}_i = \sum_{i<j} \int \boldsymbol{S}_{ij} . (d\boldsymbol{r}_i - d\boldsymbol{r}_j)$$

$$= \sum_{i<j} \int \boldsymbol{S}_{ij} . d\boldsymbol{r}_{ij} \quad . \quad . \quad . \quad (15)$$

where $\boldsymbol{r}_{ij} = \boldsymbol{r}_i - \boldsymbol{r}_j =$ the vector $\overline{P_j P_i}$. This expression on the rhs of (15) will not, in general, vanish since only exceptionally will $\boldsymbol{S}_{ij} . d\boldsymbol{r}_{ij} = 0$ for all i, j—although, of course, the expression can be zero without all its terms vanishing. Thus if $\boldsymbol{S}_{ij}$ is the tension in an elastic string there will be a non-zero contribution to the work done; also if $\boldsymbol{S}_{ij}$ is a force of universal gravitation between the masses m_i and m_j.

Thus, *in writing down the energy equation for a general system of particles we must not ignore the internal forces.*

From equations (11) and (13) we can also deduce the principles of the conservation of momentum. In their most useful form these can be expressed as follows.

Suppose $\boldsymbol{e}$ is a *constant vector* such that $\boldsymbol{R} . \boldsymbol{e} = 0$ for all t. Then (11) gives

$$M \ddot{\bar{\boldsymbol{r}}} . \boldsymbol{e} = \frac{d}{dt}\{M \dot{\bar{\boldsymbol{r}}} . \boldsymbol{e}\} = 0$$

so that

$$M \dot{\bar{\boldsymbol{r}}} . \boldsymbol{e} = \boldsymbol{L} . \boldsymbol{e} = \text{constant} \quad . \quad . \quad . \quad (16)$$

Hence *linear momentum is constant in any direction in which the resiltant external force is zero.*

If now, $\boldsymbol{e}$ is such that $\boldsymbol{e}.\boldsymbol{\Gamma}(O) = 0$ for all t, then (13) gives

$$\boldsymbol{e}.\boldsymbol{H}(O) = \text{constant} \quad . \quad . \quad . \quad . \quad (17)$$

Hence the *angular momentum is constant about any line about which the external forces have zero moment.*

Example 1. Two gravitating particles. Consider two particles of masses m_1 and m_2 which attract each other according to the inverse square law, and let them be projected in an arbitrary manner.

Here we have $\boldsymbol{R} = \boldsymbol{0}$ so that the centre of mass G moves with constant velocity. There is no loss in generality if we therefore regard G as origin, and since $\boldsymbol{\Gamma} = \boldsymbol{0}$ (for every origin) the motion will be plane. Taking polar co-ordinates (r_1, θ_1) for the mass m_1 (v. Fig. 80), we have the force between P_1 and P_2 is $\dfrac{\gamma m_1 m_2}{r^2}$ where $r = r_1 + r_2$. The motion of P_1 is given by

$$m_1(\ddot{r}_1 - r_1\dot{\theta}_1^{\,2}) = -\frac{\gamma m_1 m_2}{r^2} \quad . \quad . \quad . \quad . \quad (18)$$

$$\frac{m_1}{r_1}\frac{d}{dt}(r_1^{\,2}\dot{\theta}_1) = 0 \quad . \quad . \quad . \quad . \quad . \quad (19)$$

Since $r_1 = \dfrac{m_2 r}{m_1 + m_2}$, (18) and (19) become

$$\ddot{r} - r\dot{\theta}_1^{\,2} = -\gamma(m_1 + m_2)/r^2 \quad . \quad . \quad (20)$$

and

$$\frac{d}{dt}(r^2\dot{\theta}_1) = 0 \quad . \quad . \quad . \quad . \quad . \quad (21)$$

Equations (20) and (21) show that *either particle describes a central orbit about the other.* This orbit is a conic section with the other particle at a focus. The results of Chapter VI are immediately applicable if we write $\gamma(m_1 + m_2)$ in place of μ.

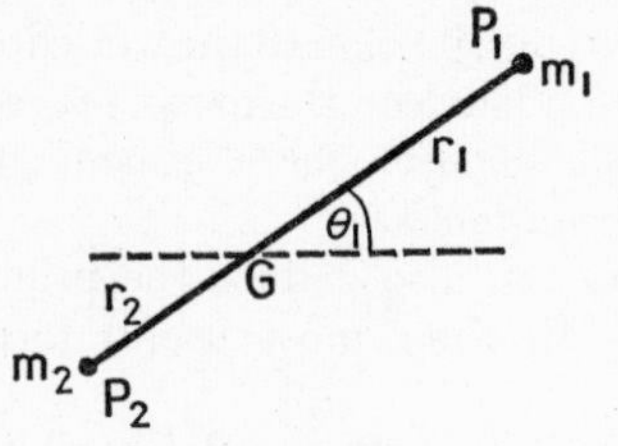

FIG. 80.

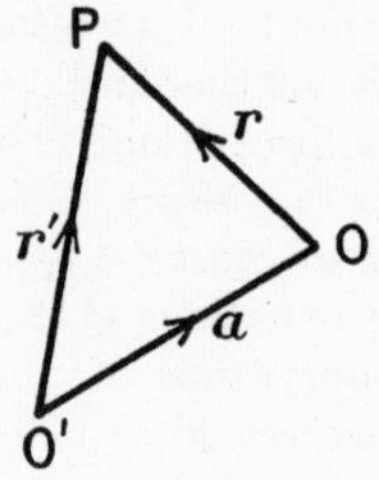

FIG. 81.

9.2 Angular momentum and its rate of change

It is important to examine the angular momentum vector $\boldsymbol{H}(O)$ when O is not necessarily a fixed point. To do this let us refer to Fig. 81

in which P is a typical particle of the system of mass m. Let O, O′ be two possible origins and let $\overline{O'O} = \boldsymbol{a}$. Let P have velocities $\boldsymbol{v}'$ and $\boldsymbol{v}$ relative to O' and O respectively. Now take O' as a fixed point and let O have velocity $\boldsymbol{u}$ (relative to O'). Then $\boldsymbol{v}' = \boldsymbol{u} + \boldsymbol{v}$ and the *angular momentum of the system relative to O* will be written $\boldsymbol{H}_r(O)$ and is clearly given by $\boldsymbol{H}_r(O) = \sum \boldsymbol{r} \times m\,\boldsymbol{v}$, summation over all the masses m being intended. We now have

$$\begin{aligned} \boldsymbol{H}(O') &= \textstyle\sum \boldsymbol{r}' \times m\,\boldsymbol{v}' \\ &= \textstyle\sum \boldsymbol{r}' \times m\,(\boldsymbol{u} + \boldsymbol{v}) \\ &= \textstyle\sum (\boldsymbol{a} + \boldsymbol{r}) \times m(\boldsymbol{u} + \boldsymbol{v}) \\ &= \textstyle\sum \boldsymbol{a} \times m\,\boldsymbol{v}' + \sum \boldsymbol{r} \times m(\boldsymbol{u} + \boldsymbol{v}) \\ &= \boldsymbol{a} \times (\textstyle\sum m\,\boldsymbol{v}') + (\sum m\,\boldsymbol{r}) \times \boldsymbol{u} + \boldsymbol{H}_r(O) \end{aligned}$$

giving $\boldsymbol{H}(O') = \boldsymbol{a} \times M\,\bar{\boldsymbol{v}}' + \bar{\boldsymbol{r}} \times M\,\boldsymbol{u} + \boldsymbol{H}_r(O)$ . . . (1)

where $\bar{\boldsymbol{v}}'$ = the velocity of G (relative to the fixed origin O')

and $\bar{\boldsymbol{r}}$ = the position vector $\overline{OG}$.

Clearly (1) becomes much simpler in the case $G \equiv O \equiv O'$, for then $\boldsymbol{a} = \bar{\boldsymbol{r}} = \boldsymbol{0}$ and so

$$\boldsymbol{H}(G) = \boldsymbol{H}_r(G) \qquad (2)$$

i.e. the angular momentum of a system of particles about G, the centre of mass, is independent of the motion of G.

Differentiating (1) gives

$$\frac{d}{dt}\boldsymbol{H}(O') = \frac{d}{dt}\boldsymbol{H}_r(O) + \dot{\boldsymbol{a}} \times M\,\bar{\boldsymbol{v}}' + \boldsymbol{a} \times M\,\dot{\bar{\boldsymbol{v}}}' + \dot{\bar{\boldsymbol{r}}} \times M\,\boldsymbol{u} + \bar{\boldsymbol{r}} \times M\,\dot{\boldsymbol{u}}$$

Firstly, let us consider the case of $O \equiv O'$, i.e. $\boldsymbol{a} = \boldsymbol{0}$ and $\dot{\boldsymbol{a}} = \boldsymbol{u}$. This gives

$$\frac{d}{dt}\boldsymbol{H}(O') = \left[\frac{d}{dt}\boldsymbol{H}_r(O)\right]_{O \equiv O'} + \bar{\boldsymbol{r}} \times M\frac{d\boldsymbol{u}}{dt} \qquad (3)$$

Secondly, take $O \equiv O' \equiv G$ so that $\bar{\boldsymbol{r}} = \boldsymbol{0}$. Then (3) gives

$$\frac{d}{dt}\boldsymbol{H}(G) = \frac{d}{dt}\boldsymbol{H}_r(G) \qquad (4)$$

i.e. the rate of change of $\boldsymbol{H}(G)$ is independent of the motion of G. These results (2) and (4) illustrate the dynamical significance of the centre of mass.

It follows from (4) and 9.1(13) that

$$\frac{d}{dt}\boldsymbol{H}_r(G) = \boldsymbol{\Gamma}(G) \qquad (5)$$

Finally, writing $G \equiv O$, $\bar{\boldsymbol{r}} = \boldsymbol{0}$, equation (1) gives

$$\boldsymbol{H}(O') = \boldsymbol{H}_r(G) + \boldsymbol{a} \times M\,\bar{\boldsymbol{v}}' \qquad (6)$$

i.e. $\boldsymbol{H}(O') = \boldsymbol{H}_r(G) +$ the angular momentum about O' of a particle M situated at G and moving with G.

9.3 The equations governing the motion of a rigid body

Consider a material body occupying a region Ω of space and whose density is the scalar point function $\rho(\boldsymbol{r})$. Then its *total mass* is $M = \int_\Omega \rho(\boldsymbol{r})\, d\Omega$, and its *centre of mass* is the point $G(\bar{\boldsymbol{r}})$, defined by

$$M\,\bar{\boldsymbol{r}} = \int_\Omega \rho(\boldsymbol{r})\,\boldsymbol{r}\, d\Omega \quad . \quad . \quad . \quad (1)$$

The body is also called a *rigid body* if

$$(\boldsymbol{r}_i - \boldsymbol{r}_j)^2 = \text{constant, for all } t \quad . \quad . \quad . \quad (2)$$

where $\boldsymbol{r}_i$ and $\boldsymbol{r}_j$ are any two points of the body, i.e. points at which $\rho(\boldsymbol{r}) \neq 0$. We have seen the consequences of this condition of rigidity in 3.5.

Now it is tempting to regard a rigid body as a set of particles possessing the additional condition (2), the body being divided up into masses $m_i = \rho\, d\Omega$ for the purpose. Before we emphasise the logical difficulties involved by such a device we can deduce certain important consequences, from the results of 9.1.

Equations 9.1(11) and 9.1(13), 9.2(5) will immediately apply. Furthermore, (2) implies that

$$\boldsymbol{r}_{ij}.\boldsymbol{dr}_{ij} = 0 = \boldsymbol{S}_{ij}.\boldsymbol{dr}_{ij} \quad (\text{all } i, j)$$

and so expression 9.1(15) is zero. Thus the internal forces $\boldsymbol{S}_{ij}$ play no part in the energy equation, and therefore no part in the general kinetic problem. This is inherent in the work of Huygens (v. 1.2).

The difficulties in this view of the kinetics of a rigid body are : (i) the number of particles of the system is infinite so that the summations of 9.1 must be replaced by limiting processes ; and (ii) since $\boldsymbol{r}_{ij} = \boldsymbol{0}$ for every pair of adjacent particles, the nature of the internal forces $\boldsymbol{S}_{ij}$ is not obvious : in particular there is no obvious reason why $\boldsymbol{S}_{ij}$ should be a line vector.

We shall regard (i) as a problem of the calculus, involving as it does questions of integrability.

With regard to (ii) we shall give *D'Alembert's Principle* as an alternative foundation.*

Since we do not wish to specify the forces which account for the conditions of rigidity (2) we shall merely refer to them as the *forces of constraint*. The word *constraint* is used dynamically to denote any specific geometrical condition which a system is subject to : thus for a rigid body equations (2) represent a constraint. Generally, it follows that " internal forces " includes " forces of constraint " although the converse is not true.

* Jean Le Rond D'Alembert, French mathematician, 1717–83.

Regarding the body as composed of a set of typical elementary particles of masses m_i, as before, let the external forces be represented by $\boldsymbol{R}_i$. If the particles were, in fact free, they would move according to the equations $m_i \ddot{\boldsymbol{r}}_i = \boldsymbol{R}_i$, but because of the constraints the particles will only move according to the equations $m_i \ddot{\boldsymbol{r}}_i = \boldsymbol{P}_i$, where the $\boldsymbol{P}_i$ are the *effective forces*. Thus the whole set of forces $\{\boldsymbol{R}_i - \boldsymbol{P}_i\}$ must be in equilibrium with the whole set of " forces of constraint." But the latter set of forces is already in equilibrium by the law of action-reaction. Hence the set of forces $\{\boldsymbol{R}_i - \boldsymbol{P}_i\}$ is itself in equilibrium : this is D'Alembert's Principle. It can be otherwise expressed in the forms :

(I) the external forces $\{\boldsymbol{R}_i\}$ are in equilibrium with the negative effective forces $\{-m_i \ddot{\boldsymbol{r}}_i\}$;

(II) the external forces $\{\boldsymbol{R}_i\}$ are equivalent to the effective forces $\{m_i \ddot{\boldsymbol{r}}_i\}$;

(III) the principle of virtual work can be applied to the set of forces $\{\boldsymbol{R}_i - m_i \ddot{\boldsymbol{r}}_i\}$, i.e.

$$\sum_i (\boldsymbol{R}_i - m_i \ddot{\boldsymbol{r}}_i).d\boldsymbol{r}_i = 0 \qquad . \qquad . \qquad (3)$$

Using (3), let the rigid body suffer an infinitesimal displacement $d\boldsymbol{x}$ and an infinitesimal rotation $\boldsymbol{e}\, d\theta$ (v. 3.4 and 3.5). Then

$$d\boldsymbol{r}_i = d\boldsymbol{x} + d\theta\, \boldsymbol{e} \times \boldsymbol{r}_i \quad \text{(all } i\text{)}$$

and (3) gives

$$\sum_i (\boldsymbol{R}_i - m_i \ddot{\boldsymbol{r}}_i).(d\boldsymbol{x} + d\theta\, \boldsymbol{e} \times \boldsymbol{r}_i) = 0$$

which gives

$$d\boldsymbol{x}.\left\{\sum_i (\boldsymbol{R}_i - m_i \ddot{\boldsymbol{r}}_i)\right\} = 0$$

and

$$d\theta\, \boldsymbol{e}.\left\{\sum_i (\boldsymbol{r}_i \times \boldsymbol{R}_i - \boldsymbol{r}_i \times m_i \ddot{\boldsymbol{r}}_i)\right\} = 0$$

since $d\boldsymbol{x}$ and $\boldsymbol{e}\, d\theta$ are independent of each other.

These give

$$M \ddot{\bar{\boldsymbol{r}}} = \boldsymbol{R} \qquad . \qquad . \qquad . \qquad . \qquad (4)$$

and, O being fixed,

$$\frac{d}{dt} \boldsymbol{H}(O) = \boldsymbol{\Gamma}(O) \qquad . \qquad . \qquad . \qquad . \qquad (5)$$

being the equations of 9.1(11) and 9.1(13). To these we can clearly add 9.2(5), viz.,

$$\frac{d}{dt} \boldsymbol{H}_r(G) = \boldsymbol{\Gamma}(G) \qquad . \qquad . \qquad . \qquad . \qquad (6)$$

We can also deduce the energy equation as a first integral of these equations of motion. Thus, suppose the external forces are conservative, possessing a potential function $V(\boldsymbol{r})$, then from (3) we have

$$\sum_i (\boldsymbol{R}_i - m_i \ddot{\boldsymbol{r}}_i).\dot{\boldsymbol{r}}_i = 0$$

giving $$\sum_i \int m_i(\dot{\boldsymbol{r}}_i \,.\, \ddot{\boldsymbol{r}}_i)\, dt + V(\boldsymbol{r}) = K, \quad \text{a constant}$$

i.e. $$T + V = K \qquad (7)$$

where T is given by 9.1(5).

To find T write $\dot{\boldsymbol{r}}_i = \dot{\bar{\boldsymbol{r}}} + \dot{\boldsymbol{s}}_i$, where $\dot{\bar{\boldsymbol{r}}}$ is the velocity of the centre of mass G. Then we have

$$T = \tfrac{1}{2}M\, \dot{\bar{\boldsymbol{r}}}^2 + \dot{\bar{\boldsymbol{r}}}.\sum_i m_i\, \dot{\boldsymbol{s}}_i + \tfrac{1}{2}\sum_i m_i\, \dot{\boldsymbol{s}}_i^2$$

and since $\boldsymbol{s}_i$ is relative to G, $\sum_i m_i\, \boldsymbol{s}_i = \boldsymbol{0} = \sum_i m_i\, \dot{\boldsymbol{s}}_i$.

Hence $$T = \tfrac{1}{2}M\, \dot{\bar{\boldsymbol{r}}}^2 + \tfrac{1}{2}\sum_i m_i\, \dot{\boldsymbol{s}}_i^2 \qquad (8)$$

consisting of "the kinetic energy of a particle of mass M at G" plus "the kinetic energy of the motion relative to G."

9.4 The inertia tensor

Suppose a rigid body is moving with angular velocity $\boldsymbol{\omega}$ about a fixed point O of itself. Taking O as origin, let $P(\boldsymbol{r})$ be the position of a typical element of mass m.

Then $$\begin{aligned}\boldsymbol{H}(O) &= \sum \boldsymbol{r} \times m\,\boldsymbol{v} \\ &= \sum m\{\boldsymbol{r} \times (\boldsymbol{\omega} \times \boldsymbol{r})\} \quad \text{by 3.4(3) and 3.5}\end{aligned}$$

Using 2.12(1) we get

$$\boldsymbol{H}(O) = \sum m\{r^2\boldsymbol{\omega} - (\boldsymbol{r}.\boldsymbol{\omega})\boldsymbol{r}\} \qquad (1)$$

By 2.14(3a) we know that the nine elements $a^r b^s$ $(r, s = 1, 2, 3)$ formed from the components of the two vectors $\boldsymbol{a} = (a^1, a^2, a^3)$ and $\boldsymbol{b} = (b^1, b^2, b^3)$ form the components of a *second-order tensor*. These nine quantities may be regarded as generated by the *open product* $\boldsymbol{ab}$ of the two vectors $\boldsymbol{a}$ and $\boldsymbol{b}$. Such a quantity may quite naturally arise in our vector algebra via such terms as (e.g.) $(\boldsymbol{a}.\boldsymbol{b})\boldsymbol{c}$ which we can agree to write as $\boldsymbol{a}.(\boldsymbol{bc})$. Similarly (e.g.) equation 2.12(1) can be written as

$$\begin{aligned}\boldsymbol{a} \times (\boldsymbol{b} \times \boldsymbol{c}) &= (\boldsymbol{a}.\boldsymbol{c})\boldsymbol{b} - (\boldsymbol{a}.\boldsymbol{b})\boldsymbol{c} \\ &= \boldsymbol{a}.(\boldsymbol{cb} - \boldsymbol{bc})\end{aligned}$$

and the rhs involves a "scalar" product between the vector $\boldsymbol{a}$ and the second-order tensor $(\boldsymbol{cb} - \boldsymbol{bc})$. It follows that (1) involves some sort of second-order tensor and we intend to show that this tensor, when we have properly identified it, is of great dynamical significance.

We shall find it convenient to use a single symbol to represent a second-order tensor : we shall use script capitals. Thus (e.g.) we might represent the tensor $\boldsymbol{ab}$ by $\mathscr{S}$, and then

$$\boldsymbol{c}.\mathscr{S} = \boldsymbol{c}.(\boldsymbol{ab}) = (\boldsymbol{c}.\boldsymbol{a})\boldsymbol{b}$$

whereas

$$\mathscr{S}.\boldsymbol{c} = (\boldsymbol{ab}).\boldsymbol{c} = \boldsymbol{a}(\boldsymbol{b}.\boldsymbol{c})$$

These equations define the *direct product* between a vector and a tensor. We use the word " direct " and not " scalar " since the result of the product is not a scalar, although evaluating the product does in fact involve a genuine scalar product. The *cross product*, $\boldsymbol{c} \times \mathscr{S}$ or $\mathscr{S} \times \boldsymbol{c}$ can also be interpreted, e.g. $\boldsymbol{c} \times \mathscr{S} = \boldsymbol{c} \times (\boldsymbol{ab}) = (\boldsymbol{c} \times \boldsymbol{a})\boldsymbol{b} = \boldsymbol{db}$, but is unnecessary, as the sequel will show.

If we write $\boldsymbol{a} = a_1\,\boldsymbol{i} + a_1\,\boldsymbol{j} + a_3\,\boldsymbol{k}$ and $\boldsymbol{b} = b_1\,\boldsymbol{i} + b_2\boldsymbol{j} + b_3\,\boldsymbol{k}$ we see that $\mathscr{S} = \boldsymbol{ab}$ can be expressed in its *nonion form*, viz.,

$$\begin{aligned}\mathscr{S} = a_1b_1\,\boldsymbol{ii} &+ a_1b_2\,\boldsymbol{ij} + a_1b_3\,\boldsymbol{ik} + \\ a_2b_1\,\boldsymbol{ji} &+ a_2b_2\,\boldsymbol{jj} + a_2b_3\,\boldsymbol{jk} + \\ a_3b_1\,\boldsymbol{ki} &+ a_3b_2\,\boldsymbol{kj} + a_3b_3\,\boldsymbol{kk}\end{aligned}$$

Provided the frame of reference $(\boldsymbol{ijk})$ is clearly understood it follows that every second-order tensor $\mathscr{T}$ can be adequately represented by a *square matrix*, let us say,

$$\mathscr{T} = \begin{pmatrix} t_{11} & t_{12} & t_{13} \\ t_{21} & t_{22} & t_{23} \\ t_{31} & t_{32} & t_{33} \end{pmatrix} \quad . \quad . \quad . \quad . \quad (2)$$

When $t_{rs} = t_{sr}$ we say $\mathscr{T}$ is *symmetric* ; when $t_{rs} = -t_{sr}$ so that $t_{rr} = 0$ we say $\mathscr{T}$ is *antisymmetric*. An important example of a symmetric tensor is the open product $\boldsymbol{rr}$. An important example of an antisymmetric tensor is the *vector product*. Thus

$$\boldsymbol{a} \times \boldsymbol{b} = \begin{pmatrix} 0 & -a_3 & a_2 \\ a_3 & 0 & -a_1 \\ -a_2 & a_1 & 0 \end{pmatrix}.\boldsymbol{b}$$

so that operating upon $\boldsymbol{b}$ in cross product with $\boldsymbol{a}$ is equivalent to operating upon $\boldsymbol{b}$ in direct product with the antisymmetric tensor whose matrix representation is

$$\begin{pmatrix} 0 & -a_3 & a_2 \\ a_3 & 0 & -a_1 \\ -a_2 & a_1 & 0 \end{pmatrix}$$

Using the nonion form we see that (e.g.)

$$\begin{aligned}\mathscr{T}.\boldsymbol{a} &= \mathscr{T}.(a_1\,\boldsymbol{i} + a_2\boldsymbol{j} + a_3\,\boldsymbol{k}) \\ &= (t_{11}a_1 + t_{12}a_2 + t_{13}a_3)\boldsymbol{i} + (t_{21}a_1 + t_{22}a_2 + t_{23}a_3)\boldsymbol{j} \\ &\quad + (t_{31}a_1 + t_{32}a_2 + t_{33}a_3)\boldsymbol{k}\end{aligned}$$

which shows that " direct product " is equivalent to " matrix multiplication " of row-into-column. Thus

$$\mathscr{T}.\boldsymbol{a} = \begin{pmatrix} t_{11} & t_{12} & t_{13} \\ t_{21} & t_{22} & t_{23} \\ t_{31} & t_{32} & t_{33} \end{pmatrix} \begin{pmatrix} a_1 \\ a_2 \\ a_3 \end{pmatrix} \quad . \quad . \quad . \quad (3)$$

The algebra of these symbols $\mathscr{T}$ cannot be complete until we define (i) the identity of addition (zero), (ii) the identity of multiplication (unity, idemfactor) and (iii) the inverse of $\mathscr{T}$, viz. $\mathscr{T}^{-1}$. Using our knowledge of elementary matrix theory we have the *nul tensor*

$$\mathscr{O} = \begin{pmatrix} 0 & 0 & 0 \\ 0 & 0 & 0 \\ 0 & 0 & 0 \end{pmatrix} \quad . \quad . \quad . \quad . \quad (4)$$

the *idemfactor*

$$\mathscr{I} = \begin{pmatrix} 1 & 0 & 0 \\ 0 & 1 & 0 \\ 0 & 0 & 1 \end{pmatrix} \quad . \quad . \quad . \quad . \quad (5)$$

and the *inverse*

$$\mathscr{T}^{-1} = \frac{1}{\Delta} \begin{pmatrix} T_{11} & T_{12} & T_{13} \\ T_{21} & T_{22} & T_{23} \\ T_{31} & T_{32} & T_{33} \end{pmatrix} \quad . \quad . \quad (6)$$

where $\Delta = \det(\mathscr{T}) \neq 0$, $T_{rs} =$ the cofactor of t_{sr} in Δ. We can easily verify that $\mathscr{T}.\mathscr{T}^{-1} = \mathscr{T}^{-1}.\mathscr{T} = \mathscr{I}$, and the form of $\mathscr{I}$ is seen to be correct by 2.11(2) since

$$\boldsymbol{r}.\mathscr{I} = \boldsymbol{r}.(\boldsymbol{ii} + \boldsymbol{jj} + \boldsymbol{kk}) = (\boldsymbol{r}.\boldsymbol{i})\boldsymbol{i} + (\boldsymbol{r}.\boldsymbol{j})\boldsymbol{j} + (\boldsymbol{r}.\boldsymbol{k})\boldsymbol{k} = \boldsymbol{r} \quad (\text{all } \boldsymbol{r})$$

To return to the dynamical problem, we can now write (1) as follows :

$$\begin{aligned} \boldsymbol{H}(O) &= \sum m\{\boldsymbol{r}^2 \mathscr{I}.\boldsymbol{\omega} - \boldsymbol{r}(\boldsymbol{r}.\boldsymbol{\omega})\} \\ &= \{\sum m(\boldsymbol{r}^2 \mathscr{I} - \boldsymbol{rr})\}.\boldsymbol{\omega} \end{aligned}$$

Hence we can introduce the *intertia tensor* at $O, \mathscr{J}(O)$, defined by

$$\mathscr{J}(O) = \sum m(\boldsymbol{r}^2 \mathscr{I} - \boldsymbol{rr}) \quad . \quad . \quad . \quad . \quad (7)$$

whence

$$\boldsymbol{H}(O) = \mathscr{J}(O).\boldsymbol{\omega} \quad . \quad . \quad . \quad . \quad . \quad . \quad (8)$$

$\mathscr{J}(O)$ is symmetric ; it is defined entirely by the mass distribution of the body in relation to the given frame of reference at O.

Let us now consider the kinetic energy of the body. We have

$$T = \tfrac{1}{2} \sum m\, \boldsymbol{v}^2 = \tfrac{1}{2} \sum m(\boldsymbol{\omega} \times \boldsymbol{r}).(\boldsymbol{\omega} \times \boldsymbol{r})$$

i.e.

$$T = \tfrac{1}{2} \sum m\{\boldsymbol{\omega}^2 \boldsymbol{r}^2 - (\boldsymbol{\omega}.\boldsymbol{r})(\boldsymbol{r}.\boldsymbol{\omega})\}$$

which gives

$$T = \tfrac{1}{2}\boldsymbol{\omega}.\mathscr{J}(O).\boldsymbol{\omega} \quad . \quad . \quad . \quad . \quad . \quad . \quad . \quad (9)$$

It only remains to find the components of $\mathscr{J}(O)$. Writing $\boldsymbol{r} = x\,\boldsymbol{i} + y\,\boldsymbol{i} + z\,\boldsymbol{k}$ we get

$$\mathscr{J}(O) = \sum m[(x^2 + y^2 + z^2)\mathscr{I} - (x\,\boldsymbol{i} + y\,\boldsymbol{j} + z\,\boldsymbol{k})(x\,\boldsymbol{i} + y\,\boldsymbol{i} + z\,\boldsymbol{k})]$$

giving the matrix representation

$$\mathscr{I}(O) = \begin{pmatrix} A & -H & -G \\ -H & B & -F \\ -G & -F & C \end{pmatrix} \quad . \quad . \quad . \quad (10)$$

where $A = \sum m(y^2 + z^2)$, $\quad B = \sum m(z^2 + x^2)$, $\quad C = \sum m(x^2 + y^2)$

$F = \sum myz$, $\quad G = \sum mzx$, $\quad H = \sum mxy$.

The quantities A, B, C are called the *moments of inertia* about the x-, y-, z-axes respectively, whilst the quantities F, G, H are called the *products of inertia* w.r.t. the yz-axes, the zx-axes, and the xy-axes It will frequently happen that in practice these dynamical constants are evaluated by integration.

If the rigid body is in general motion, let the centre of mass G have velocity $\bar{\boldsymbol{v}}$ and let $\overline{OG} = \bar{\boldsymbol{r}}$, where O is a fixed origin in space. Then 9.2(6) and (8) show that

$$\boldsymbol{H}(O) = \bar{\boldsymbol{r}} \times M\,\bar{\boldsymbol{v}} + \mathscr{I}(G).\boldsymbol{\omega} \quad . \quad . \quad . \quad (11)$$

and 9.3(8) and (9) show that

$$T = \tfrac{1}{2}M\,\bar{\boldsymbol{v}}^2 + \tfrac{1}{2}\boldsymbol{\omega}.\mathscr{I}(G).\boldsymbol{\omega} \quad . \quad . \quad . \quad (12)$$

9.5 Calculating the inertia tensor

The following result shows that it is sufficient to know the inertia tensor at the centre of mass, G. Suppose we are given $\mathscr{I}(G)$ w.r.t. a set of axes at G and suppose we wish to find $\mathscr{I}(O)$ at any other point O w.r.t. a *parallel* set of axes at O. Write $\overline{GO} = \boldsymbol{a}$ and $\overline{GP} = \boldsymbol{r}$, then $\overline{OP} = \boldsymbol{r} - \boldsymbol{a}$ and

$$\mathscr{I}(O) = \sum m\{(\boldsymbol{r} - \boldsymbol{a})^2\mathscr{I} - (\boldsymbol{r} - \boldsymbol{a})(\boldsymbol{r} - \boldsymbol{a})\}$$

that is

$$\mathscr{I}(O) = \mathscr{I}(G) + M(\boldsymbol{a}^2\,\mathscr{I} - \boldsymbol{aa}) \quad . \quad . \quad . \quad . \quad (1)$$

since $\sum m\,\boldsymbol{r} = \boldsymbol{0}$. Equation (1) includes the well-known "parallel axes" theorem. Thus if the moment of inertia about (say) the x-axis at O is denoted by A' and that about the x-axis at G by A, we get from (1),

$$\begin{aligned} A' &= \text{coefficient of } \boldsymbol{ii} \text{ in } \mathscr{I}(O) \\ &= A + M(a_2{}^2 + a_3{}^2) \\ &= \text{coefficient of } \boldsymbol{ii} \text{ in rhs} \end{aligned}$$

i.e.

$$A' = A + Mh^2 \quad . \quad . \quad . \quad . \quad . \quad . \quad (2)$$

where h = perpendicular distance between the two parallel axes. (1) also gives a similar result for products of inertia ; thus

$$F' = F + Ma_2a_3 \quad . \quad . \quad . \quad . \quad . \quad (3)$$

Example 1. *To find $\mathscr{I}(G)$ for a uniform rod AB of length $2a$.*

Take the $\boldsymbol{i}$-axis along the rod as shown in Fig. 82. The element of mass at $x\,\boldsymbol{i}$ will be $\rho\,dx$,where $M = 2a\rho$. Hence

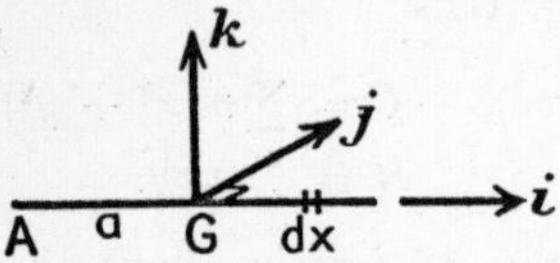

FIG. 82.

$$\mathscr{I}(G) = \int_{-a}^{+a} (x^2\,\mathscr{I} - x^2\,\boldsymbol{ii})\rho\,dx$$
$$= (\mathscr{I} - \boldsymbol{ii}) \int_{-a}^{+a} \rho x^2\,dx$$
$$= M\frac{a^2}{3}(\mathscr{I} - \boldsymbol{ii}) = M\frac{a^2}{3}(\boldsymbol{jj} + \boldsymbol{kk})$$

The matrix representation w.r.t. $(\boldsymbol{i}, \boldsymbol{j}, \boldsymbol{k})$ will be

$$\mathscr{I}(G) = M\frac{a^2}{3}\begin{pmatrix} 0 & 0 & 0 \\ 0 & 1 & 0 \\ 0 & 0 & 1 \end{pmatrix}$$

In this case all the products of inertia vanish. If we want the moment of inertia, I, about any axis perpendicular to the rod through one end, say A, (2) gives

$$I = M\frac{a^2}{3} + Ma^2 = \tfrac{4}{3}Ma^2 \quad . \quad . \quad . \quad (4)$$

Generally, if the moment of inertia of a body about some line, λ, is written in the form $I = Mk^2$, where M is the total mass, then we call k the **radius of gyration** of the body about λ.

Example 2. *To find $\mathscr{I}(G)$ for a uniform solid sphere of radius a.*

Since G is the centre of the sphere take the orthonormal triad $(\boldsymbol{ijk})$ as any set of mutually perpendicular diameters. Then by symmetry we have $F = G = H = 0$, and

$$A = B = C = \tfrac{1}{3}(A + B + C)$$
$$= \tfrac{2}{3}\int_{\Omega} \rho(x^2 + y^2 + z^2)\,d\Omega$$

where $\frac{4}{3}\pi a_3\rho = M$ and $d\Omega = r^2 \sin\theta\,dr\,d\theta\,d\phi$.

Hence $$A = B = C = \frac{2\rho}{3}\int_0^{2\pi}\int_0^{\pi}\int_0^{a} r^4 \sin\theta\,dr\,d\theta\,d\phi -$$
$$= \frac{2\rho}{3} \times \frac{a^5}{5} \times 2 \times 2\pi$$

so that $$A = B = C = \tfrac{2}{5}Ma^2 \quad . \quad . \quad . \quad . \quad . \quad (5)$$

and $$\mathscr{I}(G) = \tfrac{2}{5}Ma^2\begin{pmatrix} 1 & 0 & 0 \\ 0 & 1 & 0 \\ 0 & 0 & 1 \end{pmatrix} = \tfrac{2}{5}Ma^2\mathscr{I} \quad . \quad . \quad (6)$$

Example 3. *To find $\mathscr{I}(G)$ for a uniform solid circular cylinder of radius a and height $2h$.*

Take the $\boldsymbol{i}$-axis along the axis of the cylinder through the centre of mass G, and let $\boldsymbol{j}$, $\boldsymbol{k}$ be any perpendicular vectors forming an orthonormal triad with $\boldsymbol{i}$.

We have, using cylindrical polar co-ordinates, r, θ, z,

$$A = \int_{-h}^{+h}\int_0^{2\pi}\int_0^a \rho\,.\,r^2\,.\,r\,dr\,d\theta\,dz$$

where $2\pi a^2 h\rho = M$. Hence $A = M\dfrac{a^2}{2}$, and

$$B = C = \int_{-h}^{+h}\int_0^{2\pi}\int_0^a \rho(r^2\sin^2\theta + z^2)r\,dr\,d\theta\,dz$$
$$= M\left(\frac{h^2}{3} + \frac{a^2}{4}\right)$$

Similarly $F = G = H = 0$. Hence we have the matrix representation

$$\mathscr{I}(G) = M\begin{pmatrix} \frac{1}{2}a^2 & 0 & 0 \\ 0 & \frac{1}{3}h^2 + \frac{1}{4}a^2 & 0 \\ 0 & 0 & \frac{1}{3}h^2 + \frac{1}{4}a^2 \end{pmatrix} \qquad (7)$$

Example 4. *A plane lamina of mass M.*

Let the plane of the lamina be that defined by $\boldsymbol{i}$ and $\boldsymbol{j}$ at G. Then since $z = 0$ at all points of the lamina we get

$$A = \sum my^2\,; \quad B = \sum mx^2\,; \quad C = A + B\,. \qquad (8)$$

Also $F = G = 0$; $H = \sum mxy$. Hence, in this case

$$\mathscr{I}(G) = \begin{pmatrix} A & -H & 0 \\ -H & B & 0 \\ 0 & 0 & A + B \end{pmatrix} \qquad (9)$$

As an example, take the case of the *positive quadrant of an ellipse*, $\dfrac{x^2}{a^2} + \dfrac{y^2}{b^2} = 1$, and let us find $\mathscr{I}(O)$. Then, writing $\xi = \dfrac{x}{a}$, $\eta = \dfrac{y}{b}$,

$A = \displaystyle\iint \rho y^2\,dx\,dy = \rho ab^3 \iint_S \eta^2\,d\xi\,d\eta$, where S is the positive quadrant of the unit circle $\xi^2 + \eta^2 = 1$. Writing $\xi = r\cos\theta$, $\eta = r\sin\theta$ we get

$$A = \rho ab^3\int_0^{\pi/2}\int_0^1 r^3\sin^2\theta\,dr\,d\theta = \frac{\pi}{16}\rho ab^3 = M\frac{b^2}{4}$$

Similarly $B = M\dfrac{a^2}{4}$, so that $C = \dfrac{M}{4}(a^2 + b^2)$.

Then $\quad H = \rho\displaystyle\iint xy\,dx\,dy = \rho a^2b^2\iint_S \xi\eta\,d\xi\,d\eta$

$$= \rho a^2b^2\int_0^{\pi/2}\int_0^1 r^3\cos\theta\sin\theta\,dr\,d\theta = \frac{\pi}{16}\rho a^2b^2 = M\frac{ab}{4}$$

Finally (9) becomes

$$\mathscr{I}(O) = \frac{M}{4}\begin{pmatrix} b^2 & -ab & 0 \\ -ab & a^2 & 0 \\ 0 & 0 & a^2+b^2 \end{pmatrix}$$

If we take the *whole ellipse* M is replaced by M' and, by symmetry $H = 0$. Since O is now the centre of mass G, we have

$$\mathscr{I}(G) = \frac{M'}{4}\begin{pmatrix} b^2 & 0 & 0 \\ 0 & a^2 & 0 \\ 0 & 0 & a^2+b^2 \end{pmatrix} \quad . \quad . \quad . \quad . \quad (10)$$

When the axes $(\boldsymbol{ijk})$ at the point O are so chosen that $F = G = H = 0$ (i.e. $\mathscr{I}(O)$ is purely diagonal) we say that $\boldsymbol{i}, \boldsymbol{j}, \boldsymbol{k}$ are *principal axes* at O. This property clearly represents the symmetry of the mass distribution w.r.t. these particular axes at O. Although we shall discuss general properties of principal axes in Chapter XIII, we shall examine the problem for a lamina immediately.

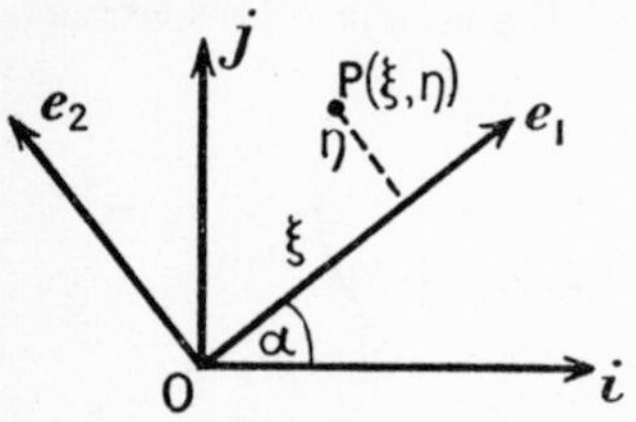

FIG. 83.

Given axes $\boldsymbol{i}, \boldsymbol{j}$ *at* O *in the plane of a lamina, to find the principal axes* $\boldsymbol{e}_1, \boldsymbol{e}_2$ *at* O.

From Fig. 83, we have

$$\boldsymbol{e}_1 = \cos\alpha\,\boldsymbol{i} + \sin\alpha\,\boldsymbol{j}\,; \quad \boldsymbol{e}_2 = -\sin\alpha\,\boldsymbol{i} + \cos\alpha\,\boldsymbol{j}$$

Hence

$$\left.\begin{aligned} \xi &= (\boldsymbol{r}.\boldsymbol{e}_1) = \cos\alpha(\boldsymbol{r}.\boldsymbol{i}) + \sin\alpha(\boldsymbol{r}.\boldsymbol{j}) = x\cos\alpha + y\sin\alpha \\ \text{and} \quad \eta &= -x\sin\alpha + y\cos\alpha \end{aligned}\right\} \quad . \quad (11)$$

Now suppose that we know the dynamical constants A, B, H w.r.t. the axes $\boldsymbol{i}, \boldsymbol{j}$ and write A', B', H' for the corresponding quantities w.r.t. the axes $\boldsymbol{e}_1, \boldsymbol{e}_2$. Using (11) we get

$$A' \sum m\eta^2 = \sum m\{y^2\cos^2\alpha - 2\sin\alpha\cos\alpha\,xy + x^2\sin^2\alpha\}$$

which is $\quad A' = A\cos^2\alpha - H\sin 2\alpha + B\sin^2\alpha \quad . \quad . \quad (12)$

Similarly $\quad B' = A\sin^2\alpha + H\sin 2\alpha + B\cos^2\alpha \quad . \quad . \quad (13)$

and $\quad H' = H\cos 2\alpha - \frac{1}{2}(B-A)\sin 2\alpha \quad . \quad . \quad . \quad (14)$

Hence $(\boldsymbol{e}_1\boldsymbol{e}_2)$ are principal axes at O in the plane of the lamina provided $H' = 0$, i.e. provided

$$\tan 2\alpha = \frac{2H}{B-A} \quad . \quad . \quad . \quad . \quad (15)$$

Example 5. A uniform lamina is bounded by the spiral $r = ae^{k\theta}$ and the radii $\theta = 0$ and $\theta = \pi$. Prove that at O the principal axes make angles α, $\alpha + \pi/2$ with Ox, where

$$\tan 2\alpha = -\frac{1}{2k}$$

and find the three principal moments of inertia. (L.U.)

We have $$A = \rho \int_0^\pi \int_0^{r_1} y^2 . r \, dr \, d\theta$$

where $r_1 = ae^{k\theta}$, $y = r \sin \theta$,

so that $$A = \rho \frac{a^4}{4} \int_0^\pi \sin^2 \theta \, e^{4k\theta} \, d\theta$$

Similarly $$B = \rho \frac{a^4}{4} \int_0^\pi \cos^2 \theta \, e^{4k\theta} \, d\theta$$

and $$H = \rho \frac{a^4}{4} \int_0^\pi \cos \theta \sin \theta \, e^{4k\theta} \, d\theta$$

These give $$A = \rho \frac{a^4}{8} . \frac{(e^{4k\pi} - 1)}{4k(1 + 4k^2)}$$

$$B = \rho . \frac{a^4}{8} . \frac{(e^{4k\pi} - 1)(1 + 8k^2)}{4k(1 + 4k^2)}$$

$$H = \rho \frac{a^4}{16} . \frac{1 - e^{4k\pi}}{1 + 4k^2}$$

Hence $$B - A = \rho \frac{a^4}{8} . \frac{(e^{4k\pi} - 1) . 2k}{1 + 4k^2}$$

so that $$\tan 2\alpha = -\frac{1}{2k}$$ Q.E.D.

Also (12) and (13) give the principal moments as

$$A' = \frac{(e^{4k\pi} - 1)}{16(1 + 4k^2)} . \rho a^4 . \left\{ \frac{1 + 4k^2}{2k} + \frac{1 + 2k^2}{\sqrt{1 + 4k^2}} \right\}$$

and $$B' = \frac{(e^{4k\pi} - 1)}{16(1 + 4k^2)} . \rho a^4 \left\{ \frac{1 + 4k^2}{2k} - \frac{1 + 2k^2}{\sqrt{1 + 4k^2}} \right\}$$

Exercise IX

1. Two bodies of mass M, $m (M > m)$ attract each other with a force $\lambda Mm/d^2$ when at a distance d apart, λ being a constant. Initially they are moving in the same straight line with velocities U, u respectively in the same sense and are at distance r apart. Prove that the smaller mass will overtake the larger after a time

$$\{\lambda(M + m)\}^{-1/2} \{r/(1 + w)\}^{3/2} \{\pi - (1 - w^2)^{1/2} - \cos^{-1} w\}$$

where

$$1 - w = \frac{r(U - u)^2}{\lambda(M + m)}$$ (L.U.)

2. Two particles of masses m_1, m_2 move in their mutual field. The attractive force is along the line joining them and of magnitude $Gm_1 m_2 / |\boldsymbol{r}|^2$, where $\boldsymbol{r}$ is the position vector of either particle relative to the other. Show that

$$|\boldsymbol{r}|^3 \ddot{\boldsymbol{r}} = -G(m_1 + m_2)\boldsymbol{r}$$

Given that the initial separation of the particles is R, and that they are projected at speeds v_1, v_2 respectively in directions inclined at an angle α, show that the relative orbit is an ellipse, a parabola or a hyperbola, according as $v_1^2 + v_2^2 - 2v_1v_2 \cos \alpha$ is less than, equal to, or greater than $2G(m_1 + m_2)/R$. (M.T.)

3. Two masses m_1, m_2 move under the force of their mutual attraction, which is equal to $\frac{\mu}{r^2}$ when their distance apart is r. When at a great distance from m_1 the mass m_2 is projected with velocity V along a straight line whose point of nearest approach to m_1 is at a distance c from m_1. Prove that the path of m_2 relative to m_1 is a part of a hyperbola with m_1 at a focus, and show that, if c is small enough, the distance of closest approach of the two bodies is approximately $\dfrac{c^2V^2m_1m_2}{2\mu(m_1 + m_2)}$. (M.T.)

4. Two particles of mass m_1, m_2 respectively are connected by an elastic string of natural length l and modulus λ. Initially they are at rest on a smooth horizontal table at distance l apart. The mass m_1 is then suddenly projected at right angles to the string with velocity V. Prove that, in the subsequent motion, and before the string becomes slack, the greatest distance x between the particles is a root of the equation

$$m_1m_2V^2l(x + l) = \lambda(m_1 + m_2)x^2(x - l) \qquad \text{(L.U.)}$$

5. Two gravitating particles of masses m and M move under the force of their mutual attraction. Show that the centre of mass of the two particles moves with constant velocity, and that, if $\boldsymbol{r}$ is the position vector of m relative to M,

$$\ddot{\boldsymbol{r}} = -\frac{\gamma(M + m)}{r^3}\boldsymbol{r}$$

where γ is the gravitational constant.

If the orbit of m relative to M is a circle of radius a described with velocity v, show that $v = \sqrt{\{\gamma(M + m)/a\}}$.

If the relative velocity of the particle m is suddenly changed to $v + u$ without change of direction, show that, if $(u/v)^2$ is negligible, the particle will describe relative to M an ellipse of eccentricity $2u/v$. (L.U.)

6. Two particles, of masses m and m', are connected by a thread which passes through a hole at the vertex of a smooth right circular cone having its axis vertical and vertex uppermost. The particle of mass m' hangs vertically, and m describes a circle of radius c on the cone. Prove that, if slightly disturbed, it will perform small oscillations in time

$$2\pi \sqrt{\left\{\frac{c(m' + m)}{3g(m' - m \cos \alpha) \sin \alpha}\right\}}$$

2α being the vertical angle of the cone. (C.)

7. The position vectors of four particles of masses m_s relative to their centre of mass at time t are given by

$$\boldsymbol{r}_s = f(t)\, \boldsymbol{a}_s \quad (s = 1, 2, 3, 4)$$

where the $\boldsymbol{a}_s$ are constant vectors. At time $t = 0$, the particles form the vertices of a regular tetrahedron of side b, and $f(0) = 1$. Show that the motion of the particles can be ascribed to their mutual gravitational attraction provided that

$$\frac{d^2f}{dt^2} = -\frac{\gamma M}{f^2 b^3}$$

where $M = \sum_s m_s$, and γ is the gravitational constant.

Show also that, if the system starts from rest, it will contract to half its original size in a time

$$\tfrac{1}{4}(\pi + 2)\left(\frac{b^3}{2\gamma M}\right)^{\frac{1}{2}}$$ (M.T.)

8. A lamina of mass m rotates on a smooth horizontal table about a point A at distance h from its centre of mass G, its angular velocity being ω. If O is any point in the plane of the lamina and ON is the perpendicular from O on AG, show that the moment of momentum of the lamina about O is $m\omega(k^2 - hx)$, where k is its radius of gyration about A and x is the distance AN.

If the lamina is released at A and at the same instant smoothly pinned to the table at O, show that its subsequent angular velocity is $\frac{1}{2}\omega$ when O lies on a circle of radius k and centre A. (L.U.)

9. Prove that the rate of change of moment of momentum of a plane material system about a fixed axis perpendicular to its plane is equal to the moment about this axis of the external forces acting on the system.

A uniform circular disc of radius a is free to rotate in a vertical plane about a smooth horizontal axis through its centre C. An insect A, whose mass in one-tenth that of the disc, is at the lowest point of the disc and the whole system is at rest. The insect suddenly starts to crawl along the rim with uniform speed V relative to the disc; show that the initial spin of the disc is $V/6a$. If, in the subsequent motion, θ is the inclination of CA to the downward vertical, prove that

$$6a\ddot{\theta} + g \sin\theta = 0$$

Show that the component of the force exerted by the insect on the disc in the direction perpendicular to the radius is $\frac{5}{6}mg \sin\theta$ where m is the mass of the insect. (L.U.)

10. Two uniform rods AB, BC of masses m and m' respectively are smoothly hinged to one another at B and to a horizontal table at C, so that they can move in a vertical plane. Initially BC is on the table and AB is set in motion (in a sense tending to increase the angle ABC) when it is vertically above B, with angular velocity $\sqrt{(3ng/l)}$, where l is the length of AB. Show that so long as BC remains on the table

$$l\dot{\theta}^2 = 3g(n + 1 - \cos\theta)$$

where θ is the angle made by BA with the vertical.

Show also that the vertically downward component Y of the reaction at B on the rod AB is

$$Y = \tfrac{1}{4}mg\{6(1 + n)\cos\theta - 1 - 9\cos^2\theta\}$$

When $n = 2/3$, show that the condition that BC does not rise from the table is $m' > 8m/9$. (L.U.)

11. A frictionless gear box is such that when the input shaft is rotated once the output shaft rotates n times. Show that a torque G applied to the input shaft can be balanced by a torque G/n applied to the output shaft.

An electric motor capable of exerting a torque G when running at any constant speed and whose moving parts have a moment of inertia I_1 is connected through the gear box to a flywheel of moment of inertia I_2. If I_1 and I_2 are fixed, find the value of n which gives the maximum possible angular acceleration of the flywheel and show that the acceleration of the motor shaft is then half what it would be if the motor were running free. The inertia of the gear box may be neglected. (M.T.)

12. A cubical block of mass M can slide on a smooth horizontal plane and a uniform rod of mass m leans with one end on the plane and the other end against a cube-face, which is smooth, the rod being in a vertical plane parallel to a pair of faces of the cube and passing through the centre of the cube. The system is released from rest with the rod inclined at an angle α to the horizontal. Show that, when contact between the rod and the cube ceases, the inclination θ of the rod to the horizontal satisfies the equation

$$3m\sin^3\theta - 12(M + m)\sin\theta + 8(M + m)\sin\alpha = 0 \qquad \text{(L.U.)}$$

13. Two uniform rods OA, AB, of masses m_1, m_2 and of lengths $2a$, $2b$ respectively, are freely jointed at A, and the rod OA is smoothly hinged to a fixed point at O. The rods are held in a horizontal line, and then released from rest. Find the initial reactions at O and A. (L.U.)

14. Prove the formula

$$I = A\cos^2\alpha - 2H\sin\alpha\cos\alpha + B\sin^2\alpha$$

for the moment of inertia of a lamina about the line $y = x\tan\alpha$, interpreting the constants A, B and H.

Four uniform smooth rods AB, BC, CD, DA, each of mass m and length $2a$, are rigidly joined at their ends to form a square $ABCD$. A small ring P of mass m is free to slide along the rod AB and the system can turn freely about a smooth horizontal axis through A and the mid-point of CD. If the system is released from rest in a horizontal plane and turns freely under gravity, show that, for all initial positions of P on AB, the velocity v of P relative to AB when the ring reaches B for the first time is given by

$$15v^2 = 48\sqrt{5}ag\sin\theta - 100a^2\dot{\theta}^2$$

where θ is the angle between $ABCD$ and the horizontal at this instant. (L.U.)

15. If the moments and product of inertia of a plane lamina about rectangular axes Gx, Gy in its plane, where G is the centre of mass of the lamina, are A, B and F respectively, find the values of the moments and product of inertia about parallel axes through a point $P(f, g)$ in the lamina.

Prove that the locus of a point P in the plane of a uniform semi-circular lamina such that one of the principal axes at P is parallel to the bounding diameter of the lamina consists of two straight lines. (L.U.)

16. A plane distribution of matter has moments of inertia A, B and a product moment H about axes Ox, Oy in the plane. If the corresponding constants of inertia at O, for axes Ox', Oy' obtained from Ox, Oy by counter-clockwise rotation through an angle θ, are A', B' and H', show that

$$A' + B' = A + B, \quad B' - A' + 2iH' = e^{-2i\theta}(B - A + 2iH)$$

and hence or otherwise find the directions of the principal axes at O.

Prove the validity of the following geometrical construction for A', B' and H', given A, B, H and θ :

Draw the circle $x^2 + y^2 = (A + B)^2/4$. From the point P, $x = (B - A)/2$, $y = H$, draw the perpendicular PN to that diameter QR of the circle which makes an angle 2θ with the x-axis. Then NR, NQ, NP represent the inertial constants A', B', H'. (L.U.)

CHAPTER X

MOTION OF A RIGID BODY IN A PLANE

10.1 The equations of motion

If a rigid body moves in a plane, say that defined by the unit vectors $\boldsymbol{i}, \boldsymbol{j}$, its angular velocity must be of the form $\boldsymbol{\omega} = \omega\, \boldsymbol{k}$, where $\boldsymbol{k}$ is normal to the plane. Also $\omega = \dfrac{d\theta}{dt}$, where θ is the angle between any line fixed in the plane and any other line which is both fixed in the body and which moves entirely in the plane. Normally we shall refer to the body as a lamina moving in its own plane, but it is clear that our results are applicable to the motion of all types of rigid bodies which move so that (i) the angular velocity is of the form $\omega\, \boldsymbol{k}$, $\boldsymbol{k}$ being a constant unit vector, and (ii) the centre of mass of the body always moves in a fixed plane perpendicular to $\boldsymbol{k}$.

Now 9.4(8) gives

$$\boldsymbol{H}_r(G) = \mathscr{J}(G).\boldsymbol{\omega} = \mathscr{J}(G).\omega\, \boldsymbol{k}$$
$$= \begin{pmatrix} A & -H & 0 \\ -H & B & 0 \\ 0 & 0 & C \end{pmatrix} \begin{pmatrix} 0 \\ 0 \\ \omega \end{pmatrix}$$

giving
$$\boldsymbol{H}_r(G) = C\omega\, \boldsymbol{k} \qquad (1)$$

and then 9.2(6) gives, for any fixed point O of the plane,

$$\boldsymbol{H}(O) = C\omega\, \boldsymbol{k} + M(\bar{\boldsymbol{r}} \times \bar{\boldsymbol{v}})$$

Writing $\bar{\boldsymbol{r}} = \bar{x}\, \boldsymbol{i} + \bar{y}\, \boldsymbol{j}$ and $\bar{\boldsymbol{v}} = \bar{u}_1 \boldsymbol{i} + \bar{u}_2 \boldsymbol{j}$, this becomes

$$\boldsymbol{H}(O) = \{C\omega + M(\bar{x}\bar{u}_2 - \bar{y}\bar{u}_1)\}\boldsymbol{k}. \qquad (2)$$

In the special case when the lamina is turning about a fixed point O of itself we naturally use 9.1(13) with $\boldsymbol{H}(O) = \mathscr{J}(O).\omega\, \boldsymbol{k} = C'\omega\, \boldsymbol{k}$ (say), C' being the moment of inertia of the body about the axis $\boldsymbol{k}$ through O.

The kinetic energy will be given by 9.3(8) and, by 9.4(9), we have

$$\tfrac{1}{2}\sum_i m_i s_i^2 = \tfrac{1}{2}\boldsymbol{\omega}.\mathscr{J}(G).\boldsymbol{\omega}$$
$$= \tfrac{1}{2}(0 \quad 0 \quad \omega) \begin{pmatrix} A & -H & 0 \\ -H & B & 0 \\ 0 & 0 & C \end{pmatrix} \begin{pmatrix} 0 \\ 0 \\ \omega \end{pmatrix}$$
$$= \tfrac{1}{2}(0 \quad 0 \quad \omega) \begin{pmatrix} 0 \\ 0 \\ C\omega \end{pmatrix}$$
$$= \tfrac{1}{2}C\omega^2$$

Hence 9.3(8) becomes

$$T = \tfrac{1}{2}M\bar{v}^2 + \tfrac{1}{2}C\omega^2 \quad . \quad . \quad . \quad . \quad . \quad (3)$$

C being the moment of inertia about the axis $\boldsymbol{k}$ through G, giving $C = A + B$.

Example 1. A lamina is free to rotate in a horizontal plane about a point O of the lamina which is fixed in space. An insect stands on the lamina at a point A of the lamina at a distance a from O. The mass of the insect is m, and the moment of inertia of the lamina about O is mk^2. The insect then walks on the lamina, his path relative to the lamina being the straight line through A at right angles to OA. Prove that the angle through which the lamina turns does not exceed $\dfrac{\pi}{2p}$, where

$$p^2 = \frac{a^2 + k^2}{a^2} \qquad \text{(M.T.)}$$

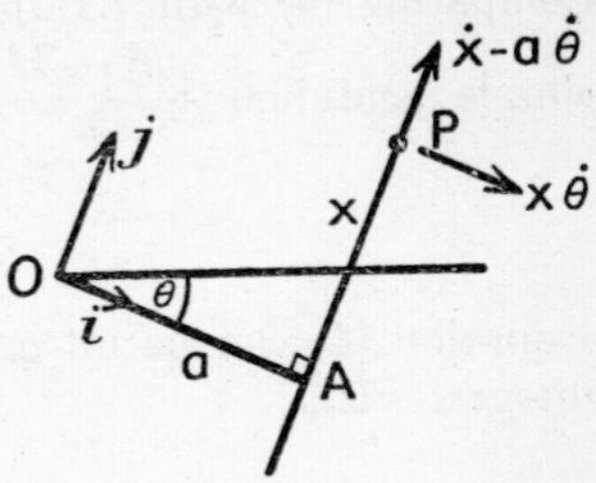

FIG. 84.

Let the insect, P, have walked a distance x while the lamina has rotated (backwards) through an angle θ. Then the velocity of P has components $(\dot{x} - a\dot{\theta})$ and $x\dot{\theta}$, as shown in Fig. 84. If this is not obvious by inspection we can deduce it as follows :

Put $\overline{OP} = \boldsymbol{r} = a\,\boldsymbol{i} + x\,\boldsymbol{j}$ and notice that the frame $\boldsymbol{i}, \boldsymbol{j}$ is rotating about $\boldsymbol{k}$ with angular velocity $-\dot{\theta}\,\boldsymbol{k}$. Then (v. 3.6) the velocity is

$$\boldsymbol{v} = \dot{x}\,\boldsymbol{j} + (-\dot{\theta}\,\boldsymbol{k}) \times (a\,\boldsymbol{i} + x\,\boldsymbol{j}) = (\dot{x} - a\dot{\theta})\boldsymbol{j} + x\dot{\theta}\,\boldsymbol{i}$$

The angular momentum of the insect about O will be

$$H_1(O) = a\,(\dot{x} - a\,\dot{\theta}) - x^2\dot{\theta} = a\dot{x} - (a^2 + x^2)\dot{\theta}$$

per unit mass, and that of the lamina will be $H_2(O) = -mk^2\dot{\theta}$. Now $\Gamma(O) = 0$ for the whole system of lamina + insect, and so $H(O) = \text{constant} = 0$ (by initial conditions).

Hence we get $$a\dot{x} - (a^2 + k^2 + x^2)\dot{\theta} = 0$$

giving $$\int_0^x \frac{a\,dx}{a^2p^2 + x^2} = \int_0^\theta d\theta$$

where $a^2 + k^2 = a^2p^2$,

or $$\frac{1}{p}\tan^{-1}\left(\frac{x}{ap}\right) = \theta$$

The greatest value of θ corresponds to $x \to \infty$ and then $\theta \to \dfrac{\pi}{2p}$.

Q.E.D.

Example 2. The compound pendulum. A rigid body swings in a vertical plane about one point O of itself which is fixed. To examine the motion.

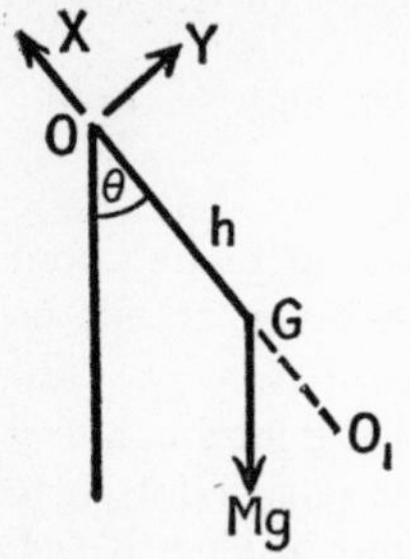

FIG. 85.

Let the line OG $(= h)$ be inclined at θ to the downward vertical at any time t, and let k be the radius of gyration of the body about a perpendicular axis through G, the centre of mass. Then, from Fig. 85, we have (v. 9.5(2) and 9.3(5))

$$\frac{d}{dt}(M(h^2 + k^2)\dot{\theta}) = -Mgh \sin \theta$$

giving

$$\ddot{\theta} = -\left(\frac{gh}{h^2 + k^2}\right) \sin \theta \quad (4)$$

Comparing (4) with 7.1(3) we see that the length of the equivalent simple pendulum is $\frac{h^2 + k^2}{h}$. The periodic time is, for small vibrations,

$$\tau = 2\pi\sqrt{\frac{h^2 + k^2}{hg}}$$

Equation (4) can be integrated once as it stands, giving the energy integral, viz.,

$$\tfrac{1}{2}(h^2 + k^2)\dot{\theta}^2 = gh \cos \theta + A \quad . \quad . \quad . \quad (5)$$

A being an arbitrary constant.

We can find the reaction at the support O by using 9.3(4). Thus since G moves in a circle of radius h, we get

$$X - Mg \cos \theta = Mh\dot{\theta}^2 \quad . \quad . \quad . \quad (6)$$

$$Y - Mg \sin \theta = Mh\ddot{\theta} \, . \quad . \quad . \quad . \quad (7)$$

(4), (5), (6) and (7) give X, Y as functions of θ.

The point O_1 on the line OG and such that $OO_1 = \frac{h^2 + k^2}{h}$ is called the *centre of oscillation*. It has been known since the time of Huygens (v. 1.2) that the centre of oscillation and the centre of suspension (i.e. O) can be interchanged without altering the periodic time τ. The length $GO_1 = \frac{k^2}{h}$ and regarding O_1 as the point of suspension the equation of motion becomes

$$\left(k^2 + \frac{k^4}{h^2}\right)\ddot{\theta} = -g.\frac{k^2}{h}.\sin \theta$$

which reduces to (4). Hence τ is unaltered.

Example 3. A particle of mass m is fixed to a point P of the rim of a uniform circular disc, centre O, mass m, and radius a. The disc is held, with its plane vertical, its lowest point in contact with a perfectly rough horizontal table, and with OP inclined at 60° to the upward vertical and is then released. When OP is inclined at θ to the upward vertical prove that

$$a(7 + 4\cos\theta)\dot{\theta}^2 = 2g(1 - 2\cos\theta)$$

Show also that when OP is first horizontal the acceleration of O is $18g/49$, and find the reaction between the disc and the table at this instant. (L.U.)

Let the system be as shown in Fig. 86 at a time $t \geqslant 0$, with O having travelled a distance x whilst OP has turned into a position where it is inclined at θ to the upward vertical. The angular velocity of the disc is $\dot{\theta}$ and since the horizontal table is perfectly rough it always rolls ; hence A is instantaneously at rest. Hence $\dot{x} - a\dot{\theta} = 0$.

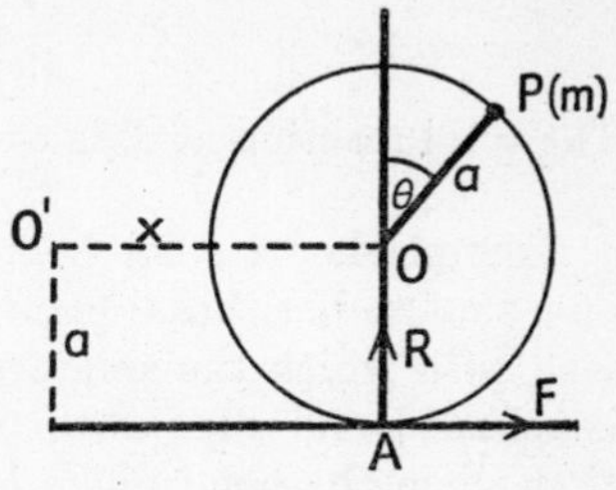

FIG. 86.

The kinetic energy of the disc is (v. (3))

$$T_1 = \tfrac{1}{2}m\dot{x}^2 + \tfrac{1}{2}.m\frac{a^2}{2}\dot{\theta}^2 = \tfrac{1}{2}.\tfrac{3}{2}ma^2\dot{\theta}^2$$

The co-ordinates of P, relative to axes through the fixed point O', are

$$\mathbf{r} = \{(x + a\sin\theta), a\cos\theta\}$$

Hence its velocity is

$$\dot{\mathbf{r}} = \{\dot{x} + a\dot{\theta}\cos\theta, - a\sin\theta\dot{\theta}\} = \{a\dot{\theta}(1 + \cos\theta), - a\dot{\theta}\sin\theta\}$$

The kinetic energy of the particle will therefore be

$$T_2 = \tfrac{1}{2}ma^2\dot{\theta}^2\{(1 + \cos\theta)^2 + \sin^2\theta\}$$

and the energy equation becomes

$$T_1 + T_2 + mga\cos\theta = K, \text{ a constant}$$

This becomes

$$a\dot{\theta}^2(7 + 4\cos\theta) + 4g\cos\theta = K', \text{ a constant}$$

When $\theta = \pi/3$, $\dot{\theta} = 0$ and so $K' = 2g$. Hence we get

$$a\dot{\theta}^2(7 + 4\cos\theta) = 2g\,(1 - 2\cos\theta) \quad . \quad . \quad (8)$$

Differentiating (8) w.r.t. t we get

$$a\ddot{\theta}(7 + 4\cos\theta) - 2a\dot{\theta}^2\sin\theta = 2g\sin\theta \quad . \quad . \quad (9)$$

When $\theta = \frac{\pi}{2}$, (8) gives $7a\dot{\theta}^2 = 2g$ and (9) gives

$$7a\ddot{\theta} - 2a\dot{\theta}^2 = 2g$$

Hence $$a\ddot{\theta} = \ddot{x} = \frac{18g}{49}$$ Q.E.D.

The centre of mass G of the system is the mid-point of OP with co-ordinates $(x + \frac{1}{2}a \sin\theta, \frac{1}{2}a \cos\theta)$. If the forces acting on the disc at A are R and F, as shown we get

$$F = 2m \frac{d^2}{dt^2}(x + \tfrac{1}{2}a \sin\theta)$$

and
$$R - 2mg = 2m \frac{d^2}{dt^2}(\tfrac{1}{2}a \cos\theta)$$

When $\theta = \pi/2$ these give the values

$$F = 2m(\ddot{x} - \tfrac{1}{2}a\dot{\theta}^2)\;; \quad R = 2mg - ma\ddot{\theta}$$

and writing $a\dot{\theta}^2 = \dfrac{2g}{7}$, $\ddot{x} = a\ddot{\theta} = \dfrac{18g}{49}$, we get

$$F = \frac{22}{49}mg \quad \text{and} \quad R = \frac{80}{49}mg$$

The total reaction at A is the resultant of these two forces.

Example 4. A solid homogeneous hemisphere of radius a is held on a smooth horizontal plane with its base parallel to a smooth vertical wall with which the spherical surface is in contact. The hemisphere is released and slips down under the action of gravity only. Show that when the hemisphere leaves the vertical wall the velocity of its centre of mass is $\frac{3}{16}\sqrt{\dfrac{15ga}{2}}$. Prove also that in the subsequent motion the inclination of the base of the hemisphere never exceeds $\cos^{-1}\frac{45}{128}$. (L.U.)

Let the base be inclined at θ to the vertical as shown in Fig. 87. Taking axes as shown, let G be the point (x, y).

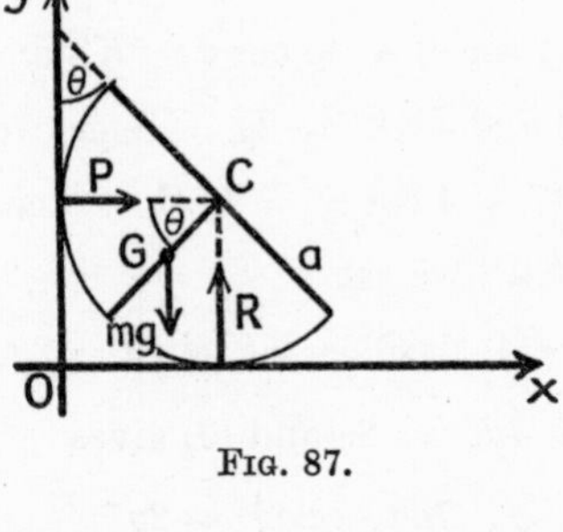

FIG. 87.

Then
$$x = a(1 - \tfrac{3}{8}\cos\theta), \quad y = a(1 - \tfrac{3}{8}\sin\theta)$$

giving
$$\dot{x} = \frac{3a}{8}\sin\theta\,\dot{\theta} \quad \text{and} \quad \dot{y} = -\frac{3a}{8}\cos\theta\,\dot{\theta}$$

Let $I(G)$ be the moment of inertia of the hemisphere about an axis through G and perpendicular to the plane of motion.

Then $$I(G) + m\left(\frac{3a}{8}\right)^2 = I(C) = \tfrac{1}{2}.\tfrac{2}{5}(2m)a^2 \qquad \text{(v. 9.5(5))}$$

which gives $$I(G) = \tfrac{83}{320}ma^2$$

The energy equation is

$$\tfrac{1}{2}m(\dot{x}^2 + \dot{y}^2) + \tfrac{1}{2}I(G)\dot{\theta}^2 + mgy = \text{constant}$$

and substituting from above, we get

$$\tfrac{1}{2}.\tfrac{2}{5}ma^2\dot{\theta}^2 + mga(1 - \tfrac{3}{8}\sin\theta) = mga$$

which is $$8a\dot{\theta}^2 = 15g\sin\theta \quad . \quad . \quad . \quad . \quad (10)$$

Now $$P = m\ddot{x} = \frac{3a}{8}m\frac{d}{dt}(\sin\theta\,\dot{\theta})$$

and so the hemisphere leaves the wall when $P = 0$, i.e. when

$$\sin\theta\,\ddot{\theta} + \cos\theta\,\dot{\theta}^2 = 0 \quad . \quad . \quad . \quad (11)$$

Using 10, $16a\ddot{\theta} = 15g\cos\theta$, and (11) gives

$$\sin\theta\cos\theta = 0 \quad \text{or} \quad \theta = \pi/2$$

Then (10) gives $\theta = \sqrt{\dfrac{15g}{8a}}$ and the velocity of G is then

$$\dot{x}_0 = \tfrac{3}{16}\sqrt{\frac{15ag}{2}}, \quad \dot{y}_0 = 0 \qquad \text{Q.E.D.}$$

When the hemisphere has left the wall $\dot{x}$ remains constant since there is zero horizontal force on the body, and so the energy equation can be written

$$\tfrac{1}{2}.\frac{9ma^2}{64}\cos^2\theta\,\dot{\theta}^2 + \tfrac{1}{2}.ma^2.\tfrac{83}{320}.\dot{\theta}^2 + mga(1 - \tfrac{3}{8}\sin\theta) = \text{constant}$$

Measuring t from the time that the hemisphere breaks contact with the wall, we have $\dot{\theta}^2 = 15g/8a$, $\theta = \dfrac{\pi}{2}$ at $t = 0$. Hence the energy equation becomes

$$f(\theta)\,\dot{\theta}^2 = \tfrac{3}{4}mga\sin\theta - \tfrac{3}{4}mga + \frac{249}{64 \times 8}mga$$

$$= \frac{3mga}{4}\{\sin\theta - \tfrac{45}{128}\} \quad . \quad . \quad . \quad . \quad (12)$$

and where $$f(\theta) = ma^2(\tfrac{83}{320} + \tfrac{9}{64}\cos^2\theta)$$

Now (12) shows that $\dot{\theta}^2 \geqslant 0$ when $\sin\theta \geqslant \tfrac{45}{128}$. Hence the least inclination to the vertical is $\sin^{-1}(\tfrac{45}{128})$; therefore the greatest inclination to the horizontal is $\cos^{-1}(\tfrac{45}{128})$. Q.E.D.

Example 5. A uniform sphere of radius a rolls without slipping on the inside of a fixed rough circular cylinder of radius b whose axis is horizontal. The sphere is started rolling at the lowest point so that the horizontal velocity u of its centre is perpendicular to the axis of the cylinder. Prove that the least value of u for which the sphere will roll right round without leaving the surface of the cylinder is given by

$$u^2 = \tfrac{27}{7}g(b - a) \qquad \text{(M.T.)}$$

Fig. 88 shows the general position of the rolling sphere after the line CG has turned through an angle θ. Let GB be a fixed radius in the sphere so chosen that B coincides with B_0 at $t = 0$. The angular velocity ω of the sphere is $\omega = \dot{\phi}$. But the arc AB equals the arc AB_0, that is

$$a(\theta + \phi) = b\theta$$

which gives $$\omega = \dot{\phi} = \left(\frac{b-a}{a}\right)\dot{\theta}. \qquad (13)$$

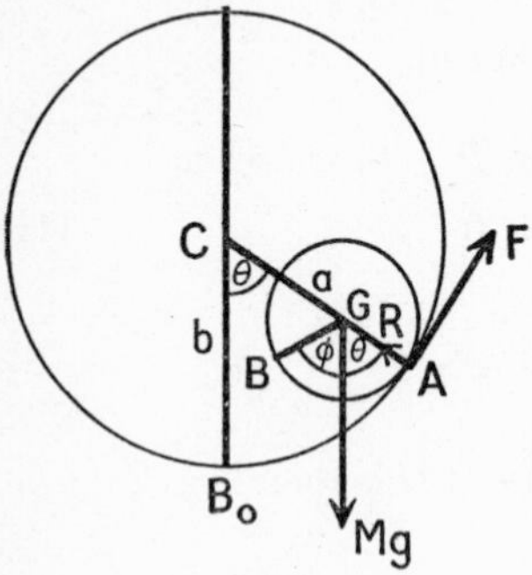

FIG. 88.

Since G moves in a circle of radius $(b - a)$ we have

$$R - Mg\cos\theta = M(b - a)\dot{\theta}^2 \qquad (14)$$

The kinetic energy of the sphere is (v. (3))

$$T = \tfrac{1}{2}M(b-a)^2\dot{\theta}^2 + \tfrac{1}{2}.\tfrac{2}{5}Ma^2.\left(\frac{b-a}{a}\right)^2\dot{\theta}^2$$
$$= \tfrac{1}{2}.\tfrac{7}{5}M(b-a)^2\dot{\theta}^2$$

and the energy equation becomes

$$\tfrac{1}{2}.\tfrac{7}{5}M(b-a)^2\dot{\theta}^2 - Mg(b-a)\cos\theta = \text{constant}$$
$$= \tfrac{1}{2}.\tfrac{7}{5}Mu^2 - Mg(b-a)$$

giving $$7(b-a)^2\dot{\theta}^2 + 10g(b-a)(1-\cos\theta) = 7u^2 \quad . \quad . \quad (15)$$

The required condition is obtained from $R \geqslant 0$ at $\theta = \pi$. When $\theta = \pi$, (15) gives

$$7(b-a)^2\dot{\theta}^2 + 20g(b-a) = 7u^2$$

and (14) then gives $R \geqslant 0$ provided

$$(b-a)\dot{\theta}^2 - g \geqslant 0$$

that is, $$\frac{u^2}{b-a} - \tfrac{20}{7}g - g \geqslant 0$$

giving $$u^2 \geqslant \tfrac{27}{7}.g.(b-a) \qquad \text{Q.E.D.}$$

Alternatively, we can consider the following *vectorial treatment*. Let the unit vector $\boldsymbol{e}$ define the line of centres CG, as shown in Fig. 89, and let the sphere have angular velocity $\boldsymbol{\omega}$. Using 9.3(4) and 9.3(6) we can write $\bar{\boldsymbol{r}} = (b - a)\boldsymbol{e}$ and

$$M(b-a)\,\ddot{\boldsymbol{e}} = -\,Mg\,\boldsymbol{k} + \boldsymbol{R} \quad (16)$$

$$\tfrac{2}{5}Ma^2\,\dot{\boldsymbol{\omega}} = a\,\boldsymbol{e} \times \boldsymbol{R} \quad . \quad (17)$$

Since A is at rest we have

$$(b-a)\dot{\boldsymbol{e}} + \boldsymbol{\omega} \times a\,\boldsymbol{e} = \boldsymbol{0} \quad (18)$$

Eliminating $\boldsymbol{R}$ between (16) and (17) gives

$$2a\,\dot{\boldsymbol{\omega}} = 5\boldsymbol{e} \times \{(b-a)\ddot{\boldsymbol{e}} + g\,\boldsymbol{k}\} \quad (19)$$

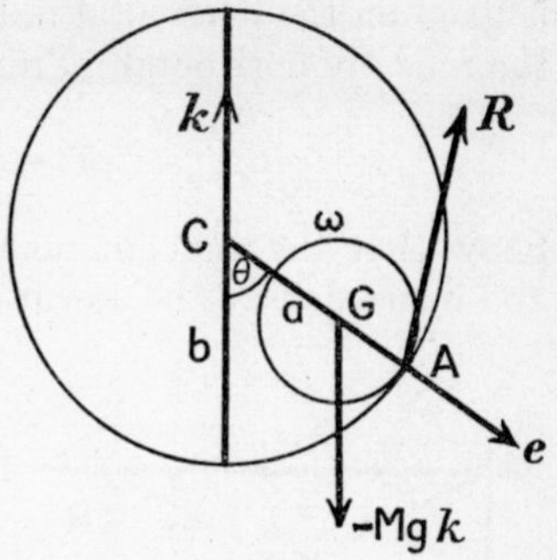

FIG. 89.

Now suppose that $\boldsymbol{n}$ is a unit vector perpendicular to the plane and forming a right-handed set with $\boldsymbol{e}$ and $\boldsymbol{k}$. Since the motion is plane it is clear that we can write

$$\boldsymbol{\omega} = -\,\omega\,\boldsymbol{n} \quad \text{and} \quad \dot{\boldsymbol{e}} = \dot{\theta}\,\boldsymbol{n} \times \boldsymbol{e} \quad (\text{v. } 3.4(3))$$

Then $\quad \dot{\boldsymbol{\omega}} = -\,\dot{\omega}\,\boldsymbol{n} \quad \text{and} \quad \ddot{\boldsymbol{e}} = \ddot{\theta}\,\boldsymbol{n} \times \dot{\boldsymbol{e}} + \dot{\theta}\,\boldsymbol{n} \times \dot{\boldsymbol{e}}$

which gives $\quad \ddot{\boldsymbol{e}} = \ddot{\theta}\,\boldsymbol{n} \times \boldsymbol{e} + \dot{\theta}^2\,\boldsymbol{n} \times (\boldsymbol{n} \times \boldsymbol{e})$

$$= \ddot{\theta}\,\boldsymbol{n} \times \boldsymbol{e} - \dot{\theta}^2\,\boldsymbol{e} \quad (\boldsymbol{n}.\boldsymbol{e} = 0)$$

Hence $\quad \boldsymbol{e} \times \ddot{\boldsymbol{e}} = \ddot{\theta}\,\boldsymbol{e} \times (\boldsymbol{n} \times \boldsymbol{e}) = \ddot{\theta}\,\boldsymbol{n}$

Now (18) gives $\quad \{(b-a)\dot{\theta} - a\omega\}(\boldsymbol{n} \times \boldsymbol{e}) = \boldsymbol{0}$

so that $\quad a\omega = (b-a)\dot{\theta} \quad (\text{cf. } (13)) \quad . \quad . \quad . \quad (20)$

Now (19) becomes

$$-\,2(b-a)\ddot{\theta}\,\boldsymbol{n} = 5(b-a)\ddot{\theta}\,\boldsymbol{n} + 5g\sin\theta\,\boldsymbol{n}$$

using the fact that $\boldsymbol{e} \times \boldsymbol{k} = \sin\theta\,\boldsymbol{n}$.

Hence we get $\quad 7(b-a)\ddot{\theta} = -\,5g\sin\theta$

which gives

$$7(b-a)\dot{\theta}^2 = 10g\cos\theta + \text{a constant}$$

$$= 10g\,(\cos\theta - 1) + \frac{7u^2}{(b-a)} \quad (\text{cf. } (15))$$

The normal reaction at A (inwards) is $S = -\,\boldsymbol{e}.\boldsymbol{R}$ so the required condition is $\quad \boldsymbol{e}.\boldsymbol{R} \leqslant 0 \quad \text{at } \theta = \pi$

(16) gives $\quad \boldsymbol{e}.\boldsymbol{R} = M(b-a)\boldsymbol{e}.\ddot{\boldsymbol{e}} + Mg\,\boldsymbol{e}.\boldsymbol{k}$

$$= -\,M(b-a)\dot{\theta}^2 - Mg\cos\theta$$

so that $\boldsymbol{e}.\boldsymbol{R} \leqslant 0$ at $\theta = \pi$ provided

$$\frac{7u^2}{(b-a)} - 20g - 7g \geqslant 0$$

giving $\quad u^2 \geqslant \tfrac{27}{7}.g(b-a) \quad$ Q.E.D.

Example 6. Two equal uniform rods AB, BC, each of mass m and length $2a$, are freely jointed at B. The end C moves on a smooth horizontal rail and the rod AB can turn freely about the end A which is fixed on the horizontal rail. The system is released from rest when the rods are horizontal. Prove that, when $\angle BAC = \theta$,

$$\dot{\theta}^2 = \frac{3g}{2a} \cdot \frac{\sin\theta}{(4 - 3\cos^2\theta)}$$

Show that the angular momentum of the system about A is $4ma^2\dot{\theta}$, and hence deduce the downward vertical reaction at C upon the rail. (M.T.)

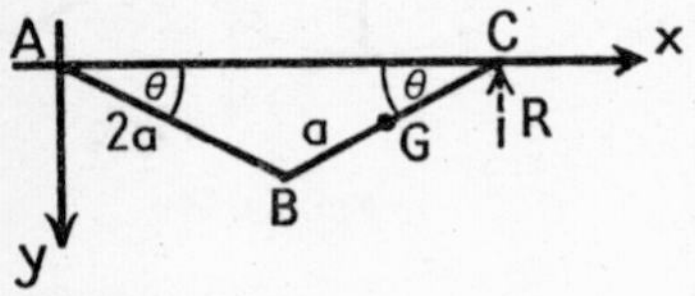

FIG. 90.

Fig. 90 shows the general position of the rods and R is the reaction of the rail on the rod BC at C. The two rods have equal and opposite angular velocities $\dot{\theta}$. Since A is a fixed point the kinetic energy of AB is (v. (3) and 9.5(4))

$$T_1 = \tfrac{1}{2} \cdot \tfrac{4}{3} ma^2 . \dot{\theta}^2$$

Let (x, y) be the co-ordinates of G, the centre of mass of BC.

Then $\quad x = 3a\cos\theta\,; \quad y = a\sin\theta$

giving $\quad \dot{x} = -3a\sin\theta\,\dot{\theta}\,; \quad \dot{y} = a\cos\theta\,\dot{\theta}$

The kinetic energy of BC is therefore

$$T_2 = \tfrac{1}{2}m(\dot{x}^2 + \dot{y}^2) + \tfrac{1}{2}.m\frac{a^2}{3}.\dot{\theta}^2$$

giving $$T_2 = \tfrac{1}{2}m\frac{a^2}{3}\dot{\theta}^2\{(1 + 3(9\sin^2\theta + \cos^2\theta)\}$$

Hence the energy equation is

$$\tfrac{1}{2}.m\frac{a^2}{3}.\{5 + 27\sin^2\theta + 3\cos^2\theta\}\dot{\theta}^2 - 2mga\sin\theta$$

$$= \text{a constant}$$

$$= 0$$

This reduces to $$2a(4 - 3\cos^2\theta)\dot{\theta}^2 = 3g\sin\theta \quad . \quad . \quad . \quad (21)$$

Q.E.D.

The angular momentum of AB about A is

$$H_1(A) = -\tfrac{4}{3}ma^2\dot{\theta}$$

To find the angular momentum $H_2(A)$ for BC we must use (2). Hence

$$H_2(A) = m(\dot{x}y - \dot{y}x) + m\frac{a^2}{3}\dot{\theta}$$

$$= -3ma^2\dot{\theta} + m\frac{a^2}{3}\dot{\theta}$$

We now get $\quad H(A) = H_1(A) + H_2(A) = -4ma^2\dot{\theta}$

the positive direction being taken as counter-clockwise about A. Using 9.3(5) we have

$$-4ma^2\ddot{\theta} = 4a\cos\theta . R \quad . \quad . \quad . \quad (12)$$

But (21) gives

$$4a(4 - 3\cos^2\theta)\ddot{\theta} + \frac{12a\cos\theta\sin\theta \,.\, 3g\sin\theta}{2a(4 - 3\cos^2\theta)} = 3g\cos\theta$$

so that

$$4a(4 - 3\cos^2\theta)\ddot{\theta} = \frac{3g\cos\theta\,(1 - 3\sin^2\theta)}{(4 - 3\cos^2\theta)}$$

Then (22) gives

$$-R = \frac{3mg}{4} \cdot \frac{(1 - 3\sin^2\theta)}{(4 - 3\cos^2\theta)^2}$$

10.2 Problems of rolling and sliding

Questions of rolling and/or sliding immediately involve questions of friction between surfaces in contact (v. 5.1(f)). Thus, consider a uniform solid sphere moving on a rough inclined plane, as in Fig. 91. Suppose, as an example, that the centre C has a velocity u down the plane and the sphere has an angular velocity ω in the direction shown. The questions which arise are :

(i) Is the point of contact, A, at rest (rolling) or is it moving (sliding)? ; and

(ii) In either case in which direction, up or down the plane, is the frictional force F at A acting?

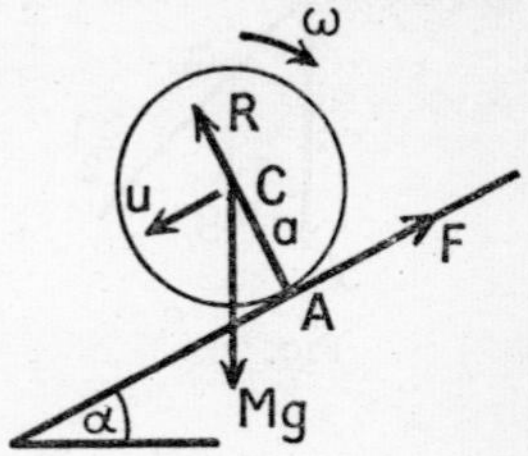

FIG. 91.

Now if u and ω are both positive quantities the velocity of A is clearly $v = u + a\omega$ down the plane. Hence $v > 0$ and A is not at rest : the sphere is sliding. Since A is moving down the plane the friction F must be acting up the plane, in an effort to stop the motion : furthermore (v. 5.1(f)) in this case $F = \mu R$.

Now suppose that ω is reversed in direction. This gives the velocity of A as $v = u - a\omega$, which might or might not vanish. Suppose in fact that $v = 0 = u - a\omega$. Then A is at rest and the sphere rolls. How to decide on the direction of F? This is decided by considering the *forces* acting on the body. The weight Mg has a component acting down the plane, and this tends to drag A down the plane. Hence F acts up the plane once more. Also it is no longer true to write $F = \mu R$, we must now have $F < \mu R$; A is in equilibrium.

We can summarize this analysis in the following conditions.

Sliding : The point of contact A has a velocity $\mathbf{v}(\neq \mathbf{0})$.
$F = \mu R$
$\mathbf{F}$ is in the direction of $-\mathbf{v}$.

Rolling : The point of contact A is at rest.
$F < \mu R$.
The direction of $\mathbf{F}$ is to oppose the remaining *forces*.

It follows that if a body is rolling in the first instance then this motion changes to sliding as soon as $F = \mu R$. Similarly, if a body is sliding in the first instance, then this motion changes to rolling as soon as " the point of contact A is at (relative) rest."

Example 1. A uniform rod is held so that one-third of its length rests on a horizontal table at right angles to an edge, the other two-thirds projecting beyond the edge, and it is then released. Show that it will rotate about the edge through an angle $\tan^{-1}(\frac{1}{2}\mu)$, where μ is the coefficient of friction, before it begins to slip. (L.U.)

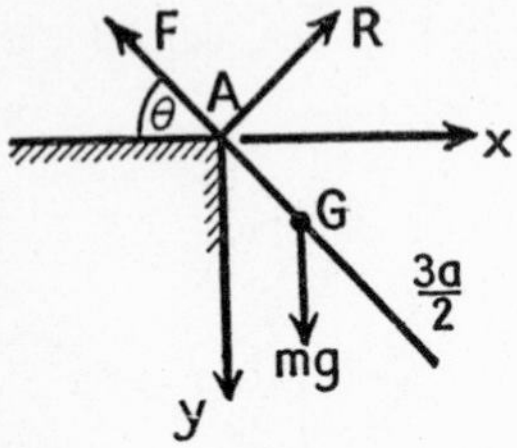

FIG. 92.

The general position is shown in Fig. 92. In the first instance the rod rolls about A since the velocity of A along AG is zero at $\theta = 0$. Let the length of the rod be $3a$, so that $AG = \frac{a}{2}$. The direction of friction is as shown. If $I(A)$ is the moment of inertia of the rod about A, we have (v. 9.3(5))

$$I(A)\ddot{\theta} = mg.\frac{a}{2}.\cos\theta \quad . \quad (1)$$

Since $I(A) = \int_{-a}^{2a} \rho z^2\,dz = 3\rho a^3 = ma^2$, (1) becomes

$$a\ddot{\theta} = \tfrac{1}{2}g\cos\theta \quad . \quad . \quad . \quad . \quad . \quad (2)$$

whence

$$a\dot{\theta}^2 = g\sin\theta \quad . \quad . \quad . \quad . \quad . \quad (3)$$

Considering the motion of G, whose co-ordinates are $x = \frac{a}{2}\cos\theta$ and $y = \frac{a}{2}\sin\theta$, we get

$$m\ddot{x} = R\sin\theta - F\cos\theta \quad . \quad . \quad . \quad (4)$$

$$m\ddot{y} = mg - R\cos\theta - F\sin\theta \quad . \quad . \quad (5)$$

Now $\ddot{x} = -\frac{a}{2}(\sin\theta\,\ddot{\theta} + \cos\theta\,\dot{\theta}^2)$, $\ddot{y} = \frac{a}{2}(\cos\theta\,\ddot{\theta} - \sin\theta\,\dot{\theta}^2)$

and using (2) and (3) these become

$$\ddot{x} = -\tfrac{3}{4}g\sin\theta\cos\theta, \quad \ddot{y} = \tfrac{1}{4}g(\cos^2\theta - 2\sin^2\theta) \quad . \quad (6)$$

Slipping occurs when $F = \mu R$ and then (4) and (5) become

$$m\ddot{x} = R(\sin\theta - \mu\cos\theta)$$

$$mg - m\ddot{y} = R(\cos\theta + \mu\sin\theta)$$

which give

$$\frac{\sin\theta - \mu\cos\theta}{\cos\theta + \mu\sin\theta} = \frac{\ddot{x}}{g - \ddot{y}}$$

$$= \frac{-\sin\theta\cos\theta}{1 + \sin\theta}, \quad \text{by (6)}$$

This easily reduces to

$$(t - \mu)(1 + 2t^2) = -t(1 + \mu t) \quad \text{with } t = \tan\theta$$

that is, $$(2t - \mu)(1 + t^2) = 0$$

Hence slipping occurs when $\tan\theta = (\frac{1}{2}\mu)$. Q.E.D.

Example 2. A uniform sphere of mass m and radius a rotating about a horizontal diameter with angular velocity ω is placed gently on the upper surface of a uniform rigid plane sheet of mass m which rests with its lower surface in contact with a rough horizontal table. The coefficient of friction between the sphere and the sheet is μ, and between the sheet and the table is $\frac{1}{4}\mu$. Prove that, if the sheet is held fixed, the sphere will travel a distance $\frac{2}{49}\cdot\frac{a^2\omega^2}{\mu g}$ before slipping ceases. If the sheet is free to slide, show that the distance relative to the sheet travelled by the sphere before it ceases to slip on the sheet is $\frac{3}{64}\cdot\frac{a^2\omega^2}{\mu g}$, and that in the same time the sheet has travelled a distance relative to the table one-third of this. (M.T.)

In Fig. 93, let the sphere have angular velocity Ω at time and let x be the distance travelled by G relative to the table. Let y measure

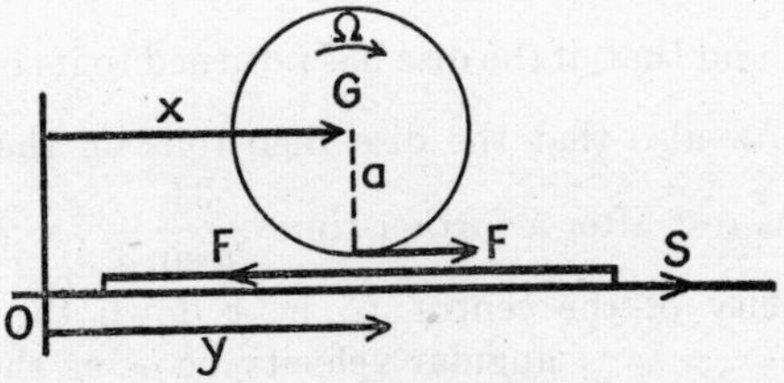

FIG. 93.

the distance travelled by the centre of mass of the sheet. The friction F acts forwards on the sphere in the first instance since the point of contact has a velocity $a\omega$ ($\neq 0$) to the left.

(i) Sheet fixed. The equations of motion for the sphere are :

$$m\ddot{x} = F = \mu R = \mu mg$$

and $$\tfrac{2}{5}ma^2\dot{\Omega} = -aF = -a\mu mg$$

These give $$\dot{x} = \mu gt\,; \quad x = \tfrac{1}{2}\mu gt^2 \quad . \quad . \quad . \quad (7)$$

and $$a\Omega = a\omega - \tfrac{5}{2}\mu gt \quad . \quad . \quad . \quad . \quad (8)$$

Slipping ceases after a time t_1, when $\dot{x} - a\Omega = 0$, that is

$$\tfrac{7}{2}\mu gt_1 - a\omega = 0$$

Hence $t_1 = \frac{2}{7}\cdot\frac{a\omega}{\mu g}$ and (7) gives $x_1 = \frac{2}{49}\cdot\frac{a^2\omega^2}{\mu g}$.

(ii) Sheet free to slide. Let S be the friction between the sheet and table, so that $S = \frac{1}{4}\mu$ (reaction) $= \frac{1}{4}\mu \times 2mg = \frac{1}{2}\mu mg$. Then equations (7) and (8) still apply for the sphere. For the sheet we have

$$m\ddot{y} = S - F = \mu mg(\tfrac{1}{2} - 1) = -\tfrac{1}{2}\mu mg$$

Hence
$$\dot{y} = -\tfrac{1}{2}\mu gt\ ;\quad y = -\tfrac{1}{4}\mu gt^2 \quad . \quad . \quad . \quad (9)$$

Slipping ceases after a time t_2, when $\dot{x} - a\Omega = \dot{y}$, that is

$$\tfrac{7}{2}\mu gt_2 - a\omega = -\tfrac{1}{2}\mu gt_2$$

Hence $t_2 = \frac{1}{4}.\frac{a\omega}{\mu g}$ and (7) and (9) give

$$x = \tfrac{1}{32}.\frac{a^2\omega^2}{\mu g}\ ;\quad y = -\tfrac{1}{64}.\frac{a^2\omega^2}{\mu g}$$

The sphere therefore moves a distance $x - y = \frac{3}{64}.\frac{a^2\omega^2}{\mu g}$ relative to the sheet.

Q.E.D.

Example 3. A uniform circular disc, of radius a, is projected, with its plane vertical, along a line of greatest slope of a plane of inclination α to the horizontal. The initial velocity of the centre of the disc is V *down* the plane and the initial angular velocity is Ω (in the sense in which the disc would roll up the plane). If the coefficient of friction between disc and plane is $2 \tan \alpha$, show that slipping ceases after a time $\frac{(V + a\Omega)}{5g \sin \alpha}$, and that, if the disc has returned to its original position, $V = a\Omega/9$. Show also that the disc then rolls on the plane, coming to instantaneous rest after a further time $\frac{3V}{2g \sin \alpha}$. (L.U.)

Let the velocity of the centre, G, be v down the plane and the angular velocity be ω, as shown in Fig. 94. At $t = 0$ the velocity of A is $V + a\Omega$ down the plane. Hence the disc slips and F acts up the plane. The equations of motion are :

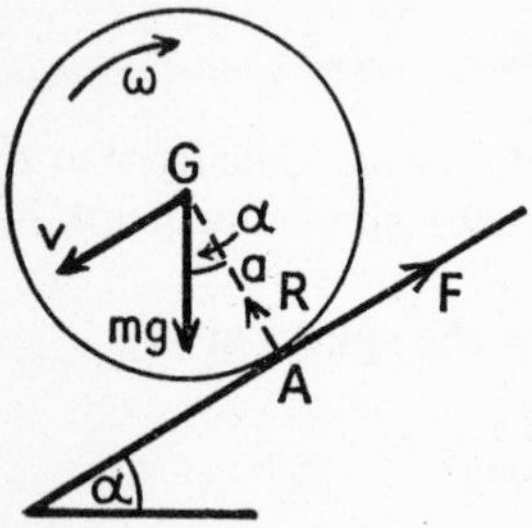

FIG. 94.

$$m\dot{v} = mg \sin \alpha - F$$
$$= mg (\sin \alpha - \mu \cos \alpha)$$

and writing $\mu = 2 \tan \alpha$, this becomes

$$\dot{v} = -g \sin \alpha \quad . \quad . \quad (10)$$

Also
$$m\frac{a^2}{2}\dot{\omega} = -aF = -a\mu.mg \cos \alpha$$

that is
$$a\dot{\omega} = -4g \sin \alpha$$

This gives
$$a\omega = a\Omega - 4gt \sin \alpha \quad . \quad . \quad . \quad . \quad (11)$$

and (10) gives
$$v = V - gt \sin \alpha \quad . \quad . \quad . \quad . \quad (12)$$

Slipping ceases when "velocity of A" $= v + a\omega = 0$. This gives

$$5gt_1 \sin \alpha = V + a\Omega \quad . \quad . \quad . \quad . \quad . \quad (13)$$

If the disc has meanwhile returned to its initial position then v has passed through the value zero (at $t = t_0$) and changed its sign so that the disc moves back up the slope. But (12) gives $t_0 = V/g \sin \alpha$ and since $t_1 = 2t_0$, (13) gives

$$10V = V + a\Omega$$

so that $9V = a\Omega$. Here we notice that even when $t = t_0$ (11) gives $a\omega = a\Omega - 4V = 5V > 0$, so that the velocity of A is still positive down the plane. Hence F still acts upwards.

While the disc now rolls up the plane, let the centre G have velocity u *up* the plane and an angular velocity ω in the same direction as shown in Fig. 94. The friction F continues to act up the plane. The equations of motion are now :

$$m\dot{u} = F - mg \sin \alpha$$
$$ma\dot{\omega} = -2F$$
$$u = a\omega$$

These give

$$3\dot{u} = -2g \sin \alpha \quad \text{and} \quad 3u = -2gt \sin \alpha + 3u_0$$

where u_0 = value of u at $t = 0$, i.e. from the start of rolling. But (12) gives

$$v = -u_0 = V - \tfrac{1}{5}(V + a\Omega) = V - \frac{10V}{5} = -V$$

Hence $3u = -2gt \sin \alpha + 3V$ and so the disc comes to instantaneous rest after a further time $\dfrac{3V}{2g \sin \alpha}$.

10.3 The instantaneous centre

We now consider the *kinematic problem* of the motion of a lamina in its own plane. In particular we can show that, however the lamina moves, there is always a point at any instant which is at rest and about which, therefore, the lamina is actually turning. This point is called the instantaneous centre : clearly its position in both the lamina and the plane will generally change with time.

Suppose the lamina occupies the whole of the xy-plane. Let its angular velocity be $\boldsymbol{\omega}$ and the velocity of the centre of mass, G, be $\boldsymbol{u}$. If P is any point of the lamina, let it have a position vector $\boldsymbol{\rho}$ w.r.t. G as origin. Its velocity $\boldsymbol{v}$ will be

$$\boldsymbol{v} = \boldsymbol{u} + \boldsymbol{\omega} \times \boldsymbol{\rho} \quad . \quad . \quad . \quad . \quad (1)$$

Taking fixed axes $\boldsymbol{i}$, $\boldsymbol{j}$ in the plane and writing $\boldsymbol{u} = u_1 \boldsymbol{i} + u_2 \boldsymbol{j}$, $\boldsymbol{\rho} = \xi \boldsymbol{i} + \eta \boldsymbol{j}$, $\boldsymbol{\omega} = \omega \boldsymbol{k}$ ($\boldsymbol{k}$ being normal to the plane, i.e. $\boldsymbol{k} = \boldsymbol{i} \times \boldsymbol{j}$), (1) becomes

$$\boldsymbol{v} = (u_1 - \eta\, \omega)\boldsymbol{i} + (u_2 + \xi\omega)\boldsymbol{j} \quad . \quad . \quad . \quad (2)$$

Hence there is a point Q which is instantaneously at rest, for values of ξ, η exist such that

$$u_1 - \eta\omega = 0\ ;\quad u_2 + \xi\omega = 0 \quad . \quad . \quad . \quad (3)$$

Now let $\boldsymbol{r}$ be the position vector $\overline{OQ}$, where O is a fixed origin in the plane, and write $\boldsymbol{\rho} = \overline{GQ}$ w.r.t. fixed axes in the lamina at G. If $\bar{\boldsymbol{r}} = OG$ we have

$$\boldsymbol{r} = \bar{\boldsymbol{r}} + \boldsymbol{\rho} = \boldsymbol{r}(t)\ ;\quad \boldsymbol{\rho} = \boldsymbol{\rho}(t) \quad . \quad . \quad . \quad (4)$$

The locus of Q in space (i.e. $\boldsymbol{r} = \boldsymbol{r}(t)$) is called the *space centrode* ; the locus of Q in the lamina (i.e. $\boldsymbol{\rho} = \boldsymbol{\rho}(t)$) is called the *body centrode.* We can now show that *the motion of the lamina is reproduced by rolling the body centrode on the space centrode.*

Since Q lies on both centrodes at any moment it is sufficient to prove that the vector velocity of Q w.r.t. the fixed plane (on the space centrode) equals that w.r.t. the lamina (on the body centrode). Thus sliding cannot occur and also the two curves will touch at Q. Since $\boldsymbol{\rho}$ is taken in a frame which rotates with the lamina, (4) gives

$$\frac{d\boldsymbol{r}}{dt} = \frac{d\bar{\boldsymbol{r}}}{dt} + \frac{d\boldsymbol{\rho}}{dt}$$

$$= \boldsymbol{u} + \frac{\partial\boldsymbol{\rho}}{\partial t} + \boldsymbol{\omega} \times \boldsymbol{\rho}$$

and by (1),

$$\frac{d\boldsymbol{r}}{dt} = \frac{\partial\boldsymbol{\rho}}{\partial t} \qquad \text{Q.E.D.}$$

Finally, we can make use of the fact that the body is instantaneously rotating about Q to find the position of Q by geometrical means.

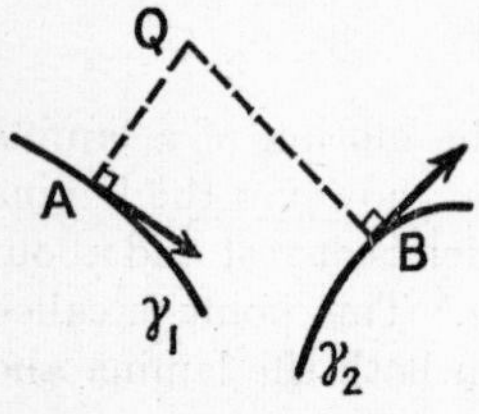

FIG. 95.

Suppose we can show that, at any instant during the motion, two points A, B of the lamina are moving along curves γ_1 and γ_2, as shown in Fig. 95. Then A must be moving perpendicular to QA (rotating about Q) and B perpendicular to QB. Hence Q is the intersection of the normals to γ_1 and γ_2 at A, B respectively.

Example 1. A bar AB moves in the plane of rectangular axes Ox, Oy, so that it always touches the parabola $y^2 = 4ax$ and the end A of the bar moves along the x-axis. Find the instantaneous centre and prove that the equation of the space centrode is

$$ay^2 + 4x(a - x)^2 = 0$$

Prove also that, referred to A as pole and AB as initial line, the equation of the body centrode is

$$r = 2a \sin\theta \sec^3\theta \qquad \text{(L.U.)}$$

Let the rod AB touch the parabola at $P\ (at^2, 2at)$ as shown in Fig. 96. Q is the intersection of the normal to $y^2 = 4ax$ at P and the normal to x-axis at A. But the tangent at P has equation $ty - x = at^2$, so that $OA = at^2$. The normal at P has equation

$$y + tx = 2at + at^3 \quad . \quad . \quad . \quad (5)$$

Hence Q is where (5) meets the line

$$x = -at^2 \quad . \quad . \quad . \quad . \quad (6)$$

This gives Q as the point $\{-at^2, 2at(1 + t^2)\}$. Eliminating t between (5) and (6) gives the *space centrode*, viz.,

$$ay^2 + 4x(a - x)^2 = 0$$

Since $\dfrac{1}{t}$ = gradient of tangent at $P = \cot\theta$, we get $AQ = r$ where

$$r = 2at(1 + t^2) = 2a \sin\theta \sec^3\theta \qquad \text{Q.E.D.}$$

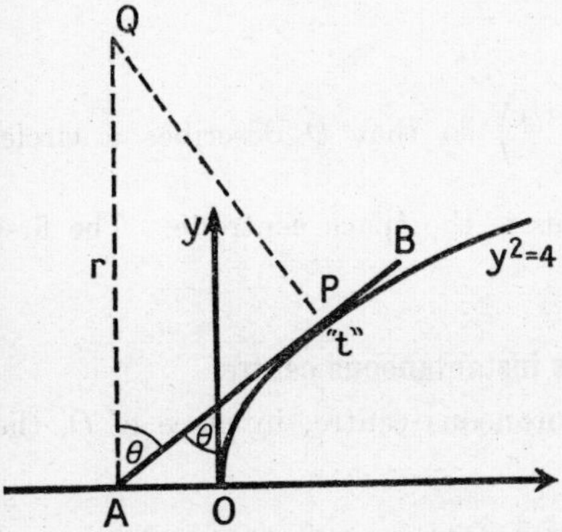

FIG. 96.

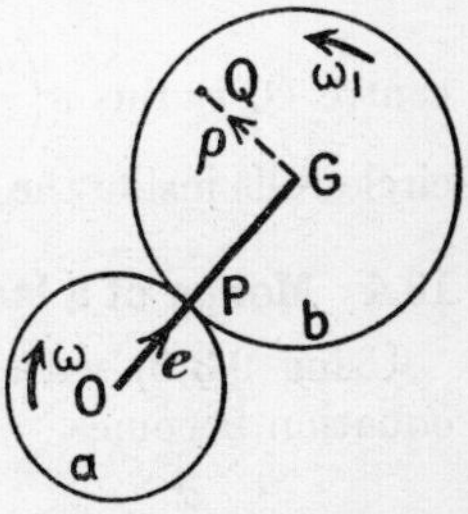

FIG. 97.

Example 2. A circular disc of radius a turns in its own plane about its centre with angular speed ω. A second circular disc of radius b, coplanar with the first, rolls in contact with it and has an angular velocity ω_1. Find the space and body centrodes for the motion of the second disc. (L.U.)

Fig. 97 shows the arrangement ; O is a fixed point in the plane. If $\boldsymbol{k}$ is a unit vector perpendicular to the plane of motion we have $\boldsymbol{\omega} = -\omega\,\boldsymbol{k}$ for one disc, and $\boldsymbol{\omega}_1 = \omega_1\,\boldsymbol{k}$ for the other. Let $\boldsymbol{e}$ be a unit vector along OG. Let $\boldsymbol{u}$ = velocity of G. The velocity of the point P is

$$\dot{\boldsymbol{P}} = -\omega\,\boldsymbol{k} \times a\,\boldsymbol{e}, \quad \text{as a point of lower disc,}$$

and $$\dot{\boldsymbol{P}} = \boldsymbol{u} + \omega_1\,\boldsymbol{k} \times (-b\,\boldsymbol{e}), \quad \text{as a point of upper disc.}$$

Also we have

$$\boldsymbol{O} = \boldsymbol{u} + \omega_1 \boldsymbol{k} \times \boldsymbol{\rho}$$

and these three equations give

$$a\omega(\boldsymbol{k} \times \boldsymbol{e}) = b\omega_1(\boldsymbol{k} \times \boldsymbol{e}) + \omega_1(\boldsymbol{k} \times \boldsymbol{\rho}) \quad . \quad . \quad (7)$$

Multiply (7) by $\times \boldsymbol{k}$, and use 2.12(1), whence

$$a\omega\, \boldsymbol{e} = b\omega_1 \boldsymbol{e} + \omega_1 \boldsymbol{\rho}$$

since $\boldsymbol{k}.\boldsymbol{e} = \boldsymbol{k}.\boldsymbol{\rho} = 0$.

Hence
$$\boldsymbol{\rho} = \left(\frac{a\omega - b\omega_1}{\omega_1}\right)\boldsymbol{e} \quad . \quad . \quad . \quad . \quad (8)$$

showing that Q describes a circle, centre G, radius $\left(\frac{a\omega - b\omega_1}{\omega_1}\right) = |\boldsymbol{\rho}|$. This is the body centrode. To find the space centrode we refer Q to the fixed point O and write $\boldsymbol{r} = \overline{OQ}$. Hence

$$\boldsymbol{r} = (a + b)\boldsymbol{e} + \boldsymbol{\rho} = \left(a + b + \frac{a\omega - b\omega_1}{\omega_1}\right)\boldsymbol{e}$$

or
$$\boldsymbol{r} = a\left(\frac{\omega + \omega_1}{\omega_1}\right)\boldsymbol{e}$$

Hence $|\boldsymbol{r}| = \text{constant} = a\left(\frac{\omega + \omega_1}{\omega_1}\right)$ so that Q describes a circle, centre O, radius $a\left(\frac{\omega + \omega_1}{\omega_1}\right)$. This is the space centrode. The first circle rolls inside the second.

10.4 Motion of a lamina about its instantaneous centre

Using 9.3(5) with Q, the instantaneous centre, in place of O, the equation becomes

$$\frac{d}{dt}\{\mathcal{J}(Q).\boldsymbol{\omega}\} = \frac{\partial}{\partial t}\{\mathcal{J}(Q).\boldsymbol{\omega}\} + \boldsymbol{\omega} \times \{(\mathcal{J}Q).\boldsymbol{\omega}\}$$
$$= \boldsymbol{\Gamma}(Q) \quad . \quad . \quad . \quad . \quad . \quad . \quad (1)$$

where we have referred $\boldsymbol{H}(Q)$ to a frame of reference moving with the lamina, that is, rotating about Q with angular velocity $\boldsymbol{\omega}$. This is an important point since the elements of $\mathcal{J}(Q)$ can sometimes remain constant in this moving frame. Now (1) gives

$$\boldsymbol{\omega}.\frac{\partial}{\partial t}\{\mathcal{J}(Q).\boldsymbol{\omega}\} = \boldsymbol{\omega}.\boldsymbol{\Gamma}(Q) \quad . \quad . \quad . \quad (2)$$

Writing $\boldsymbol{\omega} = \omega\boldsymbol{k}$, $\boldsymbol{k}$ being a unit vector perpendicular to the plane, (2) becomes

$$\tfrac{1}{2}\frac{\partial}{\partial t}\{\boldsymbol{\omega}.\mathcal{J}(Q).\boldsymbol{\omega}\} = \tfrac{1}{2}\frac{\partial}{\partial t}\{(\boldsymbol{k}.\mathcal{J}(Q).\boldsymbol{k})\omega^2\} = \omega\,\boldsymbol{k}.\boldsymbol{\Gamma}(Q)$$

using the symmetry of $\mathcal{J}(Q)$. But, by 9.5(8) and 9.5(9) $\boldsymbol{k}.\mathcal{J}(Q).\boldsymbol{k}$

$= I(Q) =$ the moment of inertia of the lamina about a perpendicular axis through Q. Hence we get

$$\frac{1}{2\omega}\frac{\partial}{\partial t}\{I(Q)\omega^2\} = \Gamma(Q) \quad . \quad . \quad . \quad (3)$$

$\Gamma(Q)$ now being the moment about Q of all the forces in the plane.

Example 1. A right cylinder, whose cross-section is any convex curve C, rolls on a horizontal plane making small oscillations under gravity about a position of stable equilibrium. Prove that the length of the equivalent simple pendulum is $\frac{k^2}{\rho - h}$, where k is the radius of gyration about the line of contact, h the height of the mass centre above the plane, and ρ the radius of curvature of C at its point of contact, all in the position of stable equilibrium. (L.U.)

The displaced position is shown in Fig. 98 ; θ and s are very small quantities. Hence $I(Q) = I(Q_0) - mh^2 + m(h^2 + s^2)$ and so $I(Q)$ differs from $I(Q_0)$ by quantities of the second order. We now have, by (3) (v. 3.6(6))

$$\frac{mk^2}{2\omega}\frac{d}{dt}(\omega^2) = \Gamma(Q)$$

$$= -mg\,(s\cos\theta - h\sin\theta)$$

Since $\omega = \dot\theta$, we get

$$k^2\ddot\theta = -g(s + h\theta)$$

$$= -g(\rho - h)\theta$$

giving $\ddot\theta = -g\left(\frac{\rho - h}{k^2}\right)\theta$ Q.E.D.

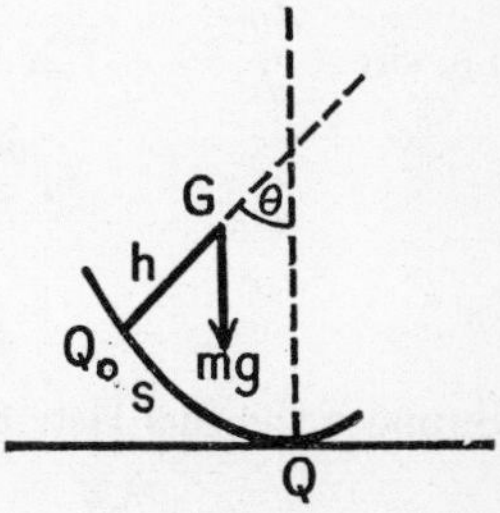

FIG. 98.

10.5 Problems of changing mass

Newton's equations for these problems are

$$\frac{d}{dt}(m\,\boldsymbol{v}) = \boldsymbol{F} \quad . \quad . \quad . \quad . \quad (1)$$

for a particle, and for a rigid body,

$$\frac{d}{dt}\{\mathscr{I}(G).\boldsymbol{\omega}\} = \boldsymbol{\Gamma}(G). \quad . \quad . \quad . \quad (2)$$

In this equation the elements of $\mathscr{I}(G)$ are functions of the time. It is often useful to write (1) and (2) in the form

$$\lim_{\Delta t \to 0}\left\{\frac{(m + \Delta m)(\boldsymbol{v} + \Delta\boldsymbol{v}) - m\,\boldsymbol{v}}{\Delta t}\right\} = \boldsymbol{F} \quad . \quad . \quad (3)$$

and $$\lim_{\Delta t \to 0}\left\{\frac{(\mathscr{I} + \Delta\mathscr{I}).(\boldsymbol{\omega} + \Delta\boldsymbol{\omega}) - \mathscr{I}.\boldsymbol{\omega}}{\Delta t}\right\} = \boldsymbol{\Gamma} \quad . \quad . \quad (4)$$

The technique may be illustrated by the following examples.

Example 1. A rocket, initially of total mass M, throws off every second a mass fM with constant velocity V. Show that it cannot rise at once unless $fV > g$ and that it cannot rise at all unless $fV > \lambda g$, where λM is the mass of the case of the rocket.

If the conditions are such that the rocket is just able to rise vertically at once, show that the greatest height it will reach is

$$\frac{V^2}{g}\{1 - \lambda + \log \lambda + \tfrac{1}{2}(\log \lambda)^2\} \qquad \text{(L.U.)}$$

Let the mass of the rocket at time t be m. Then $m = M(1 - ft)$ and if the vertically velocity is v at time t, we get the momentum at time $t + \Delta t$, as

$$(m + \Delta m)(v + \Delta v) - fM\,\Delta t\,(V - v - \Delta v)$$

a quantity of mass $\Delta m = -fM\,\Delta t$ being thrown downwards with a velocity V relative to the rocket. Hence (3) gives

$$\lim_{\Delta t \to 0}\left\{\frac{\Delta m}{\Delta t} v + m\frac{\Delta v}{\Delta t} - fMV.\frac{\Delta t}{\Delta t} + fMv\frac{\Delta t}{\Delta t}\right\} = -mg$$

i.e. since $\dfrac{dm}{dt} = -fM$,

$$m\frac{dv}{dt} - fMV = -mg$$

or

$$(1 - ft)\frac{dv}{dt} = fV - g + fgt \qquad (5)$$

Suppose the fuel lasts for a time t_1, then

$$\lambda M = M(1 - ft_1) \quad \text{and} \quad ft_1 = 1 - \lambda \qquad (6)$$

Now the rocket rises at once if $\left(\dfrac{dv}{dt}\right)_{t=0} > 0$, i.e. if $fV > g$. The rocket will never rise unless $\left(\dfrac{dv}{dt}\right)_{t=t_1} > 0$, i.e. $fV > \lambda g$.

Now, writing $fV = g$, (5) gives

$$\frac{dx}{dt} = v = -V\log(1 - ft) - gt \qquad (7)$$

and the velocity at t_1 is therefore

$$v_1 = -V\log\lambda - V(1 - \lambda) \qquad (8)$$

Also (7) integrates to give, at $t = t_1$,

$$x = \frac{V\lambda}{f}\log\lambda + \frac{V}{f}(1 - \lambda) - \tfrac{1}{2}gt_1^2$$

The final height reached will therefore be

$$x + \frac{v_1^2}{2g} = \frac{V^2}{g}\{(1 - \lambda) + \log\lambda + \tfrac{1}{2}(\log\lambda)^2\} \qquad \text{Q.E.D.}$$

Example 2. A catherine wheel, of radius a, which can turn freely about a horizontal axis, is initially of mass M and moment of inertia I about its centre. A charge is spread along the rim and ignited at time $t = 0$. While the charge is burning the rim of the wheel loses mass at a constant rate m_1 per second and, at the rim, a mass m_2 of gas is taken up per second from the atmosphere, which is at rest. The total mass $m_1 + m_2$ is discharged per second tangentially from the rim, with velocity V relative to the rim. Prove that, if θ is the angle through which the wheel has turned after t seconds, then

$$\theta = \frac{V}{a(\mu - \lambda)}\{\mu t - 1 + (1 - \lambda t)^{\mu/\lambda}\}$$

where $\lambda = m_1 a^2/I$, $\mu = (m_1 + m_2)a^2/I$. (L.U.)

Let J = the moment of inertia about the axis at time t
$= I - m_1 a^2 t$.

The mass $(m_1 + m_2)\,\Delta t$ leaves the rim with an actual velocity of $V - a\dot{\theta}$, $\dot{\theta}$ being the angular velocity of the disc. The angular momentum at time $t + \Delta t$ will be

$$(J + \Delta J)(\dot{\theta} + \Delta\dot{\theta}) - (m_1 + m_2)\Delta t\, a(V - a\dot{\theta})$$

Hence (4) becomes

$$J\ddot{\theta} + \frac{dJ}{dt}.\dot{\theta} + (m_1 + m_2)a^2\dot{\theta} = aV(m_1 + m_2)$$

giving
$$J\ddot{\theta} + m_2 a^2\dot{\theta} = aV(m_1 + m_2)$$

i.e.
$$(1 - \lambda t)\ddot{\theta} + (\mu - \lambda)\dot{\theta} = \frac{V}{a}\mu$$

Repeated integration of this equation gives

$$\theta = \frac{V}{a(\mu - \lambda)}\{\mu t - 1 + (1 - \lambda t)^{\mu/\lambda}\}$$

where $\theta = \dot{\theta} = 0$ at $t = 0$.

Exercise X

1. A lamina moves in its own plane. A point A fixed in the lamina moves on a line Ox fixed in the plane, and a line AB fixed in the lamina always touches a circle, centre O and radius a, which is fixed in the plane. Prove that the polar equation of the space centrode is

$$r\cos^2\theta = a$$

Find the polar equation of the body centrode. (M.T.)

2. A point O of the surface of a uniform sphere is freely attached to a fixed support, and the sphere is released from rest in a position where OG makes an angle α with the downward vertical, G being the centre of the sphere. Show that the motion of OG is similar to that of a simple pendulum of length $\frac{7a}{5}$. If $\alpha = \pi/2$, prove that the greatest horizontal pull on the support during the motion is $\frac{15}{14}$Mg. (M.T.)

3. A wire ABC encloses an angle β between the straight parts AB and BC. The wire moves in its own plane so that AB passes through a fixed point P, whilst BC touches a fixed circle, centre O. Prove that the space centrode is a circle which passes through O and P, and find the body centrode. (L.U.)

4. Find a formula for the period of small oscillations of a rigid body swinging freely about a fixed horizontal axis.

Two straight uniform rods AB, CD, of the same mass per unit length and of lengths $2a$ and $4a$, are rigidly attached at right angles to one another with the centre of CD at a point O of AB where AO is of length x. The system oscillates about a horizontal axis through A perpendicular to the plane of the rods. Show that the length of the equivalent simple pendulum is $(2x^2 + 4a^2)/(2x + a)$. Find the value of x for which the period is a minimum, and state briefly how the period varies as x varies from 0 to $2a$. (L.U.)

5. A thin uniform rod, one end of which can turn about a smooth hinge, is allowed to fall from a horizontal position. Prove that, when the horizontal component of the pressure on the hinge is a maximum, the vertical component is $\frac{11}{8}$ of the weight of the rod.

6. A thin uniform square plate $ABCD$, of side l and mass $3M$, is free to turn with its plane vertical about a smooth horizontal axis through A, and has a particle of mass M attached to it at C. If the plate is released from rest when AC is horizontal, prove that when it has turned through an angle θ, its angular velocity is

$$\left(\frac{5\sqrt{2}}{4}\frac{g}{l}\sin\theta\right)^{1/2},$$

and find the components along and perpendicular to AC of the reaction at the axis. (L.U.)

7. A lamina is moving in its own plane. XOY are axes in the plane, and $G(xy)$ are axes in the lamina. Find the values of $Z = X + iY$ and of $z = x + iy$ for the instantaneous velocity centre of the lamina. Hence show that if θ is $\angle(OX, Gx)$ then $dZ/dt = \text{cis}\,\theta . dz/dt$ and deduce that the body centrode rolls without slipping on the space centrode. (L.U.)

8. Prove that in general any finite displacement of a lamina in its plane can be obtained by a pure rotation of the lamina about a point I.

If a particle of the lamina moves from A to A', and the lamina rotates through an angle α, prove that I is the vertex of an isosceles triangle IAA' whose vertical angle is α.

A circular disc rolls, without slipping, on the outside of an equal circular disc which is fixed. If the centre of the rolling disc moves from A to A', prove that I is the circumcentre of the triangle OAA', where O is the centre of the fixed disc. (M.T.)

9. Define the *instantaneous centre, space-centrode* and *body-centrode* of the uniplanar motion of a lamina.

The boundary of a circular lamina of radius a touches a fixed line OA, and a fixed point P of the lamina at distance $b(< a)$ from its centre C moves on the fixed line OB, which makes an acute angle α with OA. Show that the space-centrode of the motion is a circle of radius b cosec α whose centre is the intersection of OB with a line through C parallel to OA. Show also that the body-centrode is a circle of one-half the radius of the space-centrode. (L.U.)

10. A rigid lamina is falling freely in its own plane under the action of gravity and is also rotating with an angular velocity ω about an axis perpendicular to its plane and through its centre of gravity. Show that the instantaneous centre describes, in space, a parabola of latus rectum $\{\sqrt{l} + \sqrt{(2g/\omega^2)}\}^2$, whose vertex is at a distance $\sqrt{(gl/^2\omega^2)}$ above that of the parabolic path, of latus rectum l, described by the centre of gravity of the lamina. (L.U.)

11. A compound pendulum is swinging freely about a horizontal axis with angular amplitude α (not necessarily small). The length of the equivalent simple pendulum is l. When the angular velocity of the pendulum is instantaneously zero, the axis is given a constant horizontal acceleration f in a direction perpendicular to itself. Obtain an equation of motion involving the angular co-ordinate of the pendulum and prove that the least value of f for which the body can in the subsequent motion attain the position in which the centre of mass is vertically above the axis is $g \cot \frac{\alpha}{2}$. (M.T.)

12. A rigid square $ABCD$, formed of four uniform rods each of length $2a$, lies on a smooth horizontal table, and can turn freely about one angular point A, which is fixed. An insect, whose mass is equal to that of either rod, starts from the corner B to crawl along the rod BC with uniform velocity V relative to the rod. Prove that, in any time t before the insect reaches C, the angle through which the square turns is

$$\sqrt{\frac{3}{13}} \tan^{-1}\left(\frac{Vt}{a}\sqrt{\frac{3}{52}}\right) \qquad \text{(C.)}$$

13. A ball, regarded as a uniform sphere of radius a, rolls with velocity U on a perfectly rough horizontal floor directly towards a vertical downward step of height a. If $U^2 < ag$, show that the ball will leave the edge of the step when the radius through the point of contact makes with the vertical an angle α given by

$$\cos \alpha = \frac{10}{17} + \frac{7}{17}\frac{U^2}{ag}$$

Show further that the velocity of the centre of the ball when the ball strikes the next step is $(3ga \cos \alpha)^{\frac{1}{2}}$.

14. A flexible and inextensible ribbon is coiled on the circumference of a uniform circular disc of radius r. One end is attached to the disc and the other to a fixed point. Part of the ribbon is uncoiled and is vertical and taut. The centre of the disc is at a lower level than the fixed point. The disc is allowed to fall from rest under its own weight. Show that in the period before the ribbon is completely unwound the centre of the disc descends with constant acceleration and find the magnitude of this acceleration. (M.T.)

15. A uniform wheel can rotate in a vertical plane about its centre O, which is fixed, and carries a heavy particle at a point P of its rim. Motion of the wheel is opposed by a frictional couple of constant magnitude. The system is released from rest with OP at 30° above the horizontal, and comes instantaneously to rest when OP has been carried 45° beyond the downward vertical. Prove that OP will not pass through the vertical position again. (M.T.)

16. Three equal uniform rods AB, BC, CD each of length $2a$ and mass m are freely jointed at B and C, and at the ends A and D light rings are attached which can slide freely on a fixed smooth horizontal rail. The system is released from rest when all the rods are horizontal. If in the subsequent motion θ is the angle of inclination of AB or CD to the horizontal, prove that

$$\dot{\theta}^2 = \frac{6g \sin \theta}{a(2 + 3\cos^2 \theta)}$$

Prove also that the total downward reaction on the rail is equal to $3mg$, when

$$\cos^2 \theta = \sqrt{\tfrac{7}{3}} - 1$$ (M.T.)

17. A uniform rod of mass m stands vertically on a smooth horizontal table, and is just displaced. Prove that the end on the table remains in contact with the table throughout the subsequent motion, and find the reaction on the table just before the rod becomes horizontal. (L.U.)

18. Define angular momentum about an axis for a system of particles, and in the case of motion in a plane determine conditions for which the time rate of change of angular momentum and the moment of rate of change of momentum about the same axis (not necessarily at rest) are equal.

A uniform rod is suspended in a horizontal position by two light vertical strings attached to its ends. Show that, when one string is suddenly cut, the tension in the other is instantaneously halved. (M.T.)

19. A bead of mass m can slide freely on a rigid rod which is free to rotate in a horizontal plane about a vertical axis through a fixed point O of the rod. The moment of inertia of the rod about the axis of rotation is mc^2. The system is set in motion with the bead at rest relative to the rod at a distance a from O. Prove that the differential equation of the path of the bead is

$$(a^2 + c^2)\left(\frac{dr}{d\theta}\right)^2 = (r^2 - a^2)(r^2 + c^2)$$

where r, θ are polar co-ordinates, with origin O, in the plane of motion. (M.T.)

20. A uniform thin circular hoop of radius a spinning in a vertical plane about its centre with angular velocity ω is gently placed on a rough plane of inclination α equal to the angle of friction between the hoop and the plane so that the sense of rotation is that for which the slipping at the point of contact is down a line of greatest slope. Prove that the hoop will remain stationary for a time $a\omega/g \sin \alpha$ before descending with acceleration $\frac{1}{2}g \sin \alpha$. (C.)

21. A uniform sphere is placed on the highest generator of a rough cylinder, which is fixed with its axis horizontal. Prove that, if slightly displaced, the sphere will roll on the cylinder until the plane through the centre of the sphere and the axis of the cylinder makes with the vertical an angle α satisfying the equation

$$17\mu \cos \alpha - 2 \sin \alpha = 10\mu$$

where μ is the coefficient of friction. (C.)

22. A solid homogeneous cylinder is placed on a truck, which its axis perpendicular to the length of the truck, and the truck is suddenly started, and made to move horizontally parallel to its length with given uniform velocity. Prove that the cylinder will at first slide and afterwards roll on the truck, and find the time that elapses before it begins to roll. (C.)

23. A particle is placed on a rough plane lamina which is initially horizontal, and which is free to turn about a horizontal axis through its centre of mass. Show that the particle will begin to slip when the plane has turned through an angle

$$\tan^{-1} \{\mu Ma^2/(Ma^2 + 9mc^2)\}$$

μ being the coefficient of friction, $2a$ the length of the lamina perpendicular to the axis, c the distance of the particle from that axis, and M, m the masses of the lamina and the particle.

24. A board of mass M rests on a table, and a sphere of mass m is set in motion on the upper surface of the board so that the vertical plane containing the direction of projection of its centre passes through the centre of mass of the board; the velocity of projection is V and the sphere has an angular velocity Ω about a horizontal axis perpendicular to the plane of projection. The coefficient of friction between the board and the sphere is μ, and the friction between the board and the table is neglected. Prove that after a time

$$(V - a\Omega) \bigg/ \mu g\left(1 + \frac{a^2}{k^2} + \frac{m}{M}\right)$$

the motion will become uniform, and that the velocity of the board will then be

$$\frac{M}{m}(V - a\Omega) \bigg/ \left(1 + \frac{a^2}{k^2} + \frac{M}{m}\right) \qquad \text{(C.)}$$

25. A uniform circular cylinder of mass m and radius a rests on a rough horizontal plane with its axis horizontal, and is in smooth contact along a generator with a vertical face of a uniform rectangular block of height $2a$ and mass $\frac{1}{2}m$ which also rests on the plane. The cylinder is removed and gently replaced with a spin Ω in the sense tending to maintain contact between it and the block. If μ is the coefficient of friction at either contact with the plane, show that the cylinder slips on the plane for a time $3a\Omega/7\mu g$ and that its velocity and that of the block is then $a\Omega/7$.

Show also that the cylinder subsequently rolls on the plane and that the motion ceases after a further time $4a\Omega/7\mu g$. (L.U.)

26. A uniform rod is held inclined at 30° to the vertical with its lower end in contact with a rough horizontal plane ; if the rod is released from rest and falls under gravity, show that it will not immediately slip on the plane if the coefficient of friction exceeds $(27)^{1/2}/13$, and find in this case the initial reaction on the plane. (L.U.)

27. A motor-car is of total mass M ; the wheels are of radius a and the moments of inertia of the front and back pairs of wheels about their axles are I_1, I_2 respectively ; the load carried by the back wheels is W. The car is driven by a couple applied to the back wheels, and the coefficient of friction between the tyres and the ground is μ. Prove that the back wheels will not slip if the couple is less than

$$\frac{Ma^2 + I_1 + I_2}{Ma^2+I_1} . \mu Wa \qquad \text{(L.U.)}$$

28. A uniform solid sphere, initially rotating about a horizontal diameter with angular velocity Ω, is gently placed on a rough horizontal plane. The radius of the sphere is a, and the coefficient of friction between the sphere and the plane is μ. Prove that the sphere moves a distance $2\Omega^2a^2/49\mu g$ before slipping ceases, and find the angular velocity at that instant. (L.U.)

29. A uniform solid sphere is projected up a line of greatest slope of a plane inclined at an angle α to the horixontal. Initially the sphere has no angular velocity and its centre is moving with velocity V up the plane. If the coefficient of friction between the sphere and the plane is μ, where $\mu > \frac{2}{7}\tan\alpha$, prove that the sphere will begin to roll down the plane after a time $V/(g \sin \alpha)$. (M.T.)

30. A uniform circular hoop, of radius b and mass M, hangs over a horizontal rail whose cross-section is a circle of radius a. The hoop swings without slipping on the rod, in a vertical plane at right angles to the axis of the rod. If at time t the plane through the axis of the rod and the centre of the hoop makes an angle θ with the vertical, and if the maximum value of θ in the motion is $\alpha(< \pi/2)$, prove that

$$c\dot{\theta}^2 = g(\cos\theta - \cos\alpha)$$

where $c = b - a$.

Find the least value of the coefficient of friction which will suffice to prevent slipping. (M.T.)

31. A homogeneous cylinder of mass M and radius a is free to turn about its axis which is horizontal, and the particle of mass m is placed upon it close to the highest generator. Prove that, when the particle begins to slip, the angle θ which the radius through it makes with the vertical is given by the equation

$$\mu\{(M + 6m)\cos\theta - 4m\} = M\sin\theta$$

where μ is the coefficient of friction between the particle and the cylinder. (C.)

32. A hollow circular cylinder of radius b is made to rotate about its axis, which is horizontal, with variable angular velocity ω. A uniform solid circular cylinder of radius a ($< b$) rolls without slipping inside the hollow cylinder, the axes of the two cylinders being parallel and the plane through them making an angle θ with the downward vertical. Prove that at any time

$$3(b - a)\ddot{\theta} = b\dot{\omega} - 2g\sin\theta$$

If $\dot{\omega}$ is constant and equal to kg/b and the system starts from rest with the smaller cylinder in its lowest position, find the normal component R of the reaction between the two cylinders in any position. Show that, if $2k > 7$, both $\dot{\theta}$ and R increase steadily in the subsequent motion.

Show also that, if the smaller cylinder rolls completely round inside the larger cylinder for a value of $k < 2$, it is necessary that $\dot{\theta}$ should exist when $\theta = \pi - \sin^{-1}(k/2)$ and R should be positive when $\theta = \pi - \sin^{-1}(2k/7)$. (L.U.)

33. Two equal smooth uniform circular cylinders are placed on a smooth horizontal table with their axes parallel and their curved surfaces in contact. A third equal smooth cylinder is gently placed on these so that the axes of the three cylinders are parallel and their centres of gravity lie in the same vertical plane which is also normal to the axes. The system is then released from rest. Show that the initial vertical acceleration of the upper cylinder is $g/7$ and that subsequently contact between the upper cylinder and the two lower ones will cease when the upper cylinder has fallen a distance $a\sqrt{3} - 2a\zeta$, where a is the radius of a normal cross-section of the cylinders and ζ is the positive root of the equation

$$\zeta^3 + 3\zeta - \sqrt{3} = 0 \qquad \text{(L.U.)}$$

34. A wheel can turn freely about a horizontal axis ; and a fly of mass m is at rest at the lowest point. If the fly suddenly starts off to walk along the rim of the wheel with constant velocity V relative to the rim, show that he cannot ever get to the highest point of the rim unless V is at least as great as

$$2\sqrt{\{ga(ma^2/MK^2)(1 + ma^2/MK^2)\}}$$

where a is the radius of the wheel, and MK^2 its moment of inertia about its axis. (C.)

35. A homogeneous sphere, of mass M and radius a, rests on a horizontal plane in contact with a vertical wall ; and a second homogeneous sphere, of mass m and radius $b (< a)$, is placed in contact with it and the wall, the centres being in a vertical plane at right angles to the wall. Prove that, if all the surfaces are smooth, the spheres will separate when the line joining their centres makes with the horizontal an angle θ which is given by the equation

$$(a + b)\{(M - m)\sin^3\theta + 3m\sin\theta\} = 4m\sqrt{(ab)} \qquad \text{(C.)}$$

36. A smooth circular cylinder, of mass M and radius c, is at rest on a smooth horizontal plane ; and a heavy straight rail, of mass m and length $2a$, is placed so as to rest with its length in contact with the cylinder, and to have one extremity on the ground. Prove that the inclination of the rail to the vertical in the ensuing motion (supposed to be in a vertical plane) is given by the equation

$$\tfrac{1}{2}\dot{\theta}^2\left[(\tfrac{1}{3}+\sin^2\theta)\,a^2+\frac{M}{M+m}\left(\frac{c}{1-\sin\theta}-a\cos\theta\right)^2\right]=ga\,(\cos\alpha-\cos\theta)$$

where α is the initial value of θ. (C.)

37. Obtain the equation of motion of a particle of variable mass.

A ball of mass m is moving under gravity in a medium which deposits matter, previously at rest, on the ball at a uniform rate μ per second. Show that the equation to the trajectory, referred to horizontal and vertical axes through a point on itself, may be written

$$k^2uy = kx(g + kv) + gu(1 - e^{kx/u})$$

where u, v are the horizontal and vertical components of velocity at the origin and $k = 2\mu/m$. (L.U.)

38. A particle whose mass increases through condensation of moisture at a constant time-rate m_0/τ, where m_0 is the initial mass of the particle and τ is a constant, moves freely under gravity. The particle is projected from the origin of co-ordinates with a velocity whose horizontal and vertical resolutes are u and v respectively. Prove that the co-ordinates of the particle when its mass is m are given by

$$x = u\tau \log (m/m_0)$$

$$y = \tfrac{1}{4}g\tau^2\left(1 - \frac{m^2}{m_0{}^2}\right) + (v\tau + \tfrac{1}{2}g\tau^2)\log (m/m_0)$$

the y-axis being vertically upwards.

Show also that, if $v > 0$, the greatest height attained by the particle is

$$\tfrac{1}{2}(v\tau + \tfrac{1}{2}g\tau^2)\log\left(1 + \frac{2v}{g\tau}\right) - \tfrac{1}{2}v\tau \qquad \text{(L.U.)}$$

39. A particle moving along a straight line has mass m and speed v at time t. The particle ejects matter backwards at a constant rate λm_0 with a constant velocity u relative to the particle itself. Show that the equation of motion of the particle is

$$m\frac{dv}{dt} - \lambda m_0 u = F$$

where F is the external force acting on the particle.

From a rocket which is free to move vertically upwards, matter is ejected downwards with a constant relative velocity gT at a constant rate $2M/T$. Initially the rocket is at rest and has mass $2M$, half of which is available for ejection. Neglecting air resistance and variations in the gravitational attraction, show that the greatest upward speed is attained when the mass of the rocket is reduced to M, and determine this speed.

Show also that the rocket rises to a height

$$\tfrac{1}{2}gT^2\{1 - \log 2\}^2 \qquad \text{(L.U.)}$$

40. A uniform solid sphere of radius a is at rest on a rough horizontal table. A horizontal impulse is applied to the sphere, in a vertical plane through its centre, at a height $\frac{1}{2}a$ above the table. Show that when the sphere stops slipping its linear velocity is $\frac{5}{14}$ of its initial linear velocity, and find the ratio of its angular velocity at this instant to its initial angular velocity. At what fraction of the distance travelled to this instant did the angular velocity vanish ? (L.U.)

41. A uniform solid sphere is moving in any manner on a rough horizontal plane and coefficient of friction being μ. Find equations giving the rate of change of the velocity of slipping, and show that the direction of slipping is constant. Show also that while slipping takes place the path of the centre of the sphere is a parabola, and that slipping ceases after a time $2V_0/7\mu g$, where V_0 is the initial velocity of slipping. (L.U.)

42. A particle falls from rest under gravity through a stationary cloud. The mass of the particle increases by accretion from the cloud at a rate which at any time is mkv, where m is the mass and v the speed of the particle at that instant and k is a constant. Show that after the particle has fallen a distance x

$$kv^2 = g(1 - e^{-2kx})$$

and find the distance the particle has fallen after time t. (L.U.)

43. The outer surface of a uniform spherical shell of mass M is of radius a, and the inner (concentric) surface is of radius b. A particle of mass m moves inside the shell, while the shell rolls on a horizontal plane. The friction at the inner surface is neglected. Show that the angular distance θ of the particle from the vertical diameter at time t is given by the equation

$$\tfrac{1}{2}(\tfrac{7}{5}M + m\sin^2\theta)\dot{\theta}^2 = (\tfrac{7}{5}M + m)(\cos\theta - \cos\alpha)(g/b)$$

where α is the greatest value of θ. (C.)

44. A circular cylinder, of radius a and radius of gyration k, rolls inside a fixed horizontal cylinder of radius b. Prove that the plane through the axes moves like a simple pendulum of length

$$(b - a)(1 + k^2/a^2)$$

The second cylinder is free to turn about its axis ; the first cylinder is of mass m, and the moment of inertia of the second about its axis is MK^2. Prove that the length of the equivalent simple pendulum is $(b - a)(1 + n)/n$ where $n = a^2/k^2 + mb^2/MK^2$; prove also that the pressure between the cylinders is proportional to the depth of the point of contact below a plane which is at a depth $2nb\cos\alpha/(1 + 3n)$ below the fixed axis, where 2α is the angle of oscillation. (C.)

CHAPTER XI

MOTION OF A SYSTEM UNDER IMPULSES

11.1 The equations governing the change of motion

Consider a general system of *connected particles* of masses m_i at points P_i $(i = 1, 2, \ldots n)$. By connected we shall mean that each particle is joined to at least one other by (i) a taut light inelastic string, (ii) a light rigid rod, or (iii) adjacent contact. Our analysis will therefore be applicable to a *rigid body*. Now suppose that the mass m_i is struck an impulsive blow represented by the line vector $\boldsymbol{J}_i$ (v. 1.5 and 1.6). This is an *external impulse* applied to the system. It will generate, via the " connections," a series of *internal impulses* between the particles of the system : impulsive tensions in the inelastic strings, impulsive stresses in the light rigid rods, and impulsive reactions at the points of contact (which includes such things as hinges and joints). Denote the internal impulse on m_i due to its connection to m_j by $\boldsymbol{J}_{ij}$. The change in momentum of m_i, viz. $\Delta(m_i \boldsymbol{v}_i)$, is given by (v. 1.6)

$$\Delta(m_i \boldsymbol{v}_i) = \boldsymbol{J}_i + \sum_j \boldsymbol{J}_{ij} \quad . \quad . \quad . \quad (1)$$

Hence $$\sum_i \Delta(m_i \boldsymbol{v}_i) = \Delta \sum_i (m_i \boldsymbol{v}_i) = \sum_i \boldsymbol{J}_i \text{ as in 9.1(9).}$$

This can be written $$\Delta \boldsymbol{L} = M \Delta \bar{\boldsymbol{v}} = \boldsymbol{J} \quad . \quad . \quad . \quad . \quad (2)$$

$\boldsymbol{J}$ being the vector sum of the external impulses. Since these discontinuities in momentum occur without any change in the configuration, we have $\Delta \boldsymbol{r}_i = 0$ (all i) and so (1) gives

$$\Delta(\boldsymbol{r}_i \times m_i \boldsymbol{v}_i) = \boldsymbol{r}_i \times \boldsymbol{J}_i + \boldsymbol{r}_i \times \sum_j \boldsymbol{J}_{ij}$$

This gives

$$\Delta \boldsymbol{H}(O) = \sum_i \boldsymbol{r}_i \times \boldsymbol{J}_i = \boldsymbol{K}(O) \quad . \quad . \quad . \quad (3)$$

where $\boldsymbol{H}(O)$ is the angular momentum about a fixed origin O, and $\boldsymbol{K}(O)$ is the vector moment about O of the external impulses. By 9.2(4 we have $\Delta \boldsymbol{H}(G) = \Delta \boldsymbol{H}_r(G)$ so that (3) also gives

$$\Delta \boldsymbol{H}_r(G) = \boldsymbol{K}(G) \quad . \quad . \quad . \quad . \quad (4)$$

In particular, if the angular velocity changes from $\boldsymbol{\omega}_0$ to $\boldsymbol{\omega}_1$ under the action of the impulses $\boldsymbol{J}_i$, (4) (e.g.) gives

$$\mathscr{J}(G) \cdot (\boldsymbol{\omega}_1 - \boldsymbol{\omega}_0) = \boldsymbol{K}(G) \quad . \quad . \quad . \quad (5)$$

Furthermore, when motion takes place in a plane (5) will become

$$I(G)(\omega_1 - \omega_0) = K(G) \quad . \quad . \quad . \quad (6)$$

where $I(G)$ = the moment of inertia about a perpendicular axis through G

$K(G) = |\,\mathbf{K}(G)\,| = |\,K(G)\,\boldsymbol{k}\,|$, $\boldsymbol{k}$ being perpendicular to the plane of motion.

$\boldsymbol{\omega}_1, \boldsymbol{\omega}_0 = \omega_1\,\boldsymbol{k}, \omega_0\,\boldsymbol{k}$.

When *impulses occur by way of impact* between two bodies we have, in addition, *Newton's experimental law* 1.5(4), viz.,

(the velocity of separation of the points of contact along the common normal) = $e \times$ *(the velocity of approach of the points of contact along the common normal)* . . (7)

the number e being called the *coefficient of restitution.*

Example 1. Two uniform rods AB, BC, each of mass M, are freely hinged together at B, and initially the system is at rest with the rods in line on a smooth horizontal table. Motion is set up by a blow J at right angles to the rods at A. Find the initial velocity of B and the impulsive reaction at B.

Let $AB = 2a$, $BC = 2b$, and suppose the initial velocities of G_1, G_2 are u_1, u_2 as shown in Fig. 99. Let P represent the impulsive reaction

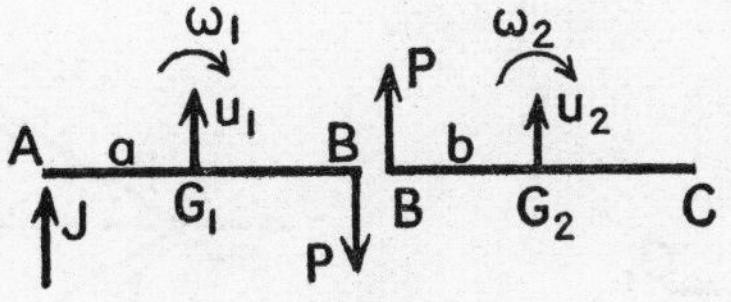

FIG. 99.

at B and suppose the initial angular velocities are ω_1 and ω_2 in the directions shown. Writing down the equations (2) and (6), we get

$$Mu_1 = J - P \quad . \quad . \quad . \quad . \quad (8)$$

$$Mu_2 = P \quad . \quad . \quad . \quad . \quad . \quad (9)$$

$$\tfrac{1}{3}Ma^2\omega_1 = a(J + P) . \quad . \quad . \quad . \quad (10)$$

$$\tfrac{1}{3}Mb^2\omega_2 = bP \quad . \quad . \quad . \quad . \quad . \quad (11)$$

Since B is a joint its velocity as a point of AB must equal its velocity as a point of BC. This gives an *equation of constraint,*

$$u_1 - a\omega_1 = u_2 + b\omega_2 . \quad . \quad . \quad . \quad (12)$$

(8), (9), (10), (11) give

$$Mu_2 = J - Mu_1\,; \quad Ma\omega_1 = 6J - 3Mu_1\,; \quad Mb\omega_2 = 3J - 3Mu_1$$

and substituting in (12), we get $4Mu_1 = 5J$, so that

$$Ma\omega_1 = \tfrac{9}{4}J\,; \quad Mu_2 = -\tfrac{1}{4}J\,; \quad Mb\omega_2 = -\tfrac{3}{4}J$$

Also (9) gives $P = -\frac{1}{4}J$ showing its direction to be opposite to that shown in Fig. 99. In this connection we can find the point (say) X about which AB commences to turn, the instantaneous centre. Let $G_1X = x$, so that the velocity of X is $u_1 - x\omega_1 = 0$. This gives $x = \frac{5a}{9}$.

Finally the initial velocity of B is $u_1 - a\omega_1 = -J/M$.

Example 2. The centre of percussion. A lamina can turn in its own plane about a fixed point O of itself : to find the point O_1 on the line OG which is such that when the lamina is struck an impulsive blow J at O_1 and perpendicular to OG there is zero impulsive reaction at O. Such a point O_1 is called a centre of percussion.

Let the lamina acquire an initial angular velocity ω about O, as shown in Fig. 100. Let $OG = h$ and let the moment of inertia about G, $I(G)$, be Mk^2. Hence we get, with $OO_1 = x$,

$$I(O)\omega = M(h^2 + k^2)\omega = xJ \quad . \quad . \quad . \quad (13)$$

We also have

$$M(h\omega) = J - P \quad . \quad . \quad . \quad . \quad (14)$$

for the motion of G. Writing $P = 0$, (13) and (14) give

$$h^2 + k^2 = xh$$

so that

$$x = \frac{h^2 + k^2}{h} \quad \text{(cf. 10.1, Ex. 2)}$$

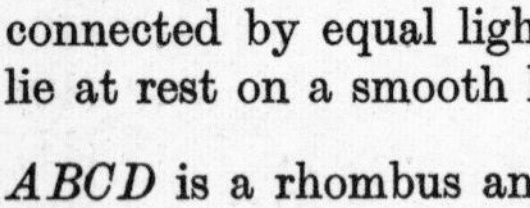

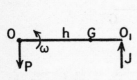

FIG. 100.

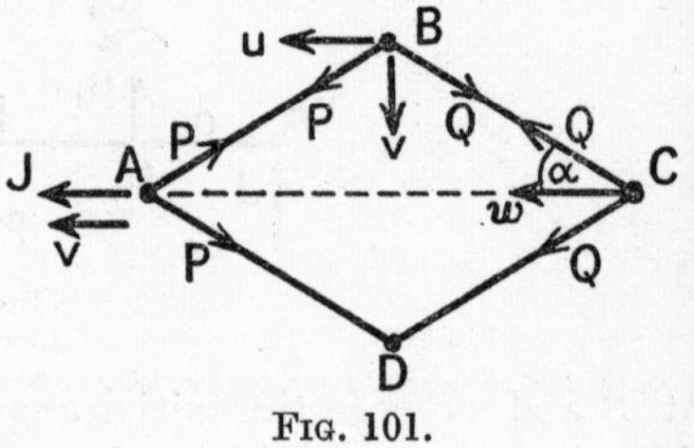

FIG. 101.

Example 3. Four equal particles A, B, C, D, each of mass m, are connected by equal light inextensible strings AB, BC, CD, DA and lie at rest on a smooth horizontal table with the strings taut, so that $ABCD$ is a rhombus and angle $BAD = 2\alpha\left(\alpha < \frac{\pi}{4}\right)$. The particle A is given a velocity V along the table in the direction of CA (produced). Find the initial velocity of the particle C and prove that the initial kinetic energy is

$$2mV^2/(1 + 2\sin^2\alpha) \qquad \text{(L.U.)}$$

Suppose the impulsive blow applied at A is J and that the impulsive tensions in the strings are P, Q, as shown in Fig. 101. The equations are

$$mV = J - 2P\cos\alpha \quad . \quad . \quad . \quad . \quad (15)$$
$$mu = (P - Q)\cos\alpha \quad . \quad . \quad . \quad . \quad (16)$$
$$mv = (P + Q)\sin\alpha \quad . \quad . \quad . \quad . \quad (17)$$
$$mw = 2Q\cos\alpha \quad . \quad . \quad . \quad . \quad (18)$$

plus two equations of constraint,

$$V\cos\alpha = u\cos\alpha + v\sin\alpha \quad . \quad . \quad . \quad (19)$$
$$w\cos\alpha = u\cos\alpha - v\sin\alpha \quad . \quad . \quad . \quad (20)$$

(18), (19), (20) give

$$w = 2u - V = \frac{2Q}{m}\cos\alpha \quad . \quad . \quad . \quad (21)$$

(16), (17), (18) give

$$v\cos\alpha - u\sin\alpha = w\sin\alpha \quad . \quad . \quad . \quad (22)$$

(20), (22) give

$$w = u(\cos^2\alpha - \sin^2\alpha)$$

so that (21) gives

$$w = \frac{V}{2\sec 2\alpha - 1} = \frac{V\cos 2\alpha}{1 + 2\sin^2\alpha} \quad . \quad . \quad (23)$$

Hence $u = \dfrac{V}{1 + 2\sin^2\alpha}$, $v = \dfrac{V\sin 2\alpha}{1 + 2\sin^2\alpha}$ giving a kinetic energy $T = \frac{1}{2}m.\{V^2 + 2(u^2 + v^2) + w^2\}$, which reduces to the given expression.

Example 4. Two smooth vertical walls are at a distance a apart. A particle is projected from the foot of one wall with a velocity V at an elevation α, in a vertical plane perpendicular to the walls. It strikes the walls alternately, the second wall n times and then returns to the point of projection. Show that

$$e^{2n-1}(1 - e)V^2\sin 2\alpha = ga(1 - e^{2n}),$$

where e is the coefficient of restitution between the particle and each wall.

Show also that the direction of motion of the particle on reaching the point of projection is inclined at $\tan^{-1}(e^{1-2n}\tan\alpha)$ to the horizontal. (L.U.)

Since the walls are smooth the vertical velocity at each impact suffers no discontinuity. Hence the vertical motion is free motion under gravity, giving a *time of flight* t_0, where

$$t_0 = \frac{2V\sin\alpha}{g} \quad . \quad . \quad . \quad . \quad (24)$$

Before the first collision the horizontal velocity is $u = V\cos\alpha$. At the first collision this changes to u_1 in the reversed direction where, by (7), $u_1 = eu$. Since the horizontal velocity otherwise remains constant we get, after the rth collision, $u_r = eu_{r-1}$. The total number of impacts being $2n - 1$, we get

$$t_0 = \frac{a}{u} + \frac{a}{u_1} + \ldots + \frac{a}{u_{2n-1}}$$
$$= \frac{a}{u}\{1 + e^{-1} + e^{-2} + \ldots + e^{-(2n-1)}\}$$
$$= \frac{a}{u}\frac{(1 - e^{-2n})}{1 - e^{-1}} = \frac{a}{e^{2n-1}.V\cos\alpha}\cdot\frac{(e^{2n} - 1)}{(e - 1)}$$

Using (24) we get

$$e^{2n-1}(1 - e)V^2 \sin 2\alpha = ga(1 - e^{2n}) \qquad \text{Q.E.D.}$$

On regaining the point of projection the downward vertical velocity is $V \sin \alpha$ and the horizontal velocity is u_{2n-1}. Hence the velocity is inclined at θ to the horizontal where

$$\tan\theta = \frac{V\sin\alpha}{u_{2n-1}} = \frac{V\sin\alpha}{e^{2n-1}\,V\cos\alpha} = e^{1-2n}.\tan\alpha \qquad \text{Q.E.D.}$$

Example 5. Surmounting a step. The centre of a uniform sphere of radius a, which rolls without slipping on a rough horizontal table, is moving in a straight line with constant velocity U. The sphere strikes a circular cylinder of radius $\frac{1}{2}a$ which lies on, and is fixed to, the table; the axis of the cylinder is perpendicular to the direction of U. If there is no rebound at impact, and no slipping at or after impact, prove that the sphere will surmount the cylinder if $121U^2 > 630\,ga$. (L.U.)

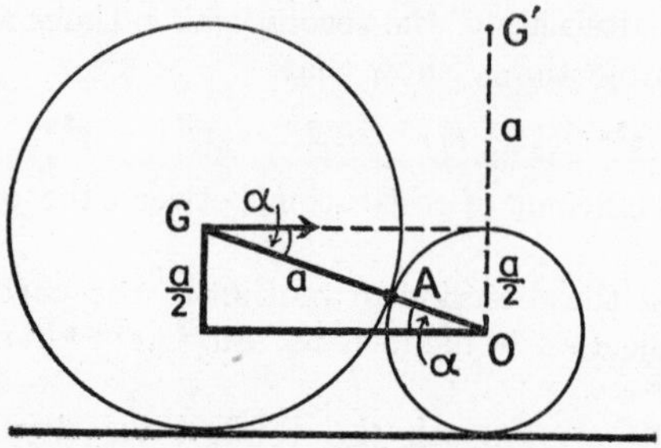

FIG. 102.

Fig. 102 shows the position on impact, at A. Since the impulsive reaction acts at A we have $K(A) = 0$ so that (3) gives

$$H(A) = \text{a constant} \qquad . \quad . \quad . \quad (25)$$

Before impact the sphere has angular velocity ω where $U = a\omega$. Hence, by 9.4(11), the angular momentum about A is

$$H_0(A) = MUa \sin \alpha + \tfrac{2}{5}Ma^2\left(\frac{U}{a}\right)$$
$$= \tfrac{11}{15}MUa, \quad \text{since } \sin \alpha = \tfrac{1}{3}.$$

Let the sphere begin to turn about A with angular velocity Ω immediately after impact. Then

$$H_1(A) = I(A)\Omega = \tfrac{7}{5}Ma^2\Omega$$

Then (25) gives $$\tfrac{7}{5}a\Omega = \tfrac{11}{15}U \quad . \quad . \quad . \quad . \quad (26)$$

The sphere will surmount the cylinder if it possesses enough energy for G to rise to G', i.e. through a height a. This requires

$$\tfrac{1}{2}M \,.\, \tfrac{7}{5}a^2 \,.\, \Omega^2 > Mga$$

Using (26), we get $$121U^2 > 630ga \qquad \text{Q.E.D.}$$

Example 6. A uniform square plate $OXAY$ is suspended freely from the corner O, and when at rest is struck at X in a direction normal to the plate. With OX, OY as axes of reference, show that it begins to turn about the line $3y = 4x$. (L.U.)

Take unit vectors $\boldsymbol{i}$, $\boldsymbol{j}$ along OX, OY as shown in Fig. 103, and let $\boldsymbol{k} = \boldsymbol{i} \times \boldsymbol{j}$. The impulse at X can be written $\boldsymbol{J} = J\,\boldsymbol{k}$ and suppose the angular velocity is $\boldsymbol{\omega} = \omega_1\,\boldsymbol{i} + \omega_2\,\boldsymbol{j} + \omega_3\,\boldsymbol{k}$. We now have

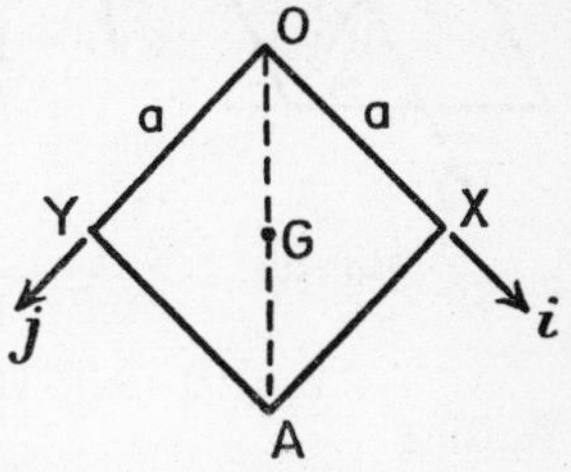

FIG. 103.

$$\boldsymbol{H}(O) = \mathscr{I}(O)\,.\,\boldsymbol{\omega} = a\,\boldsymbol{i} \times J\,\boldsymbol{k} \,. \quad (27)$$

where

$$\mathscr{I}(O) = \begin{pmatrix} A & -H & 0 \\ -H & A & 0 \\ 0 & 0 & 2A \end{pmatrix} = A\,\boldsymbol{ii} + A\,\boldsymbol{jj} + 2A\,\boldsymbol{kk} - H\,\boldsymbol{ij} - H\,\boldsymbol{ji}$$

Hence (27) gives $$\boldsymbol{k}\,.\,\mathscr{I}(O)\,.\,\boldsymbol{\omega} = 0 \quad . \quad . \quad . \quad . \quad (28)$$

and $$\boldsymbol{i}\,.\,\mathscr{I}(O)\,.\,\boldsymbol{\omega} = 0 \quad . \quad . \quad . \quad . \quad (29)$$

(28) is simply $$2A\omega_3 = 0$$

whilst (29) gives $$A\omega_1 - H\omega_2 = 0 \quad . \quad . \quad . \quad . \quad (30)$$

Now

$$A = \rho \int_0^a \!\! \int_0^a y^2\, dx\, dy = M\frac{a^2}{3} \quad \text{and} \quad H = \int_0^a \!\! \int_0^a \rho xy\, dx\, dy = M\frac{a^2}{4}$$

Hence (30) becomes $$4\omega_1 + 3\omega_2 = 0$$

Since $\boldsymbol{\omega}$ defines the line about which the lamina turns, this line has equation $$4x - 3y = 0 \qquad \text{Q.E.D.}$$

Example 7. A uniform square lamina, of mass M and side $2a$, is free to rotate about its centre O, which is fixed. When the lamina is horizontal and rotating with angular velocity Ω about a vertical axis, a particle of mass m, falling vertically, strikes the lamina and adheres to it at a point distant b from 0. If u is the speed of the particle immediately before impact, show that, after impact, the particle begins to move in a direction inclined at an angle $\tan^{-1}\dfrac{2b\lambda\Omega}{(\lambda^2-1)u}$ to the downward drawn vertical, where $\lambda = \dfrac{3mb^2}{Ma^2}+1$. Show that the impulsive reaction at O is inclined at an angle $\tan^{-1}\dfrac{2b\lambda\Omega}{(\lambda+1)u}$ to the upwards drawn vertical. (L.U.)

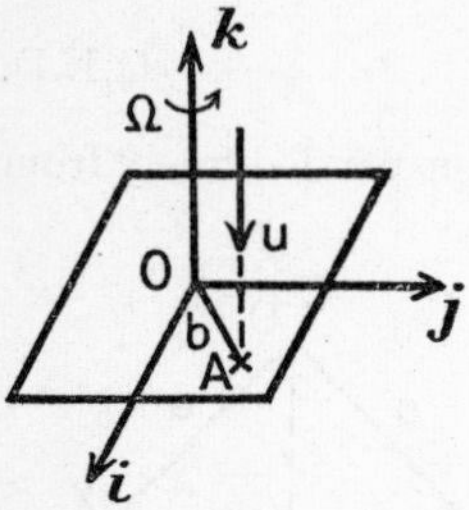

FIG. 104.

Take principal axes $\boldsymbol{i}$, $\boldsymbol{j}$, $\boldsymbol{k}$ at 0, as shown in Fig. 104, and let the particle strike the lamina at A where $\overline{OA} = \boldsymbol{r} = x\,\boldsymbol{i} + y\,\boldsymbol{j}$ and $x^2+y^2=b^2$. The particle will experience an impulse $\boldsymbol{J}$ (say) on impact and its velocity will change from $-u\,\boldsymbol{k}$ to $\boldsymbol{v}$. The lamina's angular velocity will change from $\Omega\,\boldsymbol{k}$ to $\boldsymbol{\omega}$. The equations will be

$$m(\boldsymbol{v}+u\,\boldsymbol{k}) = \boldsymbol{J} \quad . \quad . \quad (31)$$

and $$\mathscr{I}(O).(\boldsymbol{\omega}-\Omega\,\boldsymbol{k}) = \boldsymbol{r}\times -\boldsymbol{J} \quad . \quad (32)$$

Eliminating $\boldsymbol{J}$ and writing $\boldsymbol{v} = \boldsymbol{\omega}\times\boldsymbol{r}$, we get

$$\mathscr{I}(O).(\boldsymbol{\omega}-\Omega\,\boldsymbol{k}) + m\,\boldsymbol{r}\times(\boldsymbol{\omega}\times\boldsymbol{r}+u\,\boldsymbol{k}) = \boldsymbol{0} \quad . \quad (33)$$

Writing

$$\mathscr{I}(O) = M\frac{a^2}{3}\begin{pmatrix}1 & 0 & 0\\0 & 1 & 0\\0 & 0 & 2\end{pmatrix} \quad \text{and} \quad \boldsymbol{r}\times(\boldsymbol{\omega}\times\boldsymbol{r}) = r^2\boldsymbol{\omega}-(\boldsymbol{r}.\boldsymbol{\omega})\boldsymbol{r},$$

(33) becomes

$$M\frac{a^2}{3}\{\omega_1\,\boldsymbol{i}+\omega_2\,\boldsymbol{j}+2(\omega_3-\Omega)\boldsymbol{k}\} + mb^2\,\boldsymbol{\omega} - m(x\omega_1+y\omega_2)(x\,\boldsymbol{i}+y\,\boldsymbol{j})$$
$$+\,mu(y\,\boldsymbol{i}-x\,\boldsymbol{j}) = \boldsymbol{0} \quad . \quad . \quad . \quad (34)$$

But (33) also gives $\quad \boldsymbol{r}.\mathscr{I}(O).(\boldsymbol{\omega}-\Omega\,\boldsymbol{k}) = 0$

that is,
$$(x \quad y \quad 0)\begin{pmatrix}1 & 0 & 0\\0 & 1 & 0\\0 & 0 & 2\end{pmatrix}\begin{pmatrix}\omega_1\\ \omega_2\\ \omega_3-\Omega\end{pmatrix} = 0$$

This gives the equation

$$x\omega_1 + y\omega_2 = 0 \quad . \quad . \quad . \quad . \quad (35)$$

Hence (34) and (35) give

$$\left(M\frac{a^2}{3}+mb^2\right)\omega_1 = -\,muy$$
$$\left(M\frac{a^2}{3}+mb^2\right)\omega_2 = mux$$
$$2M\frac{a^2}{3}(\omega_3-\Omega) = -\,mb^2\omega_3$$

These can be written

$$\lambda\omega_1 = -(\lambda - 1)\frac{uy}{b^2}\ ; \quad \lambda\omega_2 = (\lambda - 1)\frac{ux}{b^2}\ ; \quad (\lambda + 1)\omega_3 = 2\Omega \qquad (36)$$

If the angle between $\boldsymbol{v}$ and $-\boldsymbol{k}$ is α it is clear that

$$\tan\alpha = \frac{|\boldsymbol{v} \times (-\boldsymbol{k})|}{\boldsymbol{v}.(-\boldsymbol{k})} \quad . \quad . \quad . \quad (37)$$

But $\boldsymbol{v} = \boldsymbol{\omega} \times \boldsymbol{r}$, and so $\boldsymbol{v} \times (-\boldsymbol{k}) = -\omega_3 \boldsymbol{r}$ and $\boldsymbol{v}.(-\boldsymbol{k}) = x\omega_2 - y\omega_1$ $= (\lambda - 1)\frac{u}{\lambda}$ by (36). Hence (37) gives

$$\tan\alpha = \frac{2b\lambda\Omega}{(\lambda^2 - 1)u} \qquad \text{Q.E.D.}$$

Let the impulsive reaction at O be $\boldsymbol{P}$. The centre of mass, G, of the whole system is at $\bar{\boldsymbol{r}} = \dfrac{m}{M+m}\boldsymbol{r}$, and if it begins to move with velocity $\bar{\boldsymbol{v}}$, we get

$$\begin{aligned}\boldsymbol{P} &= (M + m)\bar{\boldsymbol{v}} - mu(-\boldsymbol{k}) \\ &= m\,\boldsymbol{v} + mu\,\boldsymbol{k}, \quad \boldsymbol{v} = \boldsymbol{\omega} \times \boldsymbol{r} \quad . \quad . \quad . \quad (38)\end{aligned}$$

If $\boldsymbol{P}$ is inclined at β to $\boldsymbol{k}$ we get, as before

$$\tan\beta = \frac{|\boldsymbol{P} \times \boldsymbol{k}|}{\boldsymbol{P}.\boldsymbol{k}} \quad . \quad . \quad . \quad . \quad (39)$$

(38) gives $\quad |\boldsymbol{P} \times \boldsymbol{k}| = |-m\omega_3 \boldsymbol{r}| = m\omega_3 b$

and $\quad \boldsymbol{P}.\boldsymbol{k} = m(y\omega_1 - x\omega_2) + mu = m\frac{u}{\lambda}$

Hence (36) and (39) give $\tan\beta = \dfrac{2b\lambda\Omega}{(\lambda + 1)u}$ Q.E.D.

11.2 Some relevant theorems

Since equations 11.1(2) and 11.1(3) involve only the externally applied impulses and since the internal impulses are equal and opposite, forming a nul system, we can apply the formalism of the *Principle of Virtual Work* to the system of line vectors $\{\Delta m_i \boldsymbol{v}_i\ ;\ -\boldsymbol{J}_i\}$: the total internal impulses will do zero " work " in a general displacement. Of course, the " work done " has dimension *energy* × *time*, since an impulse has dimension *force* × *time* : we use the word " work ' in this section with this understanding.

If the particle m_i at $\boldsymbol{r}_i$ changes its velocity from $\boldsymbol{v}_i$ to $\boldsymbol{v}_i'$ under the action of the applied impulses we can therefore write

$$\sum_i m_i(\boldsymbol{v}_i' - \boldsymbol{v}_i).d\boldsymbol{r}_i = \sum_i \boldsymbol{J}_i.d\boldsymbol{r}_i \quad . \quad . \quad . \quad (1)$$

where the $d\boldsymbol{r}_i$ represent a possible displacement, compatible with the constraints of the system.

Theorem I. *The change of kinetic energy of the system is*

$$T' - T = \sum_i \boldsymbol{J}_i . \left(\frac{\boldsymbol{v}_i + \boldsymbol{v}_i'}{2}\right)$$

Proof: A set of possible displacements in (1) is given by $d\boldsymbol{r}_i = \boldsymbol{v}_i\, dt$; similarly by $d\boldsymbol{r}_i = \boldsymbol{v}_i'\, dt$. These are the actual displacements just before and just after the impulses $\boldsymbol{J}_i$ are applied. Substituting in (1) and adding, we get

$$\sum m_i(\boldsymbol{v}_i'^2 - \boldsymbol{v}_i^2) = \sum \boldsymbol{J}_i . (\boldsymbol{v}_i + \boldsymbol{v}_i') \qquad \text{Q.E.D.}$$

This theorem may be illustrated by Example 3 of 11.1.

In that problem there is only one applied impulse, viz. J. The kinetic energy generated is therefore $\frac{1}{2}JV$. Now equations 11.1(15), 11.1(16) and 11.1(18) give

$$mV = J - 2mu - mw$$

Hence

$$J = \frac{mV}{1 + 2\sin^2 a}\{1 + 2\sin^2 a + 2 + \cos 2a\}$$

$$= \frac{4mV}{1 + 2\sin^2 a}$$

giving the kinetic energy, $\dfrac{2mV^2}{1 + 2\sin^2 a}$

Theorem II (Bertrand's theorem). *For a given set of applied impulses $\{\boldsymbol{J}_i\}$ the kinetic energy after their application is greater than it would be if the same impulses $\{\boldsymbol{J}_i\}$ acted but in conjunction with additional constraints (of the kind which do no work).*

Proof: Let the additional constraints result in the particle m_i acquiring a velocity $\boldsymbol{v}_i''$ after the impulses are applied, as distinct from $\boldsymbol{v}_i'$ without these constraints. Let the kinetic energy after the impulses act be T'' and T' for the cases of "additional constraints" and "without additional constraints" respectively. Now in (1) we can write $d\boldsymbol{r}_i = \boldsymbol{v}_i''\, dt$ in both sets of circumstances. Hence we get

$$\sum m_i(\boldsymbol{v}_i' - \boldsymbol{v}_i).\boldsymbol{v}_i'' = \sum \boldsymbol{J}_i.\boldsymbol{v}_i''$$

and
$$\sum m_i(\boldsymbol{v}_i'' - \boldsymbol{v}_i).\boldsymbol{v}_i'' = \sum \boldsymbol{J}_i.\boldsymbol{v}_i''$$

Hence
$$\sum m_i \boldsymbol{v}_i''^2 = \sum m_i \boldsymbol{v}_i'.\boldsymbol{v}_i''$$

Therefore
$$T' - T'' = \tfrac{1}{2}\sum m_i \boldsymbol{v}_i'^2 - \tfrac{1}{2}\sum m_i \boldsymbol{v}_i''^2$$
$$= \tfrac{1}{2}\sum m_i(\boldsymbol{v}_i' - \boldsymbol{v}_i'')^2 > 0 \qquad \text{Q.E.D.}$$

Theorem III (Kelvin's theorem). *If a system is set in motion by impulses in such a way that the points of application move with prescribed velocities then the kinetic energy of the system is less than that acquired in any other kinematically possible motion with the relevant prescribed velocities.*

Proof: Let the actual velocities be $\boldsymbol{v}_i'$ and let $\boldsymbol{v}_i''$ be kinematically possible, subject to the points of application having prescribed velocities. Then in (1) we have $\boldsymbol{v}_i = \boldsymbol{0}$ (the system is initially at rest), and we can write $d\boldsymbol{r}_i = \boldsymbol{v}_i'\,dt$ or, equally well, $d\boldsymbol{r}_i = \boldsymbol{v}_i''\,dt$. Since the points of application have prescribed velocities those $\boldsymbol{v}_i'$ which occur in $\sum \boldsymbol{J}_i.\boldsymbol{v}_i'$ must equal the corresponding $\boldsymbol{v}_i''$ which occur in $\sum \boldsymbol{J}_i.\boldsymbol{v}_i''$. Hence (1) gives

$$\begin{aligned}\sum m_i \boldsymbol{v}_i'.\boldsymbol{v}_i' &= \sum \boldsymbol{J}_i.\boldsymbol{v}_i' \\ &= \sum \boldsymbol{J}_i.\boldsymbol{v}_i'' \\ &= \sum m_i \boldsymbol{v}_i'.\boldsymbol{v}_i'' \\ &= \tfrac{1}{2}\sum m_i\{\boldsymbol{v}_i'^2 + \boldsymbol{v}_i''^2 - (\boldsymbol{v}_i' - \boldsymbol{v}_i'')^2\}\end{aligned}$$

Hence $$T'' - T' = \tfrac{1}{2}\sum m_i(\boldsymbol{v}_i' - \boldsymbol{v}_i'')^2 > 0 \qquad \text{Q.E.D.}$$

This theorem means that the kinetic energy generated by impulses, which are such that the points of application are to have prescribed velocities, must be a *minimum*. When the conditions of Bertrand's theorem apply then, in contrast, we can find the motion by stating that the kinetic energy is to be a *maximum*.

Example 1. Ox_1, Ox_2, Ox_3 are rectangular axes at the centre O of a uniform cube of mass M and side $2a$, the axes being parallel to the sides of the cube. The cube is set in motion from rest by an impulse applied at the point (a, a, a), the impulse being such that the initial velocity of this point is (u_1, u_2, u_3). Show that the kinetic energy is

$$\frac{M}{22}\{5(u_1^2 + u_2^2 + u_3^2) + 6(u_2u_3 + u_3u_1 + u_1u_2)\} \qquad \text{(M.T.)}$$

Let the centre of mass, O, acquire a velocity $\bar{\boldsymbol{v}}$ and let the cube acquire an angular velocity $\boldsymbol{\omega}$. Then the kinetic energy will be

$$T = \tfrac{1}{2}M\,\bar{\boldsymbol{v}}^2 + \tfrac{1}{2}\boldsymbol{\omega}.\mathscr{I}(O).\boldsymbol{\omega}$$

where $\mathscr{I}(O) = 2M\dfrac{a^2}{3}\mathscr{I}$. Since $\bar{\boldsymbol{v}} = \boldsymbol{u} - a\,\boldsymbol{\omega} \times (\boldsymbol{i} + \boldsymbol{j} + \boldsymbol{k})$, $\boldsymbol{i}, \boldsymbol{j}, \boldsymbol{k}$ being taken along Ox_1, Ox_2, Ox_3 respectively, we get

$$\frac{2T}{M} = (u_1^2 + u_2^2 + u_3^2) - 2a\{\omega_1(u_3 - u_2) + \omega_2(u_1 - u_3) + \omega_3(u_2 - u_1)\}$$

$$+ 3a^2(\omega_1^2 + \omega_2^2 + \omega_3^2) - a^2(\omega_1 + \omega_2 + \omega_3)^2 + \frac{2a^2}{3}(\omega_1^2 + \omega_2^2 + \omega_3^2)$$

The values of ω_1, ω_2, ω_3 must be chosen to make $\dfrac{2T}{M} = T_1$ a minimum, by Kelvin's theorem. Hence we get

$$\frac{\partial T_1}{\partial \omega_1} = -2a(u_3 - u_2) + \frac{22}{3}a^2\omega_1 - 2a^2(\omega_1 + \omega_2 + \omega_3) = 0 \qquad (2)$$

$$\frac{\partial T_1}{\partial \omega_2} = -2a(u_1 - u_3) + \frac{22}{3}a^2\omega_2 - 2a^2(\omega_1 + \omega_2 + \omega_3) = 0 \qquad (3)$$

$$\frac{\partial T_1}{\partial \omega_3} = -2a(u_2 - u_1) + \frac{22}{3}a^2\omega_3 - 2a^2(\omega_1 + \omega_2 + \omega_3) = 0 \quad . \quad (4)$$

Adding these gives $\omega_1 + \omega_2 + \omega_3 = 0$, whence

$$a\omega_1 = \frac{3}{11}(u_3 - u_2)\,; \quad a\omega_2 = \frac{3}{11}(u_1 - u_3)\,; \quad a\omega_3 = \frac{3}{11}(u_2 - u_1) \quad (5)$$

These are equivalent to

$$a\,\boldsymbol{\omega} = \frac{3}{11}(\boldsymbol{i} + \boldsymbol{j} + \boldsymbol{k}) \times \boldsymbol{u}$$

Substituting from (5) we get

$$\frac{2T}{M} = (u_1^2 + u_2^2 + u_3^2) - \left(\frac{6}{11} - \frac{3}{11}\right)\{(u_3 - u_2)^2 + (u_1 - u_3)^2 + (u_2 - u_1)^2\}$$

$$= \frac{1}{11}\{5(u_1^2 + u_2^2 + u_3^2) + 6(u_2u_3 + u_3u_1 + u_1u_2)\} \qquad \text{Q.E.D.}$$

If we are given the impulse $\boldsymbol{J} = (J_1\boldsymbol{i} + J_2\boldsymbol{j} + J_3\boldsymbol{k})$ at the point (a, a, a) we can find the kinetic energy by applying Bertrand's theorem. Thus, additional constraints may be imposed by specifying linear relations between the angular velocity components, (e.g.) making the cube turn about a smooth pin which threads it. Now the kinetic energy must be a maximum, as ω_1, ω_2, ω_3 vary. Hence (2), (3), (4) are applicable, together with the equation

$$M\,\bar{\boldsymbol{v}} = M\,\boldsymbol{u} - Ma\,\boldsymbol{\omega} \times (\boldsymbol{i} + \boldsymbol{j} + \boldsymbol{k}) = \boldsymbol{J}$$

This gives, with (5),

$$\frac{1}{M}\boldsymbol{J} = \boldsymbol{u} + \frac{3}{11}\boldsymbol{e} \times (\boldsymbol{e} \times \boldsymbol{u}), \quad \boldsymbol{e} = \boldsymbol{i} + \boldsymbol{j} + \boldsymbol{k}$$

$$= \boldsymbol{u} + \frac{3}{11}\{(\boldsymbol{e}.\boldsymbol{u})\boldsymbol{e} - 3\boldsymbol{u}\}$$

so that $$\boldsymbol{J} = \frac{M}{11}\{5\boldsymbol{u} + 3(u_1 + u_2 + u_3)(\boldsymbol{i} + \boldsymbol{j} + \boldsymbol{k})\}$$

Hence $$5u_r = 11J_r - \frac{33}{14}(J_1 + J_2 + J_3) \quad (r = 1, 2, 3)$$

and T follows as a function of (J_1, J_2, J_3).

Theorem IV (Carnot's theorem). *When smooth constraints are suddenly introduced into a self-contained system the kinetic energy is decreased by an amount equal to the quantity* $\frac{1}{2}\sum m_i(\boldsymbol{v}_i' - \boldsymbol{v}_i)^2$.

Proof: Since $\boldsymbol{J}_i = \boldsymbol{0}$, all i, we can write $d\boldsymbol{r}_i = \boldsymbol{v}_i'\,dt$ in (1), to give

$$\sum m_i(\boldsymbol{v}_i' - \boldsymbol{v}_i).\boldsymbol{v}_i' = 0$$

Hence
$$T - T' = \tfrac{1}{2}\sum m_i(\boldsymbol{v}_i^2 - \boldsymbol{v}_i'^2)$$
$$= \tfrac{1}{2}\sum m_i(\boldsymbol{v}_i^2 - 2\boldsymbol{v}_i.\boldsymbol{v}_i' + \boldsymbol{v}_i'^2)$$
$$= \tfrac{1}{2}\sum m_i(\boldsymbol{v}_i' - \boldsymbol{v}_i)^2 \qquad \text{Q.E.D.}$$

Exercise XI

1. Two equal uniform rods, AB, BC, each of mass M, are freely jointed at B and are on a smooth horizontal table, so that ABC is a straight line; the rods move horizontally with velocity U perpendicular to ABC. The rod AB impinges at its mid-point on an inelastic stop. Show that the loss of kinetic energy is $4MU^2/7$. (M.T.)

2. Two uniform rods of the same length and each of mass m are freely hinged and lie in the same straight line on a smooth horizontal table. The free end of one rod is suddenly jerked into motion with velocity v at right angles to its length. Prove that the kinetic energy of the resulting motion of the system is $\frac{1}{7}mv^2$.

Show also that, if the rods had been rigidly joined, the kinetic energy produced would have been $\frac{1}{4}mv^2$. (M.T.)

3. Two equal uniform rods AB and BC, each of mass M and length $2a$, are smoothly hinged together at B and hang freely from A. A horizontal impulse J is applied at C. Find the velocities with which B and C start to move. (M.T.)

4. (i) A uniform rod, of length $2a$, moving with speed u perpendicularly to its length without rotation, receives a blow in the same direction at one end, which increases the speed of the centre by half its value. Find the angular velocity of the rod after the blow, and show that its kinetic energy has been trebled.

(ii) Two uniform rods AB, BC of equal line density and of lengths a and $2a$ respectively are smoothly jointed at B and placed in line; the rod BC is struck at P by a blow at right angles to BC, P lying between C and G, the mid-point of BC. If, after the blow, the angular velocities of AB and BC are equal in magnitude and of the same sense, prove the distance GP is $a/7$. (L.U.)

5. A uniform straight rigid rod AB (M, $2a$, centre G) has a small ring (m) attached to A, the ring being free to slide along a smooth horizontal wire. A particle (m) is attached to B. The system is hanging at rest under g when a horizontal blow of magnitude P is applied to B parallel to the wire. Show that the velocity imparted to B is

$$\frac{4P(M + 3m)}{(M + 2m)(M + 6m)}$$

and find the kenitic energy generated.

Show that, if the rod just reaches the horizontal position in the subsequent motion, $P^2 = (2/3)(M + 2m)(M + 6m)ga$. (L.U.)

6. n equal uniform rods A_0A_1, A_1A_2, . . . $A_{n-1}A_n$, each of mass m are freely jointed and lie on a smooth horizontal plane in a straight line. The system can turn about A_0 (fixed) and an impulse P is applied at A_n perpendicular to the line of the rods. If the velocity of A_s is v_s prove

$$v_{s+2} + 4v_{s+1} + v_s = 0 \quad (s = 0, 1, 2, \ldots n - 2)$$

If $n = 3$ prove that

$$mv_3 = 45P/13. \quad \text{(L.U.)}$$

7. Four particles of equal masses are tied at equal intervals to a thread, and the system is placed on a smooth table so as to form part of a regular polygon whose angles are each $\pi - \alpha$. Prove that, if an impulse is applied to one of the end particles in the direction of the thread attached to it, the kinetic energy generated is greater than it would be if the particles were constrained to move in a circular groove, and the impulse were applied tangentially, in the ratio $\cos^2 \alpha + 4 \sin^2 \alpha : \cos^2 \alpha + 2 \sin^2 \alpha$. (C.)

8. Two equal rigid rods AB, BC of negligible masses carry four equal particles, attached at A, C and at the middle points of the rods. The rods being freely hinged at B, and laid out straight, the end A is struck with an impulse at right angles to the rods. Prove that the magnitudes of the velocities of the particles are in the ratios $9 : 2 : 2 : 1$. (C.)

9. Three particles of equal mass are attached at equal intervals to a rigid rod of negligible mass, and, the system being at rest, one of the extreme particles is struck by a blow at right angles to the rod. Prove that the kinetic energy imparted to the system, when the other extreme particle is fixed, and the rod turns about it, is less than it would be if the system were free in the ratio $24 : 25$. (C.)

10. Points A_r, B_r have co-ordinates $(2ra, a)$ and $(2ra, -a)$ respectively $(r = 0, 1, 2, \ldots n)$. A framework is constructed of n rods $A_{r-1}B_r$ and n rods $B_{r-1}A_r$ $(r = 1, 2, \ldots n)$, each uniform and of mass m, the rods being smoothly jointed at their cross-over points $C_r\{(2r - 1)a, 0\}$, $r = 1, 2, \ldots n)$. Impulses $(I, -J)$ and (I, J) are applied to the framework at A_0 and B_0 respectively when it is at rest. If A_0 and B_0 have zero x-resolutes of velocity immediately afterwards, find I in terms of J and n, and show that the x-resolutes of velocity of A_n and B_n are each equal to $3J/m(4n^2 + 1)$. (L.U.)

11. Three particles A, B, C of equal mass are placed on a smooth plane inclined at an angle α to the horizontal, and B, C are connected with A by threads of length $h \sec \alpha$ which make equal angles α with the line of greatest slope through A on opposite sides of it, the line BC being below the level of A. If A is struck by a blow along the line of greatest slope, so as to start to move down this line with velocity V, find when the threads become tight, and prove that the velocity of A immediately afterwards is

$$V/(3 - 2 \sin^2 \alpha) + 2gh \sin \alpha / V \qquad \text{(C.)}$$

12. A particle of mass M is projected with velocity V in a direction making an angle θ with the horizontal, being attached to the point of projection by an inextensible thread of length $V^2 \operatorname{cosec}^2 \theta / 2g$. Prove that impulsive tension when the thread becomes tight is $MV \cos^2 \theta \operatorname{cosec} \theta$, and that, immediately after the change of motion, the tension is $Mg(1 - 2 \sin^4 \theta)$. (C.)

13. Four equal particles are attached at the corners of a rhombus formed of four threads each of length a; and the system is moving on a horizontal plane with uniform velocity u in the direction of the longer diagonal AC, when the end A of that diagonal is suddenly fixed. Prove that the sides of the rhombus begin to turn with angular velocity $2u \sin \alpha/a\ (1 + 2 \sin^2 \alpha)$, where 2α is the acute angle of the rhombus. (C.)

14. A ball is projected with velocity V from a point of a plane inclined at an angle α to the horizontal; the direction of projection is at right angles to the plane, and the coefficient of restitution between the ball and the plane is e. Prove that, before ceasing to bound, it will have described a length $2V^2 \sin \alpha/g \cos^2 \alpha\ (1 - e)^2$ along the plane. (C.)

15. From one corner A of a rectangular billiard table $ABCD$ a ball is projected in a direction making an angle α with the side AB; it strikes first the side BC, then AD, then DC, then BC again, and then returns to A. Prove that, if e is the coefficient of restitution, $AB : AD = e^2 \cot \alpha : 1 + e^2$. (C.)

16. A particle is projected inside a smooth tube of equal mass, which is closed at both ends and lies on a smooth table. Prove that the distance travelled through by the tube when the particle has made $(n + 1)$ impacts is $a(1 - e^n)/(e^n - e^{n+1})$ or $a(1 - e^{n+1})/(e^n - e^{n+1})$ according as n is even or odd, $2a$ being the length of the tube, and e the coefficient of restitution to each impact. (C.)

17. A sphere of radius a rolling on a rough table with velocity V comes to a slit of breadth b perpendicular to its path. Prove that, if there is no restitution, the condition that it should cross the slit without jumping is

$$V^2 > \tfrac{100}{7}ga\ (1 - \cos \alpha) \sin^2 \alpha\ (14 - 10 \sin^2 \alpha)/(7 - 10 \sin^2 \alpha)^2$$

where $b = 2a \sin \alpha$ and $17ga \cos \alpha > V^2 + 10ga$. (C.)

18. One end of a light inextensible string of length a is attached to a smooth horizontal floor at a point distant $b (< a)$ from a smooth vertical wall. An elastic particle of mass m is attached to the other end of the string and rests on the floor with the string taut. The particle is given a horizontal velocity u perpendicular to the string and after striking the wall it rebounds. Find the impulsive tension in the string when it again becomes taut. Show that the particle strikes the wall again in the same place if e, the coefficient of restitution between the particle and the wall, is less than $b^2/(a^2 - b^2)$. Find the velocity of the particle just before it strikes the wall for the nth time. (L.U.)

19. Three vertical walls meet a smooth horizontal plane in the sides of an isosceles right-angled triangle. A particle is projected along the plane from the mid-point of one side of the triangle to strike first the hypotenuse, then, after rebound, the other side of the triangle, and finally to return to the point of projection. Show that the angles of reflexion from the hypotenuse and the side are respectively $\cot^{-1}(1 + e)$, $\cot^{-1}(2 + e)$, where e is the coefficient of restitution at each impact. (L.U.)

20. A uniform solid cylinder of radius a rolls down a rough plane of inclination $\alpha\ (< 60°)$. When it has rolled a distance l it impinges on a perfectly rough inelastic horizontal rail at a distance $a/2$ from the inclined plane. Assuming that the cylinder remains in contact with the rail after the impact, show that it surmounts the rail if $4l \sin \alpha > 9a(1 - \sin \overline{\alpha + 30°})$ (L.U.)

21. A rigid body, whose moments of inertia about its principal axes at O are A, B, C, is at rest with O fixed. It is set in motion by an impulse I applied in the line L whose equations, referred to the principal axes at O, are $(x - a)/l = (y - b)/m = (z - c)/n$. Find the initial component angular velocities of the body.

If the line L is perpendicular to OG, where G is the centre of mass of the body, show that the impulsive reaction at O is also perpendicular to OG. (L.U.)

22. A uniform solid cube is spinning about a diagonal, when one of the edges which does not meet that diagonal suddenly becomes fixed. Prove that the energy is diminished in the ratio 1 : 12. (L.U.)

23. A uniform square lamina $OABC$ of side $2a$ has the corner O fixed and is free to turn about a hinge along the edge OC. The hinge OC is held at an angle of 45° to the vertical OZ with the lamina at rest. The point C is seized and made to describe a horizontal circle with constant angular velocity Ω so that the angle COZ is unaltered. Show that the initial spin of the lamina about OC is of magnitude

$$3\sqrt{2}\Omega/8$$

Show also that it will then make complete revolutions about OC if

$$\omega^2 > 48\sqrt{2}g/a \qquad \text{(L.U.)}$$

24. A uniform rectangular block, of edges $2a$, $2b$, $2c$, stands on a horizontal table, the edges of length $2c$ being vertical. A string is attached to one of the top corners A and is given a sudden jerk vertically upwards. Prove that the block will at once rise clear of the table if

$$c^4 - 2c^2(a^2 + b^2) - 5a^2b^2 > 0$$

If this condition is not satisfied, show that there is an impulsive pressure on the table, supposed smooth, at the corner diagonally opposite to A, given by

$$\frac{5a^2b^2 + 2c^2(a^2 + b^2) - c^4}{7a^2b^2 + 4c^2(a^2 + b^2) + c^4}T$$

where T is the impulsive tension in the string. (L.U.)

25. Three similar rods AB, BC, CD, uniform and each of mass M, are freely jointed together at B and C, and the rods are initially at rest forming three sides of a square. The end A is jerked into motion with speed u at right angles to the plane of the square. The kinetic energy acquired by the system is T_1 if the system is free and T_2 if D is held fixed. Prove

$$T_2 - T_1 = \frac{Mu^2}{4680}. \qquad \text{(M.T.)}$$

26. A circular disk of mass M, radius a, and moment of inertia MK^2 about its centre, spinning with angular velocity Ω impinges normally on a rough rod of mass m. Prove that the angular velocity immediately after impact is $(M+m)K^2\Omega/\{(M+m)K^2+ma^2\}$, there being no restitution. (C.)

27. Two rough circular disks of masses M_1, M_2, radii a_1, a_2, and radii of gyration k_1, k_2 about their centres, spinning about their centres with angular velocities Ω_1, Ω_2 impinge directly, the relative velocity of the centres before impact being V. Prove that, if there is no restitution, the kinetic energy lost in impact is

$$\frac{1}{2}\frac{V^2}{1/M_1+1/M_2}+\frac{1}{2}\frac{(a_1\Omega_1+a_2\Omega_2)^2}{1/M_1(1+a_1^2/k_1^2)+1/M_2(1+a_2^2/k_2^2)} \quad \text{(C.)}$$

28. A sphere of mass m falls vertically and impinges with velocity V against a board of mass M which is moving with velocity U on a horizontal table. The coefficient of restitution between the sphere and the board is e, and the friction between the board and the table can be neglected. Prove that, if the coefficient of friction between the sphere and the board exceeds $2MU/(7M+2m)(1+e)V$, the kinetic energy lost in the impact is $\frac{1}{2}m(1-e^2)V^2+mMU^2/(7M+2m)$ (C.)

29. A ball is let fall upon a hoop, of which the mass is $1/n$ of that of the ball; the hoop is suspended from a point in its circumference, about which it can turn freely in a vertical plane. Prove that, if e is the coefficient of restitution, and α the inclination to the vertical of the radius passing through the point at which the ball strikes the hoop, the ball rebounds in a direction making with the horizontal an angle $\tan^{-1}\{(1+\frac{1}{2}n)\tan\alpha-e\cot\alpha\}$. (C.)

30. Twelve equal rods each of length $2a$ are so jointed together that they can be the edges of a cube, and the framework moves symmetrically through a configuration in which each rod makes an angle θ with the vertical; prove that, if u is the velocity of the centre of mass, the kinetic energy is $\frac{1}{2}M(\frac{7}{3}a^2\dot{\theta}^2+u^2)$, where M is the mass of the framework, and that, if the frame strikes the ground when $\dot{\theta}=0$, then u is reduced in the ratio

$$1/(1+\tfrac{7}{27}\operatorname{cosec}^2\theta) \quad \text{(C.)}$$

31. Any number of equal uniform rods are jointed together so as to have a common extremity and placed symmetrically so as to be generators of a cone of vertical angle 2α; the system falling with velocity V strikes symmetrically a smooth fixed sphere of radius c (no restitution). Prove that the angular velocity with which each rod begins to turn is

$$V(c\cos\alpha\sim a\sin^3\alpha)/(\tfrac{4}{3}a^2\sin^2\alpha+c^2\cot^2\alpha-ac\sin 2\alpha) \quad \text{(C.)}$$

32. An infinite number of equal uniform rods are loosely jointed together, and are in a straight line and at rest when a blow P is struck at the free end of the extreme rod in a direction perpendicular to its length. Prove that the impulse exerted at the hinge at the further end of the nth rod is

$$(-1)^n P 2^{2n}\sin^{2n}\frac{\pi}{12} \quad \text{(C.)}$$

33. A set of $(2n+1)$ equal rods OA, OB, OC, . . . each of mass m and length $2a$ are freely jointed at O, and lie in one plane so that any two neighbouring rods are inclined at an angle α, $= 2\pi/(2n+1)$; an impulse P acts along OA, and ω_1, ω_2, . . . are the initial angular velocities communicated to the rods on each side of OA in order. Prove that

$$\omega_1 \operatorname{cosec} \alpha = \omega_2 \operatorname{cosec} 2\alpha = \ldots = \tfrac{3}{4}u/a,$$

where u, $= \frac{8}{5}P/\{(2n-1)m\}$, is the initial velocity of OA. (C.)

34. Three spheres of equal radius but of mass M_1, M_2, M_3 lie on a smooth horizontal table in that order with their centres collinear. The sphere of mass M_1 is projected with velocity V and without rotation directly towards M_2. Show that, whatever the value of M_2, the momentum acquired by M_3 cannot exceed

$$\frac{V(1+e)^2}{(M_1^{-\frac{1}{2}} + M_3^{-\frac{1}{2}})^2}$$

where e is the coefficient of restitution. (L.U.)

35. A rigid body is rotating with angular velocity ω under no forces about a point O which is fixed in the body and in space, when a line of particles of the body which passes through O is suddenly fixed, the line being specified by a unit vector $\mathbf{i}$. If A, B, C are the principal moments of inertia at O and if I is the moment of inertia about the new axis of rotation, prove that the loss of kinetic energy is

$$(BCp^2 + CAq^2 + ABr^2)/(2I)$$

where (p, q, r) are the components of $\mathbf{i} \times \boldsymbol{\omega}$, referred to the principal axes of inertia at O. (L.U.)

CHAPTER XII

THE LAGRANGE EQUATIONS FOR A GENERAL SYSTEM

12.1 Holonomic and non-holonomic systems

A general dynamical system will be defined by, say, n independent co-ordinates $q_1, q_2, \ldots q_n$; a complete set of these values will fix the *configuration* at a given time, t. Thus a particle will normally require $n = 3$ co-ordinates (cf. 8.3); a rigid rod moving in space will require $n = 5$ co-ordinates, viz. three for the centre of mass and two angles θ, ϕ (v. Fig. 30 of 2.15) for its orientation; two rigid rods hinged together by a universal joint and moving in space will require $n = 7$ co-ordinates, made up of three for the centre of mass of one rod and two sets of spherical polar angles θ_1, ϕ_1 and θ_2, ϕ_2. It is clear from these examples that n is a characteristic of the dynamical system, not of the three dimensional space in which the system moves. We call n the number of *degrees of freedom* possessed by the system.

Now we assume that each co-ordinate q_r is a determinate function of the time t and that, for complete generality, the Cartesian co-ordinates (x, y, z) of any point of the system will be functions of the q's and also of t (explicitly). Hence we write

$$x = x(q_1, q_2, \ldots q_n, t)$$
$$y = y(q_1, q_2, \ldots q_n, t)$$
$$z = z(q_1, q_2, \ldots q_n, t)$$

The significance of the explicit presence of t will be considered in 12.4.

As in 8.3, we can write, e.g.

$$\frac{\partial \dot{x}}{\partial \dot{q}_r} = \frac{\partial x}{\partial q_r} \quad (r = 1, 2, \ldots n) \qquad (1)$$

and

$$\frac{\partial \dot{x}}{\partial q_r} = \frac{d}{dt}\left\{\frac{\partial x}{\partial q_r}\right\}. \qquad (2)$$

Hence

$$\ddot{x}\frac{\partial x}{\partial q_r} = \ddot{x}\frac{\partial \dot{x}}{\partial \dot{q}_r}, \quad \text{by (1)}$$
$$= \frac{d}{dt}\left\{\dot{x}\frac{\partial \dot{x}}{\partial \dot{q}_r}\right\} - \dot{x}\frac{d}{dt}\left\{\frac{\partial \dot{x}}{\partial \dot{q}_r}\right\}$$
$$= \frac{d}{dt}\left\{\frac{\partial}{\partial \dot{q}_r}(\tfrac{1}{2}\dot{x}^2)\right\} - \dot{x}\frac{\partial \dot{x}}{\partial q_r}, \quad \text{by (1) and (2)}$$

i.e.

$$\ddot{x}\frac{\partial x}{\partial q_r} = \frac{d}{dt}\left\{\frac{\partial}{\partial \dot{q}_r}(\tfrac{1}{2}\dot{x}^2)\right\} - \frac{\partial}{\partial q_r}(\tfrac{1}{2}\dot{x}^2). \qquad (3)$$

Now suppose that the particle of mass m at (x, y, z) is acted upon by a force whose components parallel to the axes are (X, Y, Z). Since we intend to use D'Alembert's principle in the form 9.3(iii), these forces (X, Y, Z) need not include any forces which, in a small displacement, do no work. Thus we need not consider tensions in inelastic strings, normal reactions between surfaces in contact, reactions at smooth joints, stresses in rigid rods, or the internal forces in a rigid body.

If $\sum$ denotes summation over all the particles of the system, we now have

$$\sum m\{\ddot{x}\,\delta x + \ddot{y}\,\delta y + \ddot{z}\,\delta z\} = \sum\{X\,\delta x + Y\,\delta y + Z\,\delta z\} \qquad (4)$$

where δx, δy, δz are increments in the co-ordinates (x, y, z) of any point of the material system (v. 9.3(iii)). But it is clear that these increments depend upon the independent co-ordinates q_r $(r = 1, 2, \ldots n)$ in fact (e.g.)

$$\delta x = \frac{\partial x}{\partial q_1}\,\delta q_1 + \frac{\partial x}{\partial q_2}\,\delta q_2 + \ldots + \frac{\partial x}{\partial q_n}\,\delta q_n \quad . \quad . \qquad (5)$$

for a given t.

Now although the q's are independent it does not follow that the $\dot{q}$'s are independent (i.e. the δq's), for there may be *equations of constraint* (cf. 11.1(12)) expressing some essential relations between certain specific velocities. Suppose such a relation exists and can be written

$$a_1\,\dot{q}_1 + a_2\dot{q}_2 + \ldots + a_n\dot{q}_n = 0 \quad . \quad . \qquad (6)$$

where $a_r \equiv a_r(q_1, q_2, \ldots q_n)$ $(r = 1, 2, \ldots n)$. Now (6) cannot be integrable since this will give a relation between the q's and so less than n independent co-ordinates are needed to specify the configuration. In this case it is not possible to let q_1 increase to $q_1 + \delta q_1$ while all the other q's remain constant, because of (6).

When all the δq_r $(r = 1, 2, \ldots n)$ are independent, i.e. non-integrable equations of constraint do not exist, we call the system *holonomic*. Otherwise, when equations such as (6) do exist, we call the system *non-holonomic*. A simple case of a non-holonomic system is provided by a sphere rolling and spinning on a rough surface (v. 15.3).

We shall now obtain the Lagrange equations of motion for a holonomic system. Since the δq_r are independent we can put $\delta q_r \neq 0$, $\delta q_s = 0$, $s \neq r$, whence equations like (5) give

$$\delta x = \frac{\partial x}{\partial q_r}\,\delta q_r\,; \quad \delta y = \frac{\partial y}{\partial q_r}\,\delta q_r\,; \quad \delta z = \frac{\partial z}{\partial q_r}\,\delta q_r$$

whence (4) becomes

$$\sum m\left\{\ddot{x}\,\frac{\partial x}{\partial q_r} + \ddot{y}\,\frac{\partial y}{\partial q_r} + \ddot{z}\,\frac{\partial z}{\partial q_r}\right\} = \sum\left\{X\,\frac{\partial x}{\partial q_r} + Y\,\frac{\partial y}{\partial q_r} + Z\,\frac{\partial z}{\partial q_r}\right\}$$

Using (3), and writing the kinetic energy as

$$T = \tfrac{1}{2} \sum m(\dot{x}^2 + \dot{y}^2 + \dot{z}^2) \qquad (7)$$

we get $$\frac{d}{dt}\left(\frac{\partial T}{\partial \dot{q}_r}\right) - \frac{\partial T}{\partial q_r} = \sum \left\{X \frac{\partial x}{\partial q_r} + Y \frac{\partial y}{\partial q_r} + Z \frac{\partial z}{\partial q_r}\right\} \qquad (8)$$

for each $r = 1, 2, \ldots n$.

Now the *work done* by the forces in this displacement defined by δq_r will be, say,

$$Q_r \, \delta q_r = \sum \left\{X \frac{\partial x}{\partial q_r} + Y \frac{\partial y}{\partial q_r} + Z \frac{\partial z}{\partial q_r}\right\} \delta q_r$$

Hence (8) can be written

$$\frac{d}{dt}\left(\frac{\partial T}{\partial \dot{q}_r}\right) - \frac{\partial T}{\partial q_r} = Q_r \quad (r = 1, 2, \ldots n) \qquad (9)$$

The Q_r are the *generalised components of force* (cf. 8.3) : they may be easily identified in a specific problem by forming the incremental " work done " in a general displacement of all the forces. This will give

$$\delta W = \sum \{X \, \delta x + Y \, \delta y + Z \, \delta z\}$$

which will reduce to

$$\delta W = Q_1 \, \delta q_1 + Q_2 \, \delta q_2 + \ldots + Q_n \, \delta q_n \qquad (10)$$

12.2 The Lagrangian function L

In a *conservative* holonomic system equations (9) can be written in a more elegant form, as follows.

Since $\delta W = dW = - dV$ (v. 3.1), where V is a function of the q's (only), write

$$L = T - V \qquad (1)$$

Then $\dfrac{\partial L}{\partial \dot{q}_r} \equiv \dfrac{\partial T}{\partial \dot{q}_r}$ since V does not contain the $\dot{q}$'s, and also

$$Q_r = \frac{\partial W}{\partial q_r} = - \frac{\partial V}{\partial q_r} \quad (r = 1, 2, \ldots n)$$

Hence (9) becomes

$$\frac{d}{dt}\left(\frac{\partial L}{\partial \dot{q}_r}\right) - \frac{\partial L}{\partial q_r} = 0 \quad (r = 1, 2, \ldots n) \qquad (2)$$

We notice that 12.1(7) becomes, on writing

$$\dot{x} = \sum_{r=1}^{n} \frac{\partial q_r}{\partial x} \dot{q}_r + \frac{\partial x}{\partial t}$$

$$T = \tfrac{1}{2} g_{rs} \dot{q}_r \dot{q}_s + b_r \dot{q}_r + \tfrac{1}{2} b_0 \qquad (3)$$

where *summation* over $r, s = 1, 2, \ldots n$ is assumed, and where

$$\left.\begin{aligned} g_{rr} &= \sum m\left\{\left(\frac{\partial x}{\partial q_r}\right)^2 + \left(\frac{\partial y}{\partial q_r}\right)^2 + \left(\frac{\partial z}{\partial q_r}\right)^2\right\} \\ g_{rs} &= \sum m\left\{\frac{\partial x}{\partial q_r}.\frac{\partial x}{\partial q_s} + \frac{\partial y}{\partial q_r}.\frac{\partial y}{\partial q_s} + \frac{\partial z}{\partial q_r}.\frac{\partial z}{\partial q_s}\right\} \end{aligned}\right\} \quad . \quad (4)$$

and where

$$\left.\begin{aligned} b_r &= \sum m\left\{\frac{\partial x}{\partial q_r}.\frac{\partial x}{\partial t} + \frac{\partial y}{\partial q_r}.\frac{\partial y}{\partial t} + \frac{\partial z}{\partial q_r}.\frac{\partial z}{\partial t}\right\} \\ b_0 &= \sum m\left\{\left(\frac{\partial x}{\partial t}\right)^2 + \left(\frac{\partial y}{\partial t}\right)^2 + \left(\frac{\partial z}{\partial t}\right)^2\right\} \end{aligned}\right\} \quad . \quad . \quad (5)$$

These coefficients are functions of $(q_1, q_2, \ldots q_n)$ and of t. In the *special case when x, y, z do not contain the time explicitly*, we get $b_r = 0 = b_0$ (all r) and (3) becomes

$$T = \tfrac{1}{2} g_{rs}\, \dot{q}_r\, \dot{q}_s \quad . \quad . \quad . \quad . \quad (6)$$

where the g_{rs} are functions of the q's only, and are given by (4). In this case T is a *homogeneous quadratic function* of the $\dot{q}$'s.

Example 1. A uniform rod AB of mass m and length $2a$ is at rest at time $t = 0$, suspended from a fixed smooth horizontal rail by means of a small ring at A of mass m. A force F is applied at A along the rail. If x is the distance moved by A from its initial position O and the angle OAB is $\frac{\pi}{2} - \theta$, obtain the equations of motion of the system.

If A is constrained to move with constant acceleration g, show that the rod oscillates between the vertical $\theta = 0$ and the horizontal position $\theta = \frac{\pi}{2}$, and that

$$F = \frac{mg}{8}\{19 - 12 \sin\theta + 9(\sin 2\theta - \cos 2\theta)\} \qquad \text{(L.U.)}$$

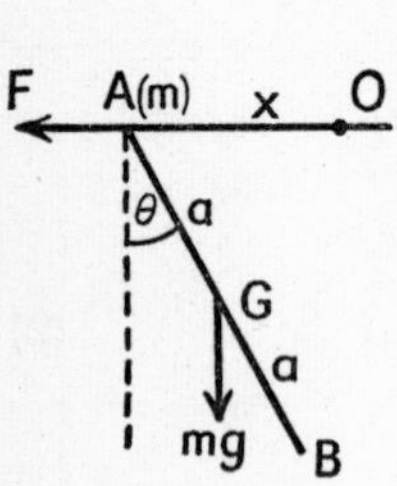

FIG. 105.

Fig. 105 shows the position at a time $t > 0$. The co-ordinates of G, the centre of mass of the rod AB, are $(x - a \sin\theta)$ horizontally and $a \cos\theta$ vertically downwards. The angular velocity of the rod is $\dot{\theta}$. Hence the kinetic energy is

$$T = \tfrac{1}{2}m\dot{x}^2 + \tfrac{1}{2}m(\dot{x} + a\cos\theta\,\dot{\theta})^2 + \tfrac{1}{2}ma^2\sin^2\theta\,\dot{\theta}^2 + \tfrac{1}{2}.m\frac{a^2}{3}\,\dot{\theta}^2$$

giving

$$T = m\{\dot{x}^2 - a\dot{x}\dot{\theta}\cos\theta + \tfrac{2}{3}a^2\dot{\theta}^2\} \quad . \quad . \quad . \quad . \quad . \quad (7)$$

In a general displacement the work done by the forces will be

$$\begin{aligned}\delta W &= F\,\delta x + mg\delta\,(a\cos\theta)\\ &= F\,\delta x - mga\sin\theta\,\delta\theta \qquad . \quad . \quad . \quad (8)\\ &= Q_x\,\delta x + Q_\theta\,\delta\theta\end{aligned}$$

The equations of motion are therefore given by 12.1(9), viz.

$$m\frac{d}{dt}\left\{2\dot{x} - a\dot{\theta}\cos\theta\right\} = Q_x = F$$

and

$$m\frac{d}{dt}\left\{-a\dot{x}\cos\theta + \tfrac{4}{3}a^2\dot{\theta}\right\} + ma\dot{x}\dot{\theta}\sin\theta = Q_\theta = -mga\sin\theta$$

These reduce to

$$2m\ddot{x} - ma\ddot{\theta}\cos\theta + ma\dot{\theta}^2\sin\theta = F \qquad . \quad . \quad (9)$$

and

$$\tfrac{4}{3}ma^2\ddot{\theta} - ma\ddot{x}\cos\theta = -mga\sin\theta \qquad . \quad . \quad (10)$$

We now write $\ddot{x} = g$, whence (10) gives

$$\tfrac{4}{3}a\ddot{\theta} = g(\cos\theta - \sin\theta)$$

so that

$$\frac{2a}{3}\dot{\theta}^2 = g(\sin\theta + \cos\theta - 1)$$

Hence $\dot{\theta}^2 \geqslant 0$ when $\sin\theta + \cos\theta - 1 \geqslant 0$

i.e. when $$\sin\left(\theta + \frac{\pi}{4}\right) \geqslant \frac{1}{\sqrt{2}} = \sin\frac{\pi}{4}, \sin\frac{3\pi}{4}$$

Therefore $$\frac{\pi}{4} \leqslant \theta + \frac{\pi}{4} \leqslant \frac{3\pi}{4}$$ Q.E.D.

Now (9) gives

$$F = 2mg - \tfrac{3}{4}mg\cos\theta\,(\cos\theta - \sin\theta) + \tfrac{3}{2}mg\sin\theta\,(\sin\theta + \cos\theta - 1)$$

reducing to the given expression.

Example 2. A bead of mass m is threaded on a smooth uniform circular wire of mass M and radius a which can rotate freely about a fixed horizontal diameter AB. At time t the bead is at an angular distance θ from A and the plane of the wire makes an angle ϕ with the horizontal plane through AB; find the Lagrangian equations of motion.

If when $t = 0$, $\theta = \alpha$, $\dot{\theta} = \phi = \dot{\phi} = 0$

prove $(M + 2m\sin^2\alpha)a\ddot{\phi} = 2mg\sin\alpha$

at $t = 0$

and find the initial value of $\dddot{\phi}$. (L.U.)

Taking axes at G, the centre of the circle, as shown in Fig. 106, we have the co-ordinates of P as $x = a\sin\theta\cos\phi$, $y = a\cos\theta$, $z = a\sin\theta\sin\phi$. Hence the kinetic energy of the particle at P is $\frac{1}{2}ma^2(\dot{\theta}^2 + \sin^2\theta\,\dot{\phi}^2)$. The moment of

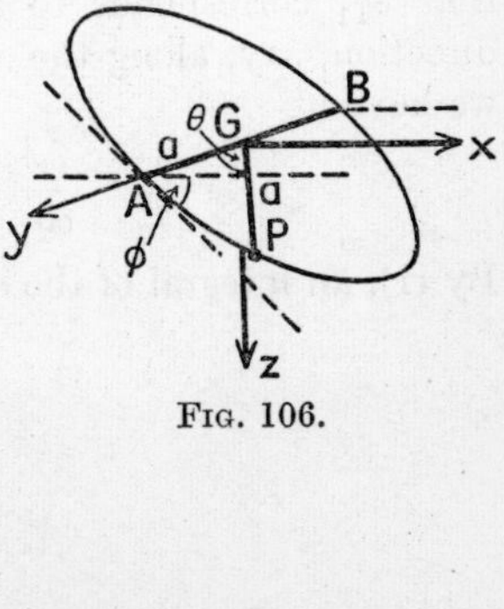

FIG. 106.

inertia of the ring about AB is $M\frac{a^2}{2}$, and so the kinetic energy of the ring is $\frac{1}{2}.M\frac{a^2}{2}.\dot{\phi}^2$. The forces are conservative, being constant gravity only, and so $V = -mgz = -mga \sin\theta \sin\phi$. Using 12.1(9), or 12.2(2), we get

$$L = m\frac{a^2}{2}(\dot{\theta}^2 + \sin^2\theta\,\dot{\phi}^2) + \tfrac{1}{2}.M\frac{a^2}{2}\dot{\phi}^2 + mga \sin\theta \sin\phi$$

and

$$ma\ddot{\theta} - ma \sin\theta \cos\theta\,\dot{\phi}^2 - mg \cos\theta \sin\phi = 0 \quad . \quad (11)$$

$$\frac{d}{dt}\left\{ma \sin^2\theta\,\dot{\phi} + \frac{Ma}{2}\dot{\phi}\right\} - mg \sin\theta \cos\phi = 0 \quad . \quad (12)$$

At $t = 0$, (12) gives

$$(2m \sin^2\alpha + M)a\ddot{\phi} = 2mg \sin\alpha \qquad \text{Q.E.D.}$$

(11) shows that the initial value of $\ddot{\theta}$ is zero. Performing the differentiation in (12) gives

$$a(2m \sin^2\theta + M)\ddot{\phi} + 4ma \sin\theta \cos\theta\,\dot{\theta}\dot{\phi} - 2mg \sin\theta \cos\phi = 0$$

and differentiating this again and putting $t = 0$ afterwards, we get

$$(2m \sin^2\alpha + M)a\dddot{\phi} = 0$$

Hence the initial value of $\dddot{\phi}$ is zero.

12.3 Cyclic co-ordinates

A co-ordinate q_k is called *cyclic* (or *ignorable*) when it does not occur explicitly in L, $\dot{q}_k$ only being present. Hence 12.2(2) becomes, $r = k$,

$$\frac{d}{dt}\left(\frac{\partial L}{\partial \dot{q}_k}\right) = 0$$

giving *an integral of the equations of motion* in the form

$$\frac{\partial L}{\partial \dot{q}_k} = \text{constant} \quad . \quad . \quad . \quad . \quad (1)$$

Two particular cases of cyclic co-ordinates are involved in the constancy of (i) linear momentum, and (ii) angular momentum about an axis.

The conservation of linear momentum. Suppose q_1 is cyclic and that δq_1 corresponds to a translation of the system in some fixed direction, say, along the x-axis. Then for every point of the system we have

$$\frac{\partial x}{\partial q_1} = 1\,; \quad \frac{\partial y}{\partial q_1} = \frac{\partial z}{\partial q_1} = 0 \quad . \quad . \quad . \quad (2)$$

By (1), an integral of the equations of motion will be

$$\frac{\partial T}{\partial \dot{q}_1} = \frac{\partial L}{\partial \dot{q}_1} = \text{constant}$$

But $$\frac{\partial T}{\partial \dot{q}_1} = \sum m\left\{\dot{x}\frac{\partial \dot{x}}{\partial \dot{q}_1} + \dot{y}\frac{\partial \dot{y}}{\partial \dot{q}_1} + \dot{z}\frac{\partial \dot{z}}{\partial \dot{q}_1}\right\}, \quad \text{v. 12.1(1)},$$
$$= \sum m\dot{x}$$
$$= \text{the linear momentum along the } x\text{-axis.}$$

Hence linear momentum is constant in any direction in which the system can move without altering the potential energy.

The conservation of angular momentum. Now suppose q_1 is cyclic and that δq_1 corresponds to a rotation of the system about a fixed axis in space. Take this axis as the z-axis, and write, for all points of the system, $x = r\cos\phi$, $y = r\sin\phi$, where $d\phi = dq_1$.

Then $$\frac{\partial x}{\partial q_1} = \frac{\partial x}{\partial \phi} = -r\sin\phi = -y$$

and $$\frac{\partial y}{\partial q_1} = \frac{\partial y}{\partial \phi} = r\cos\phi = x$$

whilst $$\frac{\partial z}{\partial q_1} = 0$$

Now $$\frac{\partial T}{\partial \dot{q}_1} = \text{constant} = \sum m\left\{\dot{x}\frac{\partial x}{\partial q_1} + \dot{y}\frac{\partial y}{\partial q_1} + z\frac{\partial z}{\partial q_1}\right\}$$
$$= \sum m(x\dot{y} - y\dot{x})$$
$$= \text{angular momentum about } Oz$$

Hence the angular momentum about an axis, λ, is constant if the system can be rotated about λ without altering the potential energy.

Example 1. A fine smooth diametral canal is bored through a uniform sphere of mass M and contains a particle of mass m. The system moves freely under no external forces, the particle being initially at the centre of the sphere, which is then turning about a diameter of the sphere perpendicular to the canal with angular velocity Ω. If the system is slightly disturbed, prove that the angular velocity of the sphere when the particle reaches its surface is

$$2\Omega(M + m)/(2M + 7m) \qquad \text{(L.U.)}$$

Since linear momentum is constant, there being no external forces, the centre of mass G continues to move with constant velocity in a straight line. If the centre of the sphere is the point O and the particle is at P then G lies on OP (in the canal) and $OG = \left(\frac{m}{M+m}\right)x$, where $x = OP$. At $t = 0$, G coincides with O and the angular momentum about the perpendicular diameter through G (and therefore O) is $\frac{2}{5}Ma^2\Omega$. At a later time it is still the angular momentum about the same axis through G (not through O) which is conserved. If the angular velocity of the sphere is ω when $OP = x$ and $OG = \bar{x}$, we get

$$\{\tfrac{2}{5}Ma^2 + M\bar{x}^2 + m(x - \bar{x})^2\}\omega \quad = \tfrac{2}{5}Ma^2\Omega$$

i.e. $$\{2a^2(M+m)^2 + 5m^2x^2 + 5mMx^2\}\omega = 2a^2(M+m)^2\Omega$$

When $x = a$ we get

$$(2M^2 + 9mM + 7m^2)\omega = 2(M+m)^2\Omega$$

so that $$\omega = \frac{2(M+m)\Omega}{2M+7m}$$ Q.E.D.

12.4 The energy integral

When T does not contain the time explicitly we can deduce the conservation of energy as follows. Since T is given 12.2(6) Euler's theorem on homogeneous functions gives

$$\sum_{r=1}^{n} \dot{q}_r \frac{\partial T}{\partial \dot{q}_r} = 2T \quad . \quad . \quad . \quad . \quad (1)$$

Now
$$\frac{dL}{dt} = \sum_{r=1}^{n} \ddot{q}_r \frac{\partial L}{\partial \dot{q}_r} + \sum_{r=1}^{n} \dot{q}_r \frac{\partial L}{\partial q_r}$$

$$= \sum_{r=1}^{n} \ddot{q}_r \frac{\partial L}{\partial \dot{q}_r} + \sum_{r=1}^{n} \dot{q}_r \frac{d}{dt}\left(\frac{\partial L}{\partial \dot{q}_r}\right) \quad \text{by 12.2(2)}$$

$$= \frac{d}{dt}\left\{\sum_{r=1}^{n} \dot{q}_r \frac{\partial L}{\partial \dot{q}_r}\right\}$$

$$= \frac{d}{dt}(2T) \quad \text{by (1) and 12.2(1)}$$

Hence
$$\frac{d}{dt}(T+V) = 0$$

giving
$$T + V = \text{constant} \quad . \quad . \quad . \quad (2)$$

The *principles of conservation* discussed in the last two sections, viz. those of *momentum* and *energy*, should be regarded as playing an important part in Dynamics. By these principles we can rapidly obtain a view of the *system as a whole*, even when we are ignorant of the interaction of its constituent parts. The student is well advised to view some of the worked examples in these chapters from the standpoint of these principles, often as an alternative treatment. To write down (e.g.) the equation which expresses the conservation of momentum is, in fact, to write down a first integral of the equations of motion; the student who wishes both to understand dynamics and to pass his irksome examinations can hardly afford to ignore such powerful methods.

12.5 The Lagrangian equations for impulsive motion

Let the impulse J applied to a typical particle of mass m at (x, y, z) have components (J_1, J_2, J_3). If the initial and final velocity components are $\dot{x}_0, \dot{x}_1$; $\dot{y}_0, \dot{y}_1$; $\dot{z}_0, \dot{z}_1$ respectively, we have, as 11.2(1),

$$\sum m\{(\dot{x}_1 - \dot{x}_0)\,\delta x + (\dot{y}_1 - \dot{y}_0)\,\delta y + (\dot{z}_1 - \dot{z}_0)\,\delta z\} = \sum\{J_1\,\delta x + J_2\,\delta y + J_3\,\delta z\}\,. \quad (1)$$

the summation being over the particles of the system. But the rhs of (1) can be written in the form (cf. 12.1(10))

$$\delta U = Q_1'\,\delta q_1 + Q_2'\,\partial q_2 + \ldots + Q_n'\,\delta q_n \quad . \quad . \quad (2)$$

where the Q_r' $(r = 1, 2, \ldots n)$ are *generalised components of impulse.* We also notice that

$$\dot{x}\,\frac{\partial x}{\partial q_r} = \dot{x}\,\frac{\partial \dot{x}}{\partial \dot{q}_r} = \frac{\partial}{\partial \dot{q}_r}\,(\tfrac{1}{2}\dot{x}^2)$$

and writing $\delta x = \dfrac{\partial x}{\partial q_r}\,.\,\partial q_r$, etc., in (1) we get

$$\left(\frac{\partial T}{\partial \dot{q}_r}\right)_1 - \left(\frac{\partial T}{\partial \dot{q}_r}\right)_0 = Q_r' \quad (r = 1, 2, \ldots n) \quad . \quad . \quad (3)$$

Example 1. Four equal uniform rods, each of mass m and length $2a$, are freely jointed at their ends to form a rhombus $ABCD$. The rhombus is let fall from rest in a vertical plane with a diagonal vertical and strikes a fixed inelastic horizontal plane with velocity V. Prove that the angular velocity of each rod just after impact is

$$\omega = \tfrac{3}{2}\,.\,\frac{V \sin \alpha}{a(1 + 3\sin^2 \alpha)}$$

where 2α is the vertical angle of the rhombus at impact. (L.U.)

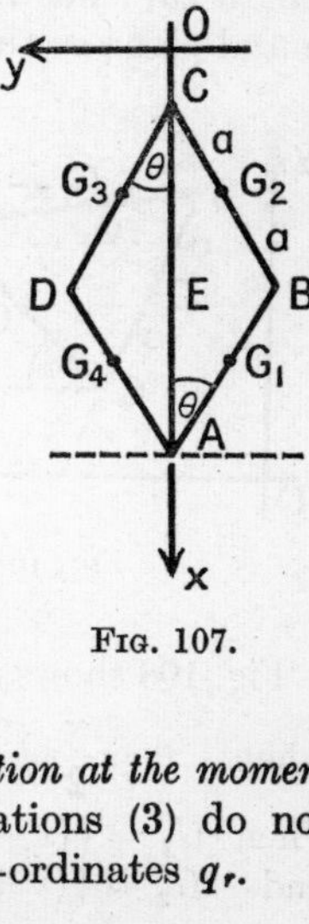

FIG. 107.

Take a fixed point O in the vertical line of the diagonal AC as origin, as shown in Fig. 107. Consider the rhombus in a general configuration, and let E, the mid-point of CA, have coordinates $(x, 0)$. Then we have co-ordinates

$G_1 = \{x + a\cos\theta,\ - a\sin\theta\}$;
$G_2 = \{x - a\cos\theta,\ - a\sin\theta\}$

which have velocities

$\dot{G}_1 = \{\dot{x} - \sin\alpha\,.\,\dot{\theta},\ - a\cos\alpha\,\dot{\theta}\}$;
$\dot{G}_2 = \{\dot{x} + a\sin\alpha\,.\,\dot{\theta},\ - a\cos\alpha\,.\,\dot{\theta}\}$

where we have written $\theta = \alpha$, *defining the configuration at the moment of impact.* This is always permissible since equations (3) do not involve any differentiations with respect to the co-ordinates q_r.

We now have

$$T = \tfrac{1}{2}.2m(2\dot{x}^2 + 2a^2\sin^2\alpha\,\dot{\theta}^2 + 2a^2\cos^2\alpha\,\dot{\theta}^2) + \tfrac{1}{2}.4m.\frac{a^2}{3}.\dot{\theta}^2$$

reducing to
$$T = 2m(\dot{x}^2 + \tfrac{4}{3}a^2\dot{\theta}^2) \quad . \quad . \quad . \quad (4)$$

Let the impulse at A be J vertically upwards. Then since $OA = x + 2a\cos\theta$, we have

$$\delta U = -J.\delta(OA) = -J\,\delta x + 2aJ\sin\theta.\delta\theta \quad . \quad (5)$$

Equations (3) become, with $\theta = \alpha$,

$$4m(\dot{x}_1 - \dot{x}_0) = -J\,; \quad \tfrac{16}{3}ma^2(\dot{\theta}_1 - \dot{\theta}_0) = 2aJ\sin\alpha \quad . \quad (6)$$

where $\dot{x}_0 = V$, $\dot{\theta}_0 = 0$. Hence (6) give

$$\dot{x}_1 = V - \frac{J}{4m}\,; \quad \dot{\theta}_1 = \frac{3J\sin\alpha}{8am} \quad . \quad . \quad . \quad (7)$$

Since the plane is inelastic A remains at rest. Hence

$$\dot{x}_1 - 2a\sin\alpha\,\dot{\theta}_1 = 0 = \frac{d}{dt}(OA)$$

and (7) now gives

$$V - \frac{2a}{3\sin\alpha}\dot{\theta}_1 - 2a\sin\alpha\,\dot{\theta}_1 = 0$$

Hence
$$\dot{\theta}_1 = \frac{3V\sin^2\alpha}{2a(1 + 3\sin^2\alpha)} \qquad \text{Q.E.D.}$$

Example 2. Three equal uniform rods AB, BC, CD, each of length $2a$, smoothly hinged at B and C, are placed on a smooth horizontal plane so that $ABCD$ is a square. An impulse I is applied at A along AD. If the initial longitudinal velocity of BC is u and the initial angular velocities of AB and CD are ω_1 and ω_2 respectively, in the sense $ABCD$, prove that

$$u : a\omega_1 : a\omega_2 = 4 : 21 : 3$$

and that the initial longitudinal velocities of AB and CD and the initial angular velocity of BC all vanish. Find the kinetic energy imparted to the system by the impulse I. (L.U.)

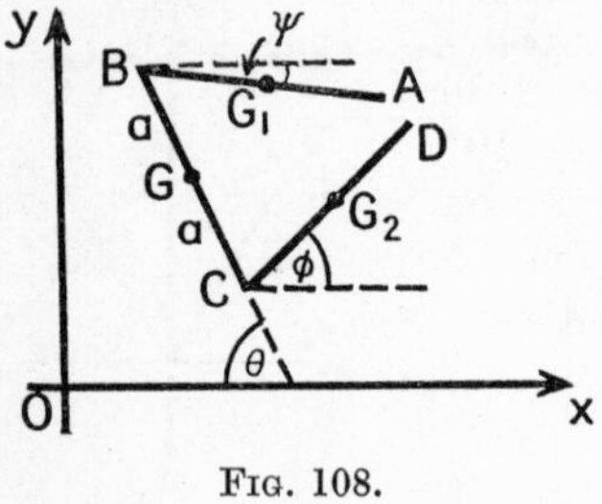

Fig. 108.

Fig. 108 shows a general configuration ; the impulse is applied when $\theta = \frac{\pi}{2}$, $\phi = \psi = 0$. Let G be the point (x, y).

Then $G_1 = \{(x - a\cos\theta + a\cos\psi),\ (y + a\sin\theta - a\sin\psi)\}$
and $G_2 = \{(x + a\cos\theta + a\cos\phi),\ (y - a\sin\theta + a\sin\phi)\}$

Differentiating and writing $\theta = \frac{\pi}{2}$, $\phi = \psi = 0$ afterwards, we get

$$\dot{G} = (\dot{x}, \dot{y})\ ;\quad \dot{G}_1 = \{(\dot{x} + a\dot{\theta}), (\dot{y} - a\dot{\psi})\}\ ;\quad \dot{G}_2 = \{(\dot{x} - a\dot{\theta}), (\dot{y} + a\dot{\phi})\}$$

Hence

$$\frac{2T}{m} = \dot{x}^2 + \dot{y}^2 + (\dot{x} + a\dot{\theta})^2 + (\dot{y} - a\dot{\psi})^2 + (\dot{x} - a\dot{\theta})^2 + (\dot{y} + a\dot{\phi})^2$$

$$+ \frac{a^2}{3}(\dot{\theta}^2 + \dot{\phi}^2 + \dot{\psi}^2)$$

$$= 3\dot{x}^2 + 3\dot{y}^2 + \frac{7a^2}{3}\dot{\theta}^2 + \tfrac{4}{3}a^2\dot{\phi}^2 + \tfrac{4}{3}a^2\dot{\psi}^2 - 2a\dot{y}\dot{\psi} + 2a\dot{y}\dot{\phi}$$

Since the ordinate of A is $y + a \sin \theta - 2a \sin \psi$, we have

$$\delta U = - I(\delta y + a \cos \theta\ \delta\theta - 2a \cos \psi\ \delta\psi)$$

or

$$\delta U = - I\delta y + 2aI\ \delta\psi$$

Equations (3) are now

$$3\dot{y}_1 - a\dot{\psi}_1 + a\dot{\phi}_1 = - I$$

$$7\frac{a^2}{3}\dot{\theta}_1 = 0 \quad = \dot{x}_1$$

$$\frac{4a^2}{3}\dot{\phi}_1 + a\dot{y}_1 = 0$$

$$\frac{4a^2}{3}\dot{\psi}_1 - a\dot{y}_1 = 2aI$$

Writing $- u = \dot{y}_1$, $\dot{\phi}_1 = \omega_2$, $\dot{\psi}_1 = - \omega_1$, we get

$$- 3u + a\omega_1 + a\omega_2 = - I$$

$$4a\omega_2 - 3u = 0$$

$$4a\omega_1 - 3u = - 6I$$

and so $\quad u : a\omega_2 = 4 : 3$, and then $\omega_1 : \omega_2 = 7 : 1$ Q.E.D.

The longitudinal velocities of AB and CD are $\dot{x}_1 \mp a\dot{\theta}_1 = 0$.

Also

$$\frac{2T}{m} = 5I^2$$

Example 3. A rod OA, of length a, is freely hinged to a fixed point O of a smooth horizontal table and smoothly jointed at A to the circumference of a uniform circular disc of radius b and centre C free to slide on the table. If, when OAC is a straight line, OA is at rest and AC is turning with angular velocity Ω, impulses are applied to OA to give it an angular velocity ω, show that the angular velocity of the disc changes instantaneously to $\Omega - \lambda^2\omega$, where $2a = 3b\lambda^2$.

If OA is thereafter constrained to rotate with the constant angular velocity ω, and $\angle OAC = \pi - \phi$, show that

$$\ddot{\phi} + \lambda^2\omega^2 \sin \phi = 0$$

and that the motion will be oscillatory if

$$(1 - \lambda)^2 < \frac{\Omega}{\omega} < (1 + \lambda)^2 \qquad \text{(L.U.)}$$

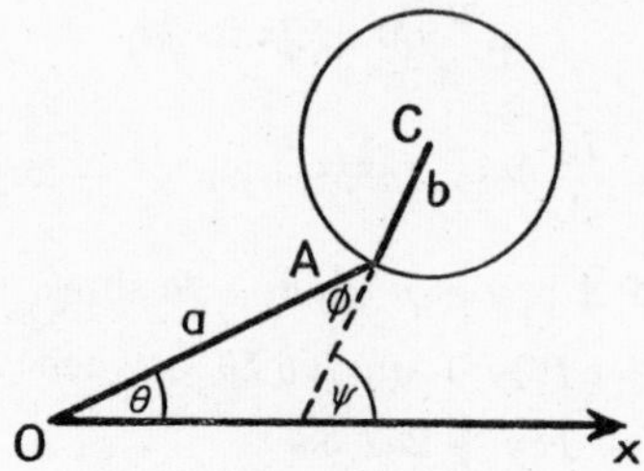

FIG. 109.

Suppose the impulses are applied when $\theta = \psi = 0$ (v. Fig. 109), and write $\dot{\psi}_0 = \Omega$, $\dot{\theta}_0 = 0$. Let the impulses applied to OA be an *impulsive couple* of moment Γ. Then we get

$$\delta U = \Gamma\, \delta\theta$$

The co-ordinates of C, the centre of mass of the disc, are

$$(a \cos \theta + b \cos \psi,\ a \sin \theta + b \sin \psi)$$

Its velocity is therefore

$$(-\, a \sin \theta\, \dot{\theta} - b \sin \psi\, \dot{\psi},\ a \cos \theta\, \dot{\theta} + b \cos \psi\, \dot{\psi})$$

and the total kinetic energy of the system will be

$$T = \tfrac{1}{2}.m\frac{a^2}{3}\dot{\theta}^2 + \frac{M}{2}\left\{\frac{b^2}{2}\dot{\psi}^2 + (a^2\dot{\theta}^2 + b^2\dot{\psi}^2 + 2ab \cos (\theta - \psi)\dot{\theta}\dot{\psi})\right\}$$

m being the mass of OA, M the mass of the disc. This becomes

$$T = \tfrac{1}{2}.\left(m\frac{a^2}{3} + Ma^2\right)\dot{\theta}^2 + \tfrac{1}{2}.\tfrac{3}{2}Mb^2\dot{\psi}^2 + Mab \cos (\theta - \psi)\dot{\theta}\dot{\psi} \qquad (8)$$

for general motion and, putting $\theta = \psi = 0$, it becomes

$$T = \frac{a^2}{2}\left(\frac{m}{3} + M\right) \dot{\theta}^2 + \tfrac{3}{2}Mb^2\dot{\psi}^2 + Mab\dot{\theta}\dot{\psi} \quad . \quad . \qquad (9)$$

for impulsive motion. Forming the " ψ " equation by (3), we get

$$\tfrac{3}{2}Mb^2(\dot{\psi}_1 - \dot{\psi}_0) + Mab(\dot{\theta}_1 - \dot{\theta}_0) = Q'\psi = 0$$

giving

$$3b(\dot{\psi}_1 - \Omega) + 2a\omega = 0$$

or

$$\dot{\psi}_1 = \Omega - \lambda^2\omega \quad (3b\lambda^2 = 2a) \qquad \text{Q.E.D.}$$

Writing $\phi = \psi - \theta$, $\dot{\theta} = \omega$ (constant) in (8) we get

$$T = \text{constant} + Mab \cos \phi . \omega^2 + M\frac{b}{2}(3b + 2a \cos \phi)\omega\dot{\phi} + \tfrac{3}{4}Mb^2\dot{\phi}^2$$

The " ϕ " equation of 12.2(2), with $V \equiv 0$, is

$$\frac{d}{dt}\{\tfrac{3}{2}b\dot{\phi} + \tfrac{1}{2}.\omega(3b + 2a \cos \phi)\} + a\omega^2 \sin \phi + a\omega\dot{\phi} \sin \phi = 0$$

which reduces to $\qquad \ddot{\phi} + \lambda^2\omega^2 \sin \phi = 0 \qquad . \quad . \quad . \quad (10)$

Integrating (10) with $\dot{\phi} = \dot{\psi} - \omega = \Omega - (1 + \lambda^2)\, \omega$ at $t = 0$,

we get $\quad \dot{\phi}^2 - 2\lambda^2\omega^2 \cos \phi = \{\Omega - (1 + \lambda^2)\omega\}^2 - 2\lambda^2\omega^2$

Hence $\dot{\phi} = 0$ for real values of ϕ (i.e. oscillatory motion) provided

$$\{\Omega - (1 + \lambda^2)\omega\}^2 - 2\lambda^2\omega^2 < 2\lambda^2\omega^2$$

which reduces to $\qquad (1 - \lambda)^2 < \frac{\Omega}{\omega} < (1 + \lambda)^2 \qquad$ Q.E.D.

Exercise XII

1. For a certain dynamical system the kinetic and potential functions are

$$T = \tfrac{1}{2}\{(1 + 2k)\dot{\theta}^2 + 2\dot{\theta}\dot{\phi} + \dot{\phi}^2\}$$
$$V = \tfrac{1}{2}n^2\{(1 + k)\theta^2 + \phi^2\}$$

where θ, ϕ are the co-ordinates, and n, k are positive constants. Write down the Lagrangian equations of motion and deduce that

$$(\ddot{\theta} - \ddot{\phi}) + n^2\left(\frac{1 + k}{k}\right)(\theta - \phi) = 0$$

Hence prove that if $\theta = \phi$, $\dot{\theta} = \dot{\phi}$ at $t = 0$, then $\theta = \phi$ for all t. (M.T.)

2. One end A of a uniform rod AB of mass m and length $2a$ can slide along a smooth vertical wire OZ, and the end B is attached to O by an inextensible string of length $2a$, so that when the string is taut, OB makes an angle θ with the downward vertical, and the plane OBA makes an angle ϕ with a fixed plane through OA. Show that the kinetic energy of the rod is

$$\tfrac{2}{3}ma^2\}(1 + 6 \sin^2 \theta)\dot{\theta}^2 + \dot{\phi}^2 \sin^2 \theta\}$$

Show that a steady motion of the system $\theta = \alpha$ is possible if $\dot{\phi} = \Omega = (9g/4a \cos \alpha)^{\frac{1}{2}}$, and find the period of the small oscillations about this steady motion, in terms of Ω and α. (L.U.)

3. A uniform solid cylinder of mass m and radius a can roll without slipping inside a thin hollow cylinder of mass M and radius b, free to turn about its axis which is horizontal. Taking θ as the angle of inclination to the vertical of the plane containing the axes of the two cylinders and ϕ as the similar angle of inclination (measured in the same sense as θ) of some axial plane fixed in the larger cylinder, show that the angular velocity ω of the smaller cylinder can be expressed in the form $a\omega = (b - a)\dot{\theta} - b\dot{\phi}$.

Obtain the kinetic energy of the system in the form

$$2T = \left(M + \frac{m}{2}\right)b^2\dot{\phi}^2 - mb(b - a)\dot{\phi}\dot{\theta} + \tfrac{3}{2}m(b - a)^2\dot{\theta}^2$$

and write down the Lagrangian equations of motion.

Prove that

$$(3M + m)(b - a)\ddot{\theta} + (2M + m)\, g \sin \theta = 0 \qquad \text{(M.T.)}$$

4. A uniform circular solid cylinder, of mass M and radius a, has a particle of mass m attached to its surface at a point equidistant from the ends. The cylinder moves in a direction perpendicular to its length on a smooth horizontal table. The horizontal displacement of the axis of the cylinder is denoted by x, and the angle that the radius through the particle makes with the downward vertical is denoted by θ. Using x and θ as Lagrangian co-ordinates, find the kinetic and potential energy functions for the system, and form the Lagrangian equations of motion. Deduce that

$$\{\tfrac{1}{2}M(M + 3m) + m^2 \sin^2 \theta\}\ddot{\theta} + m^2 \cos \theta \sin \theta\, \dot{\theta}^2 + m(M + m)n^2 \sin \theta = 0$$

where $n^2 = g/a$.

If the motion starts from rest with the particle near its lowest position, find the period of the small oscillations. (M.T.)

5. A uniform solid circular cylinder of radius a and mass m and a thin hollow circular cylinder of external radius b $(b > a)$ and mass M are mounted on the same axis with the solid cylinder inside the hollow one and able to turn freely about the common axis. The cylinders are of equal length and have light springs with one end attached to the inside of the hollow cylinder and the other end to the solid cylinder.

When the inner cylinder is turned relatively to the outer one from the position in which the springs are unstrained, a couple of total moment K per unit relative angular displacement is exerted by the springs on each cylinder. The outer cylinder can roll without slipping on a horizontal table and the system is released from rest when the relative angular displacement of the cylinders is α. Taking θ and ϕ to measure the subsequent angular displacements of the inner and outer cylinders respectively, obtain the Lagrangian equations of motion, and prove that, at any instant,

$$ma^2\theta + (2m + 4M)b^2\phi = 0 \qquad \text{(M.T.)}$$

6. A bead of mass m is threaded on a smooth uniform circular wire of mass M and radius a which can rotate freely about a fixed horizontal diameter AB. At time t the bead is at an angular distance θ from A and the plane of the wire makes an angle ϕ with the horizontal plane through AB; find the Lagrangian equations of motion.

If, when $t = 0$,

$$\theta = \alpha, \quad \dot{\theta} = \phi = \dot{\phi} = 0$$

prove that

$$(M + 2m \sin^2 \alpha)a\ddot{\phi} = 2mg \sin \alpha$$

when $t = 0$, and find the initial value of $\ddot{\phi}$. (L.U.)

7. A uniform rod OA (m ; $2a$) is pivoted at O. The rod makes θ with the downward vertical OZ and the plane AOZ makes ϕ with a fixed vertical plane. A bead $P(\lambda m)$ slides on the rod and is joined to O by a light elastic string (nmg ; a). Prove that the kinetic energy is given by

$$2T = \tfrac{4}{3}ma^2(\dot{\theta}^2 + \dot{\phi}^2 \sin^2\theta) + \lambda m(\dot{x}^2 + x^2\dot{\theta}^2 + x^2 \sin^2 \theta\dot{\phi}$$

where $x = OP$. Derive the Lagrange equations of motion and show that if a steady motion is possible with $\theta = \frac{\pi}{3}$, $x = \frac{4a}{3}$ then $\dot{\phi}^2 = \frac{3g}{2a}$ and $n = 6\lambda$. (L.U.)

8. Two equal uniform rods AB, BC (M ; $2a$) are hinged at B and move on a smooth horizontal table with the centre of gravity at rest. If 2θ is the angle between the rods and ϕ is the angle made by AC with a fixed direction in the plane prove that the kinetic energy and the angular momentum about the centre of gravity are given by

$$3T = Ma^2\{(1 + 3\cos^2\theta)\dot{\theta}^2 + (1 + 3\sin^2\theta)\dot{\phi}^2\}$$
$$3H(G) = 2Ma^2(1 + 3\sin^2\theta)\dot{\phi}$$

The ends A, C are joined by a light inextensible string whose length is almost $4a$. Initially the system rotates with angular velocity ω in the plane. Show that if the string breaks the subsequent relative motion of the rods is approximately S.H.M. of period $\pi/\omega\sqrt{3}$. (L.U.)

9. One end A of a uniform rod AB of mass m and length $2a$ is constrained to move on a smooth, straight, horizontal wire ; the rod moves in a vertical plane through the wire under its own weight and under a force X acting at B in a direction parallel to the wire. At time t, A is at a distance x from a fixed point of the wire and the rod makes an angle θ with the vertical. Derive Lagrange's equations for the rod and deduce from them that the rate at which work is done by the force X and the weight is equal to the rate of increase of the kinetic energy of the rod. (L.U.)

10. A uniform rod AB, of length l, lies on a smooth horizontal table, and is initially rotating with angular velocity Ω about one end A, which is at rest. If A is then constrained to move with constant acceleration f in a horizontal direction perpendicular to the original direction of AB, find the condition that the rod will make complete revolutions. (M.T.)

11. A thin uniform smooth wire in the form of a circle of radius a and of mass M is free to rotate about a fixed vertical diameter AB. A heavy bead of mass $4M$, threaded on the wire, is held at rest relative to the wire by means of a catch at one end of the diameter perpendicular to AB. The system is spun about AB and, when the spin is ω, the catch is released, and the system then moves freely. If $9a\omega^2 = 2g$, and θ is the angle which the radius to the bead makes with the horizontal in the subsequent motion, prove that

$$\frac{8}{9}\frac{\dot{\theta}^2}{\omega^2} = 1 + 8\sin\theta - \frac{9}{9 - 8\sin^2\theta}$$

Show also that, when the bead first comes to rest relative to the wire, the spin of the latter is 9ω. (L.U.)

12. A uniform rod, of length $2l$, can turn freely about a universal joint at one end, which is fixed. Initially the rod is inclined at an angle of 60° to the downward vertical and is then set rotating about a vertical axis through the joint with angular velocity ω. Show, by applying the principles of the conservation of energy and of angular momentum, or otherwise, that

$$4l\dot{\theta}^2 = 3l\omega^2(1 - \tfrac{3}{4}\operatorname{cosec}^2\theta) + 3g(2\cos\theta - 1)$$

where θ is the angle the rod makes with the downward vertical at time t.

Hence show that the angle θ always lies between 60° and ϕ, where

$$\cos\phi = \{\sqrt{(n^2 - n + 1)} - n\}$$

with $n = l\omega^2/4g$. (L.U.)

13. A uniform solid right circular cylinder, of mass M and radius a, rests with its axis horizontal on a horizontal table. A similar cylinder rests on the first, touching it along the highest generator, and the centre B of the upper cylinder is vertically above the centre A of the lower cylinder. All the surfaces are perfectly rough. The system is slightly disturbed from rest, and at time t the lower cylinder has turned through an angle ϕ, and the line AB has turned (in the opposite sense) through an angle θ from the upward vertical. Using θ and ϕ as Lagrangian co-ordinates, find the kinetic and potential energy functions for the system.

Prove that, so long as the cylinders remain in contact, (i) the angular velocity of AB is given by the equation

$$a\dot{\theta}^2 = 12g(1 - \cos\theta)/(17 + 4\cos\theta - 4\cos^2\theta)$$

and (ii) the path of B, referred to the tangent and normal at the highest point as axes, can be represented parametrically in the form

$$x = \tfrac{1}{3}a(\theta + 4\sin\theta)$$
$$y = 2a(1 - \cos\theta)$$

(M.T.)

14. A particle at one end of a string of length a, whose other end is attached to a fixed point, is projected horizontally with speed V with the string at an acute angle α with the downward vertical and is again moving horizontally when the string makes an acute angle β with the upward vertical, without the string going slack. Find V, and prove that $\alpha < \beta$ and $2\sin^2\alpha \geqslant \cos\beta\,(\cos\alpha - \cos\beta)$.

In the case $\beta = \pi/2$, if at time t the string makes an angle θ with the downward vertical and the vertical plane through the string has turned through an angle ϕ, show that

$$\phi = \psi + \frac{Vt}{2a}\sin\alpha$$

where $\cos^2\psi = \sin^2\alpha\cos\theta/\sin^2\theta\cos\alpha$. (L.U.)

15. A solid uniform circular cylinder of radius a and mass nm rests on a horizontal plane. A uniform plank of length λa and mass m rests transversely across it with one end on the plane. All the contacts are smooth except that between the cylinder and plane, which is rough enough to prevent slipping. The system being released from rest, obtain Lagrangian equations of motion of the system, and show that when the point of contact between the plank and cylinder comes to the end of the plank, the ratio of the angular velocities of the plank and cylinder is

$$(3n + 2)(1 + \lambda^2)/(1 + \lambda^4) \qquad \text{(L.U.)}$$

16. A heavy particle P is attached to a light rod OP of length l, freely pivoted at O. Initially OP makes an angle α ($< \frac{1}{2}\pi$) with the downward vertical. The particle is projected horizontally with velocity V. Show that P will begin to rise if

$$V^2 > gl \sin \alpha \tan \alpha$$

but that, however large V may be, it can never rise through a vertical distance greater than $2l \cos \alpha$. (M.T.)

17. A particle of mass m is attached to the surface of a uniform sphere of radius a and mass M. The sphere rotates with a constant angular velocity n about the radius to the particle, which makes a constant acute angle α with the upward vertical. The vertical plane through this diameter rotates with constant angular velocity Ω, and the whole arrangement slides along a smooth horizontal table. Show that

$$ak(2k + 7)\Omega^2 \cos \alpha - 2ank(k + 1)\Omega + 5g(k + 1) = 0$$

where $k = M/m$. (M.T.)

18. State the principle of conservation of angular momentum for a dynamical system.

A uniform thin smooth tube, of length $2a$ and mass M, is free to move in contact with a smooth horizontal plane. Initially the tube is rotating with angular velocity ω about its mid-point at which a bead of mass m is at rest. If the bead is slightly displaced, find the angular velocity of the tube when the bead reaches the end. (L.U.)

19. State the principles of conservation of energy and conservation of linear momentum.

A block of mass M at rest on a smooth horizontal table has a smooth-walled cylindrical hole of radius a with its axis horizontal, and a small bead of mass m is at rest in the hole, in the vertical plane through the centre of mass of the block. If the block is then suddenly given a velocity V along the table in a direction normal to the axis of the hole, show that the bead will just rise to the level of the axis if $V^2 = 2ga(M + m)/M$.

Prove also that when the bead is next at its lowest level the velocity of the block is $(M - m)V/(M + m)$. (L.U.)

20. The kinetic energy of a dynamical system with two degrees of freedom is

$$\tfrac{1}{2}(a\dot{q}_1^2 + 2b\dot{q}_1\dot{q}_2 + c\dot{q}_2^2)$$

where q_1, q_2 are generalised co-ordinates and a, b, c are functions of q_1, q_2 such that $a = a_0$, $b = b_0$, $c = c_0$ when $q_1 = q_2 = 0$. The system is set in motion from rest in the configuration $q_1 = q_2 = 0$ by Lagrangian components of impulse I_1, I_2. Show that the kinetic energy T_0 just after impulse is given by

$$2(a_0c_0 - b_0^2)T_0 = c_0I_1^2 - 2b_0I_1I_2 + a_0I_2^2$$

Two equal uniform rods AB, BC, each of mass m and length $2l$, are freely hinged at B and are suspended from a fixed smooth hinge at A. The system hangs in equilibrium when a horizontal impulse I is applied at C. Show that

$$7mT_0 = 12I^2 \qquad \text{(L.U.)}$$

21. Obtain Lagrange's equations of impulsive motion. Three uniform rods AB, BD, DC smoothly jointed at B and D are at rest, forming two opposite sides and a diagonal BD of a rectangle $ABCD$, where AB is $4a$, and $BC = 3a$. The rods AB and DC are of equal mass m and the rod BD is of mass $2m$. An impulse I is applied at B along the diagonal BD. Prove that the kinetic energy of the motion set up is $19I^2/125m$. (L.U.)

22. Four equal uniform rods AB, BC, CD, DA, each of length $2a$ and mass m, are freely hinged together at A, B, C, D so as to form a square, and they lie on a smooth horizontal plane. A blow mV is delivered at A in the direction AB. If u_1, u_2, u_3, u_4 are the resolutes of the velocities of AB, BC, CD, DA, respectively, parallel to AB, BC, CD, DA, respectively, show, by the Lagrangian method or otherwise, that

$$u_1 = \tfrac{5}{8}V, \quad u_2 = 0, \quad u_3 = \tfrac{1}{8}V, \quad u_4 = 0 \qquad \text{(L.U.)}$$

23. Two uniform rods OA, AB, each of mass m and length $2a$, are smoothly jointed together at A and hang in equilibrium under gravity from a fixed smooth joint at O. A horizontal impulse I is applied at B. Find the Lagrangian components of impulse if the angles which the rods make with the vertical are taken as the generalised co-ordinates of the system, and show that the kinetic energy of the rods just after impulse is $12I^2/(7m)$. (L.U.)

24. Four equal rods, each of length a and mass m, are freely jointed so as to form a rhombus, one of whose diagonals is vertical; the ends of the horizontal diagonal are joined by an elastic thread at its natural length, and the system falls through a height h to a horizontal plane (no restitution). Prove that, if any rod makes an angle θ with the vertical at time t after the impact, then

$$(1 + 3\sin^2\theta)\dot{\theta}^2 = \frac{18gh}{a^2}\,\frac{\sin^2\alpha}{1 + 3\sin^2\alpha} + \frac{6g}{a}(\cos\alpha - \cos\theta) - \frac{3\lambda}{2ma}\,\frac{(\sin\theta - \sin\alpha)^2}{\sin\alpha}$$

where α is the initial value of θ, and λ is the modulus of the thread. (C.)

25. Obtain Lagrange's equations for impulsive forces.

A uniform rod, of mass m, is moving in a plane, its longitudinal velocity being w, and the transverse velocities of its end points being u and v. Show that the kinetic energy of the rod is

$$T = \tfrac{1}{6}m(u^2 + v^2 + uv + 3w^2)$$

Three uniform rods AB, BC, CD of equal masses m, smoothly jointed together at B and C, lie on a smooth table, with AB and CD perpendicular to BC and on opposite sides of it. An impulse I is applied at D in the plane of the rods. If T is the kinetic energy generated, prove that

$$8/21 \leqslant mT/I^2 \leqslant 19/12. \qquad \text{(L.U.)}$$

26. The ends of a uniform rigid rod of mass m are moving with velocities $\mathbf{u}$, $\mathbf{v}$; prove that the kinetic energy of the rod is

$$\tfrac{1}{6}m(\mathbf{u}^2 + \mathbf{u}.\mathbf{v} + \mathbf{v}^2)$$

Three uniform rods OA, AB, BC, each of mass m, are smoothly jointed together at A, B and hang in equilibrium under gravity from a fixed smooth joint at O. An impulsive couple G is applied to the rod AB in a vertical plane through O; prove that the initial kinetic energy of the system is

$$(57G^2)/(26ml^2)$$

where l is the length of AB. (L.U.)

27. State and prove the principle of conservation of angular momentum.

A uniform thin hollow circular cylinder of radius a and mass m rolls on a rough plane, which is inclined at an angle $\pi/6$ to the horizontal, and its axis is perpendicular to the line of greatest slope. The cylinder meets a fixed inelastic perfectly rough bar placed horizontally and parallel to the inclined plane and at a perpendicular distance $\frac{1}{2}a$ from the plane. Show that, if the cylinder is to have sufficient velocity to surmount the obstacle when it reaches it, it must be allowed to roll down the plane through a distance

$$\frac{32a}{9}\left(1 - \frac{\sqrt{3}}{2}\right) \qquad \text{(L.U.)}$$

28. The ends A, B of a light rod of length $2a$ are constrained to move along two fixed smooth wires OC, OZ respectively; OC is horizontal and OZ vertically downwards. A particle of mass m is attached to each end of the rod, and a bead of mass M can slide freely along the rod. The whole system is made to rotate about OZ with constant angular velocity ω, and at time t the bead is at a distance $a + x$ from B, while the rod makes an angle θ with the upward vertical. Prove that the kinetic energy of the system is

$$2ma^2[\dot\theta^2 + \omega^2 \sin^2 \theta] + \tfrac{1}{2}M[\dot x^2 + (a^2 + 2ax \cos 2\theta + x^2)\dot\theta^2 + 2a\dot x\dot\theta \sin 2\theta + (a + x)^2\omega^2 \sin^2 \theta]$$

Show, by using Lagrange's equations, or otherwise, that the steady motion in which $x = 0$, $\theta = \alpha$ (constant), is possible only if $a\omega^2 = g \cot \alpha \operatorname{cosec} \alpha$, and

$$(M + 2m) \tan^2 \alpha = M + 4m \qquad \text{(L.U.)}$$

29. A uniform rod AB of mass m and length $2a$, attached to a fixed point O by a light elastic string OA of natural length l and modulus of elasticity λ, moves in a vertical plane through O with the string taut. At time t, OA, AB make angles θ, ϕ with the downward vertical and the length of OA is $l + x$. Prove that the kinetic energy of the rod is

$$\tfrac{1}{2}m[\dot x^2 + (l + x)^2\dot\theta^2 + \tfrac{4}{3}a^2\dot\phi^2] + ma\dot\phi[(l + x)\dot\theta \cos (\phi - \theta) - \dot x \sin (\phi - \theta)]$$

Derive Lagrange's equations of motion for the system if, in addition to gravity, an external force with horizontal and vertical components X, Y acts on the rod at B. (L.U.)

30. Two uniform rods AB, AC, each of mass m and length $2a$, are smoothly hinged together at A and move on a smooth horizontal plane. At time t the mass-centre of the pair of rods is at the point (ξ, η) referred to fixed perpendicular axes Ox, Oy in the plane, and the rods make angles $\theta \pm \phi$ with Ox. Prove that the kinetic energy of the system is

$$m[\dot{\xi}^2 + \dot{\eta}^2 + (\tfrac{1}{3} + \sin^2 \phi)a^2\dot{\theta}^2 + (\tfrac{1}{3} + \cos^2 \phi)a^2\dot{\phi}^2]$$

and derive Lagrange's equation for the system if an external force with components (X, Y) along the axes acts on the rods at A. (L.U.)

31. Two uniform rods, each of length $2a$, are freely jointed and placed on a smooth table in a straight line parallel to an edge. A cord is attached to the joint and passing over the edge of the table at right angles supports a body of mass $1/n$ of that of either rod. Prove that the angle θ through which either rod has turned at time t is given by the equation

$$\{2 + n(1 + 3 \sin^2 \theta)\}a\dot{\theta}^2 = 3g \sin \theta \qquad \text{(C.)}$$

32. Six equal uniform rods are freely jointed at a point O and have their other ends at the corners of a regular hexagon on a smooth horizontal plane, these ends being connected by six similar elastic threads in the sides of the hexagon. Initially all the threads have their natural lengths, and the rods are inclined at an angle α to the vertical. Prove that the joint will or will not reach the plane according as the ratio of the modulus of elasticity of each thread to the weight of each rod $<$ or $>$ $\sin \alpha \cos \alpha/(1 - \sin \alpha)^2$. (C.)

33. A rifled gun is mounted on a carriage without wheels. Prove that, if α is the elevation of the gun, p the pitch of the barrel, k the radius of gyration of the shot, and U, V the muzzle velocities of the shot when the carriage is (1) fixed and (2) allowed a free recoil, then

$$V^2\{k^2/p^2 + \sin^2 \alpha + M \cos^2 \alpha/(M + m)\}$$
$$= U^2(1 + k^2/p^2)\{\sin^2 \alpha + M^2 \cos^2 \alpha/(M + m)^2\}$$

where m is the mass of the shot, and M is the mass of the gun and carriage. (C.)

34. A particle is placed in a smooth elliptic tube of n times its mass at an end of the major axis, and the tube is struck by a blow parallel to the minor axis so that it starts to move parallel to this axis with velocity V. Prove that the eccentric angle ϕ of the position of the particle at any time is given by the equation

$$\left[a^2 \sin^2 \phi + b^2 \cos^2 \phi + \frac{a^2(a^2 - b^2) \sin^2 \phi}{(1 + n)k^2 - (a^2 - b^2) \sin^2 \phi}\right]\dot{\phi}^2 = V^2$$

where $2a$ and $2b$ are the principal axes of the tube, and k is its radius of gyration about an axis through its centre at right angles to its plane. (C.)

35. Two rough horizontal cylinders each of radius c are fixed with their axes inclined to each other at an angle 2α ; and a uniform sphere of radius a rolls between them, starting with its centre very nearly above the point of intersection of the highest generators. Prove that the vertical velocity of its centre in a position in which the radii to the two points of contact make angles ϕ with the horizontal is

$$\sin \alpha \cos \phi \sqrt{\{10g(a + c)(1 - \sin \phi)/(7 - 5 \cos^2 \alpha \cos^2 \phi)\}} \qquad \text{(C.)}$$

36. A pair of uniform disc wheels, each of mass m and radius a, connected by a light axle normal to each wheel through its centre, rolls with the axle horizontal down a rough plane of angle α. A light rod, of length l ($< a$), smoothly hinged at one end to the mid-point of the axle so that it can swing freely in a plane perpendicular to the axle, carries a mass $2m$ at the other end. Initially the system is held at rest with the rod normal to the inclined plane and below the axle. If, at time t after the system is released from rest, ϕ is the angle turned through by the wheels and θ the angle turned through by the rod (in the opposite sense), show that

$$5a\phi + 2l \sin \theta = 2gt^2 \sin \alpha$$

and that the rod swings over an arc $2 \tan^{-1} (\frac{1}{5} \tan \alpha)$. (L.U.)

CHAPTER XIII

FURTHER PROPERTIES OF THE INERTIA TENSOR

13.1 The eigenvalue problem

Suppose we are given an inertia tensor $\mathscr{I}(O)$ at a point O and w.r.t. an orthonormal triad $(\boldsymbol{i}, \boldsymbol{j}, \boldsymbol{k})$. Now because $\mathscr{I}(O)$ is a symmetric tensor we shall be able to show that an orthonormal triad $(\boldsymbol{e}_1, \boldsymbol{e}_2, \boldsymbol{e}_3)$ can always be found with respect to which $\mathscr{I}(O)$ is diagonal, that is say, it can be written

$$\mathscr{I}(O) = \lambda_1 \boldsymbol{e}_1\boldsymbol{e}_1 + \lambda_2 \boldsymbol{e}_2\boldsymbol{e}_2 + \lambda_3 \boldsymbol{e}_3\boldsymbol{e}_3 \quad . \quad . \quad (1)$$

with matrix representation

$$\mathscr{I}(O) = \begin{pmatrix} \lambda_1 & 0 & 0 \\ 0 & \lambda_2 & 0 \\ 0 & 0 & \lambda_3 \end{pmatrix}$$

If (1) is true then $\qquad \mathscr{I}(O).\boldsymbol{e}_r = \lambda_r \boldsymbol{e}_r \quad (r = 1, 2, 3)$

so that the scalars λ_r and the vectors $\boldsymbol{e}_r$ satisfy the equation

$$\mathscr{I}(O).\boldsymbol{e} = \lambda \boldsymbol{e} \quad . \quad . \quad . \quad . \quad . \quad (2)$$

We call the values of λ the *eigenvalues* of $\mathscr{I}(O)$, and the vectors $\boldsymbol{e}$, the *eigenvectors* of $\mathscr{I}(O)$. The eigenvectors are clearly the *principal axes* at O, the λ_r being the *principal moments of inertia* at O.

Theorem I. *Every real symmetric tensor of the second order can be reduced to the canonical form* $\lambda_1 \boldsymbol{e}_1\boldsymbol{e}_1 + \lambda_2 \boldsymbol{e}_2\boldsymbol{e}_2 + \lambda_3 \boldsymbol{e}_3\boldsymbol{e}_3$.

Proof: Our problem is to solve for λ, $\boldsymbol{e}$ the equation (2), where $\boldsymbol{e} = l\,\boldsymbol{i} + m\,\boldsymbol{j} + n\,\boldsymbol{k}$. If the elements of $\mathscr{I}(O)$ are $t_{\alpha\beta}$ $(\alpha, \beta = 1, 2, 3)$ w.r.t $(\boldsymbol{i}, \boldsymbol{j}, \boldsymbol{k})$, where $t_{\alpha\beta} = t_{\beta\alpha}$, (2) gives

$$\left.\begin{aligned} t_{11}l + t_{12}m + t_{13}n &= \lambda l \\ t_{21}l + t_{22}m + t_{23}n &= \lambda m \\ t_{31}l + t_{32}m + t_{33}n &= \lambda n \end{aligned}\right\} \quad . \quad . \quad (3)$$

(3) have a non-trivial solution in $l : m : n$ provided

$$\det\{\mathscr{I}(O) - \lambda\mathscr{I}\} = \begin{vmatrix} t_{11} - \lambda & t_{12} & t_{13} \\ t_{21} & t_{22} - \lambda & t_{23} \\ t_{31} & t_{32} & t_{33} - \lambda \end{vmatrix} = 0 \quad (4)$$

This is a cubic in λ and possesses at least one real root. In fact, since $\mathscr{I}(O)$ is symmetric, we can show that all the roots are real : thus, write $\boldsymbol{a} = \mathscr{I}(O).\boldsymbol{e} = \boldsymbol{e}.\mathscr{I}(O)$, then

$$0 < \boldsymbol{a}^2 = \lambda^2 \boldsymbol{e}^2 \quad \text{so that } \lambda^2 > 0$$

Each value of λ gives a value for $l : m : n$ from (3) and if we say that $\boldsymbol{e}$ shall be a unit vector, i.e. $l^2 + m^2 + n^2 = 1$, we find l, m, n separately.

(i) Suppose all the roots of (4) are distinct, $\lambda_1, \lambda_2, \lambda_3$. Then we solve (3) to find the eigenvectors $\boldsymbol{e}_1, \boldsymbol{e}_2, \boldsymbol{e}_3$. We notice that $\quad \mathscr{I}(O).\boldsymbol{e}_r = \lambda_r \boldsymbol{e}_r \quad$ and $\quad \mathscr{I}(O).\boldsymbol{e}_s = \lambda_s \boldsymbol{e}_s$

give $\quad \boldsymbol{e}_s.\mathscr{I}(O).\boldsymbol{e}_r = \boldsymbol{e}_r.\mathscr{I}(O).\boldsymbol{e}_s = \lambda_r(\boldsymbol{e}_s.\boldsymbol{e}_r) = \lambda_s(\boldsymbol{e}_r.\boldsymbol{e}_s)$

Hence $\lambda_r \neq \lambda_s$ implies $\boldsymbol{e}_r.\boldsymbol{e}_s = 0$. The eigenvectors therefore form an orthonormal triad at O.

(ii) Suppose two roots are equal, $\lambda_2 = \lambda_3$. Then we can find $\boldsymbol{e}_1$ and $\boldsymbol{e}_2$ from (3) and, as in (i), $\boldsymbol{e}_1$ is perpendicular to $\boldsymbol{e}_2$. Now choose $\boldsymbol{e}_3$ to be perpendicular to $\boldsymbol{e}_1$ and $\boldsymbol{e}_2$, viz. $\boldsymbol{e}_3 = \boldsymbol{e}_1 \times \boldsymbol{e}_2$.

If $\mathscr{I}(O)$ becomes
$$\begin{pmatrix} \lambda_1 & 0 & \lambda_{13} \\ 0 & \lambda_2 & \lambda_{23} \\ \lambda_{13} & \lambda_{23} & \lambda_{33} \end{pmatrix}$$
w.r.t. $(\boldsymbol{e}_1, \boldsymbol{e}_2, \boldsymbol{e}_3)$ we have
$$\lambda_{13} = \boldsymbol{e}_1.\mathscr{I}(O).\boldsymbol{e}_3 = \boldsymbol{e}_3.\mathscr{I}(O).\boldsymbol{e}_1 = \lambda_1.\boldsymbol{e}_3.\boldsymbol{e}_1 = 0$$
$$\lambda_{23} = \boldsymbol{e}_3.\mathscr{I}(O).\boldsymbol{e}_2 = \lambda_2\, \boldsymbol{e}_3.\boldsymbol{e}_2 = 0$$
$\lambda_{33} = \lambda_2$ since $\mathscr{I}(O)$ must now reduce to
$$\lambda_1 \boldsymbol{e}_1\boldsymbol{e}_1 + \lambda_2(\boldsymbol{e}_2\boldsymbol{e}_2 + \boldsymbol{e}_3\boldsymbol{e}_3).$$

(iii) Suppose $\lambda_1 = \lambda_2 = \lambda_3$. Then we can find $\boldsymbol{e}_1$ from (3), and take any other perpendicular pair $\boldsymbol{e}_2, \boldsymbol{e}_3$ so that $(\boldsymbol{e}_1, \boldsymbol{e}_2, \boldsymbol{e}_3)$ form an orthonormal triad. Suppose that, w.r.t. this new triad, $\mathscr{I}(O)$ becomes
$$\begin{pmatrix} \lambda_1 & 0 & 0 \\ 0 & \lambda_{22} & \lambda_{23} \\ 0 & \lambda_{23} & \lambda_{33} \end{pmatrix}$$
this will be the form since, e.g. $\lambda_{13} = \boldsymbol{e}_3.\mathscr{I}(O).\boldsymbol{e}_1 = \lambda_1 \boldsymbol{e}_3.\boldsymbol{e}_1 = 0$

Now the roots of the equation $\det\{\mathscr{I}(O) - \lambda\mathscr{I}\} = 0$ are invariant quantities, independent of the frame of reference, by elementary matrix theory. Hence we must have
$$(\lambda_{22} - \lambda)(\lambda_{33} - \lambda) - \lambda^2{}_{23} \equiv (\lambda_1 - \lambda)^2$$
which gives $\quad (\lambda_{22} - \lambda_{33})^2 + 4\lambda^2{}_{23} = 0$

Hence $\quad \lambda_{22} = \lambda_{33} = \lambda_1 \quad$ and $\quad \lambda_{23} = 0$

It follows that $\mathscr{I}(O)$ is diagonal w.r.t. $(\boldsymbol{e}_1, \boldsymbol{e}_2, \boldsymbol{e}_3)$. Q.E.D.

Example 1. A rigid body consists of four particles of masses m, $2m$, $3m$, $4m$ respectively situated at the points (a, a, a), $(a, -a, -a)$, $(-a, a, -a)$, $(-a, -a, a)$. The particles are rigidly connected by a light framework. Find the interia tensor at the origin and deduce that the principal moments of inertia at O are
$$(20 + 2\sqrt{5})ma^2, \quad 20ma^2, \quad (20 - 2\sqrt{5})ma^2 \qquad \text{(M.T.)}$$

With respect to the axes given, we have

$$A = \sum m(y^2 + z^2) = 20ma^2 ; \quad B = 20ma^2 ; \quad C = 20ma^2$$
$$F = \sum myz = -4ma^2 ; \quad G = -2ma^2 ; \quad H = 0$$

Hence $\mathscr{I}(O)$ has matrix representation

$$\mathscr{I}(O) = ma^2 \begin{pmatrix} 20 & 0 & 2 \\ 0 & 20 & 4 \\ 2 & 4 & 20 \end{pmatrix}$$

The principal moments of inertia at O are the values of $\lambda(ma^2)$ satisfying

$$\begin{vmatrix} (20-\lambda) & 0 & 2 \\ 0 & (20-\lambda) & 4 \\ 2 & 4 & (20-\lambda) \end{vmatrix} = 0$$

which gives $$(20-\lambda)\{(20-\lambda)^2 - 20\} = 0$$

Hence $$\lambda = 20 \quad \text{or} \quad 20 - \lambda = \pm 2\sqrt{5}$$ Q.E.D.

The *principal axes* at O are the eigenvectors corresponding to these eigenvalues. The equations (3) become, in this case,

$$\begin{aligned} (20-\lambda)l \qquad\qquad &+ \quad 2n &= 0 \\ (20-\lambda)m &+ \quad 4n &= 0 \\ 2l + \quad 4m \quad &+ (20-\lambda)n &= 0 \end{aligned}$$

Hence

$$l : m : n = \begin{vmatrix} (20-\lambda) & 4 \\ 4 & (20-\lambda) \end{vmatrix} : -\begin{vmatrix} 0 & 4 \\ 2 & (20-\lambda) \end{vmatrix} : \begin{vmatrix} 0 & (20-\lambda) \\ 2 & 4 \end{vmatrix}$$

(i) When $20 - \lambda = 0$, we get

$$l : m : n = -2 : 1 : 0$$

and $$\boldsymbol{e}_1 = \frac{1}{\sqrt{5}}(-2\boldsymbol{i} + \boldsymbol{j})$$

(ii) When $20 - \lambda = -2\sqrt{5}$, we get

$$l : m : n = 1 : 2 : \sqrt{5}$$

and $$\boldsymbol{e}_2 = \frac{1}{\sqrt{10}}(\boldsymbol{i} + 2\boldsymbol{j} + \sqrt{5}\boldsymbol{k})$$

(iii) When $20 - \lambda = +2\sqrt{5}$, we get

$$l : m : n = 1 : 2 : -\sqrt{5}$$

and $$\boldsymbol{e}_3 = \frac{1}{\sqrt{10}}(\boldsymbol{i} + 2\boldsymbol{j} - \sqrt{5}\boldsymbol{k})$$

We notice that these vectors are mutually perpendicular.

13.2 The moment of inertia about a given line

Suppose we are given $\mathscr{I}(O)$; to find the moment of inertia I of the system about the line through O defined by the unit vector $\boldsymbol{e}$

(v. Fig. 110). Let μ denote the mass of a particle at P. We have

$$\begin{aligned} I &= \sum \mu p^2 \\ &= \sum \mu \,|\, (\boldsymbol{r} \times \boldsymbol{e}) \,|^2 \\ &= \sum \mu(\boldsymbol{r} \times \boldsymbol{e})^2 \\ &= \sum \mu\{\boldsymbol{r}^2\boldsymbol{e}^2 - (\boldsymbol{r}.\boldsymbol{e})^2\} \end{aligned}$$

Hence $\quad I = \boldsymbol{e}.\mathscr{I}(O).\boldsymbol{e} \quad . \quad . \quad . \quad (1)$

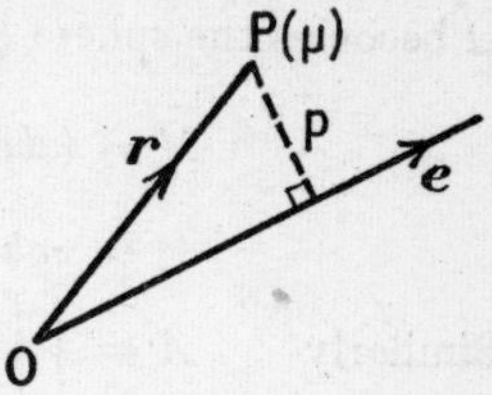

FIG. 110.

This is illustrated by the special cases, $\boldsymbol{i}.\mathscr{I}(O).\boldsymbol{i} = A, \boldsymbol{j}.\mathscr{I}(O).\boldsymbol{j} = B, \boldsymbol{k}.\mathscr{I}(O).\boldsymbol{k} = C.$

(1) also confirms the fact that, when $\mathscr{I}(O)$ is referred to its principal axes at O, the λ_r of 13.1(1) measure the moments of inertia about these axes.

If the line defined by $\boldsymbol{e}$ does not pass through O we can find I most easily by starting with $\mathscr{I}(G)$, G being the centre of mass of the system. Thus, if $\boldsymbol{e}$ passes through a point A where $\overline{GA} = \boldsymbol{a}$ we get, by 9.5(1),

$$I = \boldsymbol{e}.\mathscr{I}(A).\boldsymbol{e} = \boldsymbol{e}.\{\mathscr{I}(G) + M(\boldsymbol{a}^2\mathscr{I} - \boldsymbol{aa}\}.\boldsymbol{e} \quad . \quad (2)$$

If we must start with $\mathscr{I}(O)$ we can use 9.5(1) again in (2) to give, with $\overline{OG} = \bar{\boldsymbol{r}}$

$$I = \boldsymbol{e}.\{\mathscr{I}(O) - M(\bar{\boldsymbol{r}}^2 - \mathscr{I}\,\bar{\boldsymbol{r}}\bar{\boldsymbol{r}}) + M(\boldsymbol{a}^2\mathscr{I} - \boldsymbol{aa})\}.\boldsymbol{e}$$

We can express (1) in terms of Cartesian geometry by writing $\boldsymbol{e} = l\,\boldsymbol{i} + m\,\boldsymbol{j} + n\,\boldsymbol{k}$ and

$$\mathscr{I}(O) = \begin{pmatrix} A & -H & -G \\ -H & B & -F \\ -G & -F & C \end{pmatrix}$$

Then $$I = (l \quad m \quad n)\begin{pmatrix} A & -H & -G \\ -H & B & -F \\ -G & -F & C \end{pmatrix}\begin{pmatrix} l \\ m \\ n \end{pmatrix}$$

giving $$I = Al^2 + Bm^2 + Cn^2 - 2Fmn - 2Gnl - 2Hlm \quad . \quad (3)$$

Example 1. A solid ellipsoid has principal axes of lengths $2a$, $2b$, $2c$. The density of the material is variable in such a way that the surfaces of constant density are similar and similarly situated concentric ellipsoids, the density at points of the axis of lenth $2a$ being proportional to the distance from the centre of the ellipsoid. Prove that the square of the radius of gyration about the diameter which makes equal angles with the principal axes is

$$\tfrac{4}{27}(a^2 + b^2 + c^2) \qquad \text{(L.U.)}$$

If Ω denotes the volume of the ellipsoid the total mass is M where

$$M = \iiint_\Omega \rho\, dx\, dy\, dz$$

Transform the variables by $\xi = \dfrac{x}{a}$, $\eta = \dfrac{y}{b}$, $\zeta = \dfrac{z}{c}$. The surfaces of equal density become concentric spheres with $\rho = kr$, k a constant. Ω becomes the sphere $\xi^2 + \eta^2 + \zeta^2 = 1$ and so

$$M = (abck) \int_0^1 \int_0^\pi \int_0^{2\pi} r \cdot r^2 \sin \theta \, dr \, d\theta \, d\phi$$

$$= \pi abck$$

Similarly $A = \iiint_\Omega \rho(y^2 + z^2) \, dx \, dy \, dz = \frac{2}{9}M(b^2 + c^2)$

with $B = \frac{2}{9}M(c^2 + a^2)$ and $C = \frac{2}{9}M(a^2 + b^2)$. Also $F = G = H = 0$ by symmetry (or calculation). The line e has direction cosines $\dfrac{1}{\sqrt{3}}, \dfrac{1}{\sqrt{3}}, \dfrac{1}{\sqrt{3}}$. Hence (3) gives

$$I = \tfrac{1}{3}(A + B + C) = \tfrac{4}{27}M(a^2 + b^2 + c^2) \qquad \text{Q.E.D.}$$

13.3   The momental ellipsoid

With O as origin, let $\boldsymbol{r} = x\,\boldsymbol{i} + y\,\boldsymbol{j} + z\,\boldsymbol{k}$ be the position vector of a variable point $P(\boldsymbol{r})$. Given $\mathscr{J}(O)$, the equation

$$\boldsymbol{r} \cdot \mathscr{J}(O) \cdot \boldsymbol{r} = 1 \qquad . \qquad . \qquad . \qquad . \qquad (1)$$

is the equation of a central quadric, centre at O, for it is

$$Ax^2 + By^2 + Cz^2 - 2Fyz - 2Gzx - 2Hxy = 1 \qquad . \qquad (2)$$

This is in fact an *ellipsoid* ; for, referring $\mathscr{J}(O)$ and $\boldsymbol{r}$ to the principal axes at O (as in 13.1), (1) becomes

$$\lambda_1 \xi_1^2 + \lambda_2 \xi_2^2 + \lambda_3 \xi_3^2 = 1$$

where $\boldsymbol{r} = \xi_1 \boldsymbol{e}_1 + \xi_2 \boldsymbol{e}_2 + \xi_3 \boldsymbol{e}_3$. Since λ_1, λ_2, λ_3 are all positive, being moments of inertia, this is an ellipsoid. Also, writing $\boldsymbol{r} = r\,\boldsymbol{e}$ where $|\,\boldsymbol{e}\,| = 1$, (1) gives

$$\boldsymbol{e} \cdot \mathscr{J}(O) \cdot \boldsymbol{e} = \frac{1}{r^2} \qquad . \qquad . \qquad . \qquad . \qquad (3)$$

which is the moment of inertia about $\boldsymbol{e}$ (v, 13.2(1)). Thus if P is any point on the ellipsoid the moment of inertia about OP equals $\dfrac{1}{OP^2}$ (numerically, dimensions being ignored). Hence (1) is called the *momental ellipsoid of the body at* O.

    Theorem I.   *Given the momental ellipsoid at G; to find the momental ellipsoid with respect to parallel axes at any other point O.*

Method: If $\overline{GO} = \boldsymbol{a}$ we can use 9.5(1), whence the ellipsoid at O is

$$\boldsymbol{r} \cdot \mathscr{J}(O) \cdot \boldsymbol{r} = 1$$

or $\qquad\qquad \boldsymbol{r} \cdot \{\, \mathscr{J}(G) + M(a^2 \mathscr{J} - \boldsymbol{aa})\} \cdot \boldsymbol{r} = 1 \qquad . \qquad (4)$

Example 1. To find the momental ellipsoid at one corner of a uniform cube of mass M and side $2a$, the axes being taken along the edges of the cube.

At the centre of the cube G the parallel set of axes are principal axes (by symmetry) and we have $A = B = C = \frac{2}{3}Ma^2$; $F = G = H = 0$. Writing $\overline{GO} = \boldsymbol{a} = a(\boldsymbol{i} + \boldsymbol{j} + \boldsymbol{k})$, $a \neq |\boldsymbol{a}|$, (4) gives

$$\boldsymbol{r}.\{\tfrac{2}{3}\mathscr{I} + 3\mathscr{I} - (\boldsymbol{i}+\boldsymbol{j}+\boldsymbol{k})(\boldsymbol{i}+\boldsymbol{j}+\boldsymbol{k})\}.\boldsymbol{r} = \frac{1}{Ma^2}$$

which is
$$\tfrac{11}{3}r^2 - (x+y+z)^2 = \frac{1}{Ma^2}$$

This is
$$11(x^2+y^2+z^2) - 3(x+y+z)^2 = \frac{3}{Ma^2}$$

13.4 The ellipsoid of gyration

Let $\mathscr{J}^{-1}(O)$ be the tensor inverse to $\mathscr{J}(O)$ (v. 9.4(6)), i.e. $\mathscr{J}^{-1}.\mathscr{J} = \mathscr{J}.\mathscr{J}^{-1} = \mathscr{I}$. Then the central quadric

$$\boldsymbol{r}.\mathscr{J}^{-1}(O).\boldsymbol{r} = \frac{1}{M} \quad . \quad . \quad . \quad . \quad (1)$$

is called the *ellipsoid of gyration at the point O*. When $\mathscr{J}(O)$ is referred to its principal axes at O, viz.

$$\mathscr{J}(O) = \lambda_1 \boldsymbol{e}_1\boldsymbol{e}_1 + \lambda_2 \boldsymbol{e}_2\boldsymbol{e}_2 + \lambda_3 \boldsymbol{e}_3\boldsymbol{e}_3$$

the inverse tensor is simply

$$\mathscr{J}^{-1}(O) = \frac{1}{\lambda_1}\boldsymbol{e}_1\boldsymbol{e}_1 + \frac{1}{\lambda_2}\boldsymbol{e}_2\boldsymbol{e}_2 + \frac{1}{\lambda_3}\boldsymbol{e}_3\boldsymbol{e}_3 \quad . \quad . \quad (2)$$

which shows that the principal axes of $\mathscr{J}(O)$ are also principal axes of $\mathscr{J}^{-1}(O)$. This also follows by the argument:

$$\mathscr{J}.\boldsymbol{e} = \lambda\boldsymbol{e} \quad \text{implies} \quad \mathscr{J}^{-1}.\mathscr{J}.\boldsymbol{e} = \boldsymbol{e} = \lambda\,\mathscr{J}^{-1}.\boldsymbol{e}$$

and so
$$\mathscr{J}^{-1}.\boldsymbol{e} = \frac{1}{\lambda}\boldsymbol{e}$$

In connection with (1) we can prove the following interesting result:

The perpendicular from O to the tangent plane at P to the ellipsoid of gyration equals the radius of gyration about a line defined by this perpendicular.

To prove this, consider Fig. 111, where P is any point on the ellipsoid of gyration (1), and p is the length of the perpendicular from O to the tangent plane at P. Now (1) gives

$$d\boldsymbol{r}.\mathscr{J}^{-1}.\boldsymbol{r} = 0$$

Since $\mathscr{J}^{-1}$ is symmetric. Hence, since $d\boldsymbol{r}$ lies in the tangent plane at P, $(\mathscr{J}^{-1}.\boldsymbol{r})$ must be a

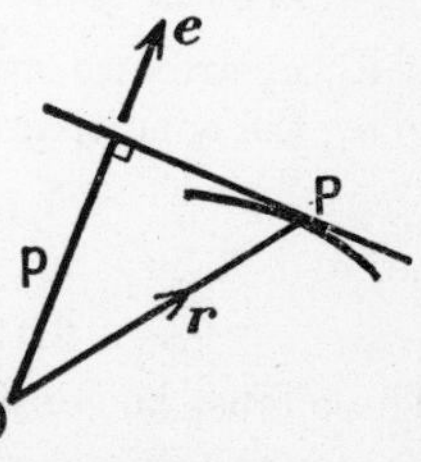

FIG. 111.

vector along the *normal* at P. Hence we can write $\boldsymbol{e} = \theta(\mathscr{I}^{-1}.\boldsymbol{r})$, where $\theta^{-1} = |\mathscr{I}^{-1}.\boldsymbol{r}|$, and $p = \boldsymbol{r}.\boldsymbol{e}$. Then the moment of inertia about the line $\boldsymbol{e}$ is

$$I = Mk^2 = \boldsymbol{e}.\mathscr{I}.\boldsymbol{e} = \theta^2(\mathscr{I}^{-1}.\boldsymbol{r}).\mathscr{I}.(\mathscr{I}^{-1}.\boldsymbol{r})$$

$$= \theta^2(\mathscr{I}^{-1}.\boldsymbol{r}).\boldsymbol{r} = \frac{\theta^2}{M} \quad \text{by (1)}$$

But $$p = \boldsymbol{r}.\boldsymbol{e} = \theta(\boldsymbol{r}.\mathscr{I}^{-1}.\boldsymbol{r}) = \frac{\theta}{M} \quad \text{by (1)}$$

Hence $$Mk^2 = Mp^2 \quad \text{and so } k = p$$ Q.E.D.

13.5 Principal axes at a point

We have already seen in 13.1 that the principal axes at O are, in fact, the eigenvectors of $\mathscr{I}(O)$. When these correspond to distinct eigenvalues λ_1, λ_2, λ_3 the momental ellipsoid at O is an equation of the form (v. 13.3)

$$\lambda_1 x^2 + \lambda_2 y^2 + \lambda_3 z^2 = 1 \quad . \quad . \quad . \quad . \quad (1)$$

When two of the eigenvalues coincide, say $\lambda_2 = \lambda_3$, (1) becomes

$$\lambda_1 x^2 + \lambda_2(y^2 + z^2) = 1$$

which is a surface of revolution about the x-axis ; a *spheroid* in fact, prolate when $\lambda_2 > \lambda_1$, oblate when $\lambda_2 < \lambda_1$. In this case the fact that the ellipsoid is a spheroid means that the choice of the principal axes $\boldsymbol{e}_2$, $\boldsymbol{e}_3$ is unlimited ; any two perpendicular diameters of the circular cross-section will suffice. When all three of the eigenvalues coincide $\lambda_1 = \lambda_2 = \lambda_3$, (1) becomes

$$x^2 + y^2 + z^2 = \frac{1}{\lambda_1}$$

which is a *sphere*. In this case any mutually perpendicular triad will serve as principal axes, because of the symmetry of the sphere.

To find the point on a given line at which it is a principal axis.

Take G, the centre of mass, as origin and the equation of the line as $\boldsymbol{r} = \boldsymbol{a} + t\,\boldsymbol{e}_1$, $\boldsymbol{e}_1$ being a unit vector. Suppose P is the point on this line at which it is a principal axis. Then P is defined by (say) t_0, and

$$\mathscr{I}(P) = \mathscr{I}(G) + M\{(\boldsymbol{a} + t_0\,\boldsymbol{e}_1)^2\mathscr{I} - (\boldsymbol{a} + t_0\,\boldsymbol{e}_1)(a + t_0\,\boldsymbol{e}_1)\}$$

If $\boldsymbol{e}_2$, $\boldsymbol{e}_3$ are two other unit vectors perpendicular to each other and to $\boldsymbol{e}_1$, the conditions that the line is a principal axis at P are

$$\boldsymbol{e}_1.\mathscr{I}(P).\boldsymbol{e}_2 = 0 = \boldsymbol{e}_1.\mathscr{I}(P).\boldsymbol{e}_3$$

i.e.
$$\boldsymbol{e}_1.\mathscr{I}(G).\boldsymbol{e}_2 - M(\boldsymbol{e}_1.\boldsymbol{a} + t_0)\boldsymbol{a}.\boldsymbol{e}_2 = 0$$
$$\boldsymbol{e}_1.\mathscr{I}(G).\boldsymbol{e}_3 - M(\boldsymbol{e}_1.\boldsymbol{a} + t_0)\boldsymbol{a}.\boldsymbol{e}_3 = 0$$

These must be consistent in t_0, hence

$$(\boldsymbol{a}.\boldsymbol{e}_3)\{\boldsymbol{e}_1.\mathscr{I}(G).\boldsymbol{e}_2\} = (\boldsymbol{a}.\boldsymbol{e}_2)\}\boldsymbol{e}_1.\mathscr{I}(G).\boldsymbol{e}_3\} \quad . \quad (2)$$

The point P is then defined by

$$t_0 = \frac{\boldsymbol{e}_1 . \mathscr{I}(G) . \boldsymbol{e}_2 - M(\boldsymbol{a} . \boldsymbol{e}_1)(\boldsymbol{a} . \boldsymbol{e}_2)}{M(\boldsymbol{a} . \boldsymbol{e}_2)} \quad . \quad . \quad (3)$$

Finally, we shall prove

Binet's Theorem. *The principal axes at a point O are the three normals at O to the three quadrics through O confocal with the ellipsoid of gyration at the mass centre G.*

Proof: The principal axes at O are the vectors $\boldsymbol{e}$ such that

$$\mathscr{I}(O) . \boldsymbol{e} = \lambda \boldsymbol{e} \quad (\lambda \text{ a scalar})$$

If $\overline{GO} = \boldsymbol{a}$, $\boldsymbol{e}$ satisfies

$$\{\mathscr{I}(G) + M(\boldsymbol{a}^2\mathscr{I} - \boldsymbol{aa})\} . \boldsymbol{e} = \lambda \mathscr{I} . \boldsymbol{e}$$

i.e. $$\{\mathscr{I}(G) + (M\,\boldsymbol{a}^2 - \lambda)\,\mathscr{I}\} . \boldsymbol{e} = M\,\boldsymbol{a}(\boldsymbol{a} . \boldsymbol{e})$$

Hence $$\boldsymbol{e} = M(\boldsymbol{a} . \boldsymbol{e})\{\mathscr{I}(G) + (M\,\boldsymbol{a}^2 - \lambda)\,\mathscr{I}\}^{-1} . \boldsymbol{a}$$

where the quantity $\{\quad\}^{-1}$ is the inverse tensor. Multiplying by $\boldsymbol{a}.$ gives

$$\boldsymbol{a} . \{\mathscr{I}(G) + (M\,\boldsymbol{a}^2 - \lambda)\mathscr{I}\}^{-1} . \boldsymbol{a} = \frac{1}{M}$$

which is the quadric confocal with

$$\boldsymbol{a} . \mathscr{I}^{-1}(G) . \boldsymbol{a} = \frac{1}{M}$$

Since there are three values of λ, there are three confocal quadrics and the normal to any one quadric is parallel to $\boldsymbol{e}$.

Q.E.D.

13.6 Equimomental systems

Let $\{M\,;\,G\}$ denote a mass system, total mass M, centre of mass G, and let primes denote a second system, i.e. $\{M'\,;\,G'\}$. Let their respective inertia tensors at a point O be denoted by $\mathscr{I}(O)$ and $\mathscr{I}'(O)$.

Definition: $\{M\,;\,G\}$ *and* $\{M'\,;\,G'\}$ *are equimomental when*

$$\mathscr{I}(O) = \mathscr{I}'(O) \textit{ for all points } O.$$

Theorem I. *$\mathscr{I}(O) = \mathscr{I}'(O)$, all O, implies $M = M'$ and G coincides with G'.*

Proof: We have $$\mathscr{I}(G) = \mathscr{I}'(G) = \mathscr{I}'(G') + M'(\boldsymbol{a}^2\mathscr{I} - \boldsymbol{aa}) \quad (1)$$

and $$\mathscr{I}'(G') = \mathscr{I}(G') = \mathscr{I}(G) + M(\boldsymbol{a}^2\mathscr{I} - \boldsymbol{aa}) \quad (2)$$

where $\boldsymbol{a} = \overline{GG'}$. Adding (1) and (2) gives

$$(M + M')(\boldsymbol{a}^2\,\mathscr{I} - \boldsymbol{aa}) = 0$$

Equating to zero the diagonal elements in $(\boldsymbol{a}^2\,\mathscr{I} - \boldsymbol{aa})$, we get

$$a_2{}^2 + a_3{}^2 = a_3{}^2 + a_1{}^2 = a_1{}^2 + a_2{}^2 = 0$$

Hence $a_1 = a_2 = a_3$ and G coincides with G'.

If O is any other point and $\overline{OG} = \mathbf{b}$, we now get

$$\mathscr{I}(O) = \mathscr{I}(G) + M(\mathbf{b}^2 \mathscr{I} - \mathbf{bb})$$
$$= \mathscr{I}'(G) + M'(\mathbf{b}^2 \mathscr{I} - \mathbf{bb}) = \mathscr{I}'(O)$$

Hence $M = M'$. Q.E.D.

Theorem II. *If $M = M'$, G coincides with G', and the moments of inertia of the two systems about every line through G are correspondingly equal, then $\{M ; G\}$ and $\{M' ; G'\}$ are equimomental systems.*

Proof: Let O be any point and $\mathbf{e}$ be an arbitrary unit vector.

Then, writing $\mathbf{b} = \overline{OG} = \overline{OG'}$, we get

$$\mathscr{I}(O) = \mathscr{I}(G) + M(\mathbf{b}^2 \mathscr{I} - \mathbf{bb})$$
$$\mathscr{I}'(O) = \mathscr{I}'(G) + M(\mathbf{b}^2 \mathscr{I} - \mathbf{bb})$$

Hence $\quad \mathscr{I}(O) - \mathscr{I}'(O) = \mathscr{I}(G) - \mathscr{I}'(G) \quad$ for all points O

Since $\quad \mathbf{e}.\mathscr{I}(G).\mathbf{e} = \mathbf{e}.\mathscr{I}'(G).\mathbf{e}$ it follows that

$$\mathbf{e}.\mathscr{I}(O).\mathbf{e} = \mathbf{e}.\mathscr{I}'(O).\mathbf{e} \quad (\text{all } \mathbf{e}) \qquad . \qquad . \qquad (3)$$

Take axes $\mathbf{i}$, $\mathbf{j}$, $\mathbf{k}$ at O and put $\mathbf{e} = l\,\mathbf{i} + m\,\mathbf{j} + n\,\mathbf{k}$, then (3) implies

$$(A - A')l^2 + (B - B')m^2 + (C - C')n^2 - 2(F - F')mn$$
$$- 2(G - G')nl - 2(H - H')lm = 0$$

for all l, m, n. Hence $A = A'$, $B = B'$, . . ., $H = H'$, and so

$$\mathscr{I}(O) = \mathscr{I}'(O) \quad \text{for all } O.$$ Q.E.D.

Corollary. In the condition $\mathbf{e}.\mathscr{I}(G).\mathbf{e} = \mathbf{e}.\mathscr{I}'(G).\mathbf{e}$, any other point may be substituted for G without affecting the result.

Example 1. A uniform rod of mass M is equimomental with three particles of masses $\frac{M}{6}$ at one end, $\frac{M}{6}$ at the other end, $\frac{2M}{3}$ at the centre of mass G.

For the inertia tensor at G of the particles is

$$\mathscr{I}'(G) = \tfrac{2}{6}Ma^2(\mathscr{I} - \mathbf{ii})$$

which should be compared with 9.5, Ex. 1. (N.B. This arrangement is not unique.)

Example 2. A uniform triangular lamina is equimomental with three particles placed at the mid-points of the sides, each of mass $\frac{M}{3}$.

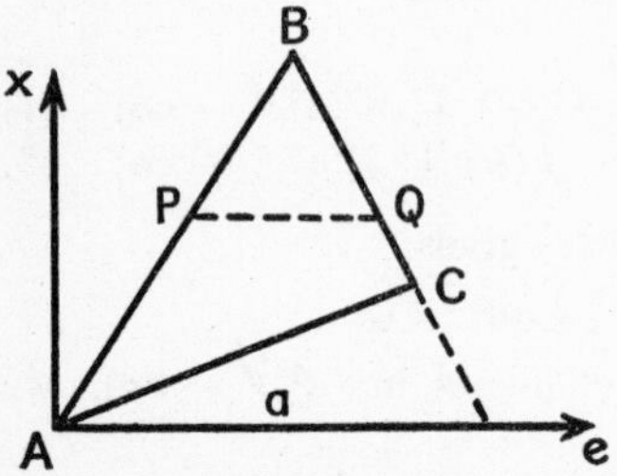

Fig. 112.

We can most readily prove this by using Theorem II (Cor.). Thus let Fig. 112 represent the triangle ABC of mass M and let $\mathbf{e}$ be an arbitrary vector in the plane of the triangle and through A. Let h, k be the perpendicular distances of B and C

from e. The moment of inertia of the triangle about e will be

$$I(e) = \int_0^h (PQ).x^2\,dx - \int_0^k (PQ).x^2\,dx$$

$$= \frac{a}{h}\int_0^h (h-x)x^2\,dx - \frac{a}{k}\int_0^k (k-x)x^2\,dx$$

$$= \frac{a}{12}(h^3 - k^3)$$

But $M = \frac{a}{2}(h-k)$ and so

$$I = \frac{M}{6}(h^2 + hk + k^2)$$

$$= \frac{M}{3}\left\{\left(\frac{h}{2}\right)^2 + \left(\frac{h+k}{2}\right)^2 + \left(\frac{k}{2}\right)^2\right\} \qquad \text{Q.E.D.}$$

N.B. Another system equimomental with the triangle is formed by three particles at the vertices, each of mass $\frac{M}{12}$, together with a a particle of mass $\frac{3}{4}M$ at the centroid. This follows by writing

$$I = \frac{M}{6}\left\{\frac{h^2}{2} + \frac{k^2}{2} + \frac{9}{2}\left(\frac{2}{3}\cdot\frac{h+k}{2}\right)^2\right\}$$

Example 3. A uniform rectangular lamina of mass M is equimomental with four particles of mass $\frac{M}{12}$ placed at the mid-points of the sides together with a particle of mass $\frac{2M}{3}$ at the centre.

This follows by writing, with the usual notation,

$$\mathscr{I}(G) = \frac{M}{3}\{a^2\,\boldsymbol{ii} + b^2\,\boldsymbol{jj} + (a^2+b^2)\boldsymbol{kk}\}$$

Exercise XIII

1. Three uniform rods, OA, OB, OC are each of unit length and mass. OB is normal to the plane COA and $\angle COA$ is 30°. Find the inertia tensor at O, taking two of the orthogonal axes as OA and OB. Deduce that the principal moments of inertia are 2/3 and $(4 \pm \sqrt{3})/6$. (L.U.)

2. A uniform right circular cone has a vertical angle of 90°. Show that the p-axes at a point P on the circumference of the base are the tangent at P to the base and two lines in the same axial plane as the diameter of the base at P, one making an angle $\frac{1}{2}$ arctan (10/21) with it. (L.N.)

3. A thin-walled rectangular box has the dimensions 9 cm. $\times$ 18 cm. $\times$ 18 cm. Calculate the radii of gyration about three principal axes and deduce that the radius of gyration about a space diagonal is $\sqrt{57}$ cm. (M.T.)

4. Find the momental ellipsoid at the vertex of a uniform solid right circular cone, of mass M, height h and vertical angle 2α. (L.U.)

5. A homogeneous solid has the form of a right circular cylinder of radius a and height $a\sqrt{3}$. P is a point on one of the circular edges. Show that the inertia quadric at P is a spheroid, the axis of which passes through the centre of the cylinder. (M.T.)

6. Define the term *equimomental systems.*

The perimeter of a uniform lamina, of mass m, is a regular hexagon $ABCDEF$ of side $2a$. Find a system of particles equimomental with the lamina and hence, or otherwise, show that the moment of inertia of the lamina about AD is $5ma^2/6$. Show also that the moment of inertia of the lamina about *any* line in its plane passing through the intersection of AD and BE has this same constant value. (L.U.)

7. State necessary and sufficient conditions that two rigid mass systems should be equimomental, and show that a uniform equilateral triangular lamina of mass M is equimomental with three particles, each of mass $M/3$, placed one at the mid-point of each side.

A uniform equilateral triangular lamina is free to rotate about one of its vertices, A, which is fixed. Show that the ratio of the periods of small oscillations about a horizontal axis through A (i) at right angles to the plane of the lamina, (ii) in the plane of the lamina, is $\sqrt{10/3}$. (L.U.)

8. A uniform right circular cone of height h and radius a is of mass M. Prove that the moment of inertia about its axis of symmetry is $3\dfrac{Ma^2}{10}$, and that the moment of inertia about a diameter of the base is $\dfrac{M}{20}(3a^2 + 2h^2)$.

9. Explain what is meant by the momental ellipsoid at a given point of a rigid body.

Find the equation of the momental ellipsoid at the vertex of a uniform solid right circular cone, of mass M, height y and vertical angle 2α. (L.U.)

10. Show how the principal axes of inertia at any point of a solid can be determined if the principal axes and principal radii of gyration at the centroid are known.

A uniform right circular cone has a vertical angle of 90°. Show that the principal axes at a point P on the circumference of the base are the tangent at P to the base and two lines in the same axial plane as the diameter of the base at P, one making an angle $\frac{1}{2}\tan^{-1}\frac{10}{21}$ with it. (L.U.)

CHAPTER XIV

MORE PROBLEMS IN THE MOTION OF A RIGID BODY

14.1 Screw motion

The motion of a rigid body can always be regarded as a certain screw motion, that is to say, a translation along a certain line λ and a simultaneous rotation about λ. The line λ, which varies with time, is the axis of the screw. To prove this we can proceed as follows.

Suppose an arbitrary origin O in the body has a velocity $\boldsymbol{u}$. Then if P is any other point of the body where $OP = \boldsymbol{s}$, and if $\boldsymbol{\omega}$ is the angular velocity of the body, P will have a velocity $\boldsymbol{v}$ where

$$\boldsymbol{v} = \boldsymbol{u} + \boldsymbol{\omega} \times \boldsymbol{s}$$

Now suppose that P is such that $\boldsymbol{v}$ is parallel to $\boldsymbol{\omega}$ (i.e. P lies on the axis of the screw), then $\boldsymbol{\omega} \times \boldsymbol{v} = \boldsymbol{0}$ and so

$$\boldsymbol{\omega} \times \boldsymbol{u} + \boldsymbol{\omega} \times (\boldsymbol{\omega} \times \boldsymbol{s}) = \boldsymbol{0}$$

i.e. $$\boldsymbol{\omega} \times \boldsymbol{u} + (\boldsymbol{\omega} . \boldsymbol{s})\boldsymbol{\omega} - \omega^2 \boldsymbol{s} = \boldsymbol{0}$$

If we take P to be such that $\boldsymbol{\omega} . \boldsymbol{s} = 0$, which is possible without any loss of generality, then we have

$$\boldsymbol{s} = \frac{\boldsymbol{\omega} \times \boldsymbol{u}}{\omega^2} \qquad . \quad . \quad . \quad . \qquad (1)$$

Hence all points on the line

$$\boldsymbol{r} = \boldsymbol{s} + \theta\, \boldsymbol{\omega} \quad (\theta \text{ a parameter}) \quad . \quad . \quad . \qquad (2)$$

have the property that they are moving parallel to the direction of $\boldsymbol{\omega}$. Equation (2) is the equation of the axis of the screw motion.

We notice that *if the motion is plane*, with $\boldsymbol{\omega} = \omega\, \boldsymbol{k}$ and $\boldsymbol{\omega} . \boldsymbol{u} = 0$, the vector $\boldsymbol{s}$ gives the *instantaneous centre* (the point where (2) cuts the plane of motion). Writing $\boldsymbol{u} = u_1 \boldsymbol{i} + u_2 \boldsymbol{j}$, (1) gives $\boldsymbol{s} = -\frac{u_2}{\omega}\boldsymbol{i} + \frac{u_1}{\omega}\boldsymbol{j} = \xi\, \boldsymbol{i} + \eta\, \boldsymbol{j}$, a result already obtained in 10.3(3).

The axis of the screw, viz. (2), is naturally called the *instantaneous axis*; its direction is defined by $\boldsymbol{\omega}$ and its position by $\boldsymbol{s}$.

Now suppose that a rigid body is given a number of simultaneous velocities, i.e. points O_α are given velocities $\boldsymbol{u}_\alpha$ ($\alpha = 1, 2, \ldots n$) and at the same instant the body is given angular velocities $\boldsymbol{\omega}_\alpha$ about lines through O_α. Choosing any point O as origin and writing $\overline{OO_\alpha} = \boldsymbol{r}_\alpha$, we can say that the resultant motion is equivalent to a velocity $\boldsymbol{u}$ at O together with a single angular velocity $\boldsymbol{\omega}$, provided

$$\boldsymbol{u} + \boldsymbol{\omega} \times \boldsymbol{r} = \sum_{a=1}^{n} \{\boldsymbol{u}_a + \boldsymbol{\omega}_a \times (\boldsymbol{r} - \boldsymbol{r}_a)\} \quad \text{for all } \boldsymbol{r}$$

This requires
$$\boldsymbol{u} = \sum_{a=1}^{n} (\boldsymbol{u}_a + \boldsymbol{r}_a \times \boldsymbol{\omega}_a) \quad . \quad . \quad . \quad . \quad (3)$$

and
$$\boldsymbol{\omega} = \sum_{a=1}^{n} \boldsymbol{\omega}_a \quad . \quad . \quad . \quad . \quad . \quad (4)$$

In this we can reduce the set $\{\boldsymbol{u}_\alpha ; \boldsymbol{\omega}_\alpha\}$ to $(\boldsymbol{u} ; \boldsymbol{\omega})$ at any *base-point* O. The axis of the resulting screw motion now follows by writing down (2) w.r.t. 0.

The *pitch of the screw*, p, is naturally related to the velocity of translation along the axis. If we write $\boldsymbol{v} \times p\,\boldsymbol{\omega}$ for the point $\boldsymbol{s}$ we get

$$\boldsymbol{u} + \boldsymbol{\omega} \times \boldsymbol{s} = p\,\boldsymbol{\omega}$$

and so
$$\boldsymbol{\omega} . \boldsymbol{u} = p\,\boldsymbol{\omega}^2$$

and
$$p = \frac{\boldsymbol{\omega} . \boldsymbol{u}}{\boldsymbol{\omega}^2} \quad . \quad . \quad . \quad . \quad (5)$$

When $p = 0$ the motion is one of pure rotation about (2).

Example 1. Three concurrent edges OX, OY, OZ of a rectangular block are of lengths a, b, c respectively. O', X', Y', Z' are the corners of the block diagonally opposite to O, X, Y, Z. The block is given small rotations about the edges OX, $Y'O'$, YX' Show that, if the resultant displacement is equivalent to a pure rotation, its axis must lie on the surface

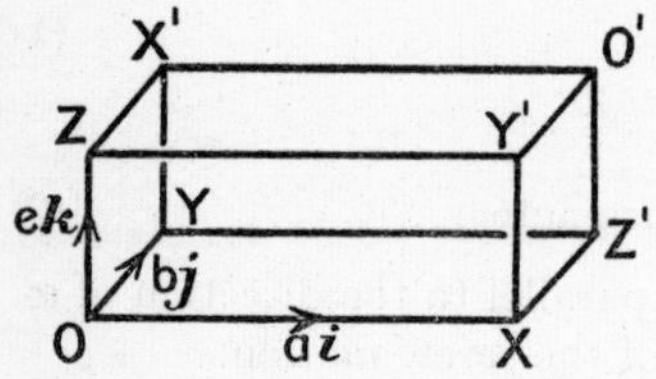

FIG. 113.

$$ayz + bzx - cxy - abz = 0$$

w.r.t. OX, OY, OZ as axes.

Let the rotations be $\boldsymbol{\omega}_1 = l\,\boldsymbol{i}$ about OX, $\boldsymbol{\omega}_2 = m\,\boldsymbol{j}$ about $Y'O'$, and $\boldsymbol{\omega}_3 = n\,\boldsymbol{k}$ about YX' (v. Fig. 113). Since $\overline{OY'} = a\,\boldsymbol{i} + c\,\boldsymbol{k}$, the system reduces to $(\boldsymbol{u} ; \boldsymbol{\omega})$ at O, where

$$\boldsymbol{u} = (a\,\boldsymbol{i} + c\,\boldsymbol{k}) \times m\,\boldsymbol{j} + b\,\boldsymbol{j} \times n\,\boldsymbol{k}$$

giving
$$\boldsymbol{u} = (nb - mc)\boldsymbol{i} + am\,\boldsymbol{k} \quad . \quad . \quad . \quad . \quad (6)$$

and
$$\boldsymbol{\omega} = l\,\boldsymbol{i} + m\,\boldsymbol{j} + n\,\boldsymbol{k} \quad . \quad . \quad . \quad . \quad . \quad (7)$$

The instantaneous axis is the line

$$\boldsymbol{r} = \boldsymbol{s} + \theta\,\boldsymbol{\omega} \quad . \quad . \quad . \quad . \quad (8)$$

where $\boldsymbol{s} = \dfrac{\boldsymbol{\omega} \times \boldsymbol{u}}{\boldsymbol{\omega}^2}$. If the motion is pure rotation, $p = \dfrac{\boldsymbol{\omega} . \boldsymbol{u}}{\boldsymbol{\omega}^2} = 0.$

Hence (8) gives, for all θ,

$$\boldsymbol{\omega} \times \boldsymbol{r} = \boldsymbol{\omega} \times \boldsymbol{s} = -\boldsymbol{u}$$

and if $\boldsymbol{r} = x\,\boldsymbol{i} + y\,\boldsymbol{j} + z\,\boldsymbol{k}$, we get

$$\begin{aligned} m(z-c) + n(b-y) &= 0 \\ lz \qquad - nx &= 0 \\ ly + m(a-x) &= 0 \end{aligned}$$

Eliminating l, m, n we get

$$\begin{vmatrix} 0 & (z-c) & (b-y) \\ z & 0 & -x \\ y & (a-x) & 0 \end{vmatrix} = 0$$

This gives $\qquad -xy(z-c) + z(b-y)(a-x) = 0 \qquad$ Q.E.D.

14.2 The polhode and herpolhode cones

Consider a rigid body which is turning about a fixed point O of itself, and let $\boldsymbol{\omega}$ be its angular velocity at any time. The instantaneous axis is now the line through O in the direction of $\boldsymbol{\omega}$. Taking moving axes, origin at O, fixed in the body we get

$$\frac{d\boldsymbol{\omega}}{dt} = \frac{\partial \boldsymbol{\omega}}{\partial t} + \boldsymbol{\omega} \times \boldsymbol{\omega} = \frac{\partial \boldsymbol{\omega}}{\partial t} \quad . \quad . \quad . \quad (1)$$

The vector $\boldsymbol{\omega}$ (instantaneous axis), passing through the fixed point O, will describe a cone, vertex at O, in the body and another cone in space The first is called the polhode cone and the second is the herpolhode cone. Now $d\boldsymbol{\omega}$ is a displacement in the tangent plane to the herpolhode cone and $\partial\boldsymbol{\omega}$ is a displacement in the tangent plane to the polhode cone. Hence (1) shows that the two cones touch along a common generator (defined by $\boldsymbol{\omega}$) and that sliding does not occur. The motion of the body about O is therefore obtained by *rolling the polhode cone on the herpolhode cone* (cf. 10.3). The following example illustrates the application of these vector methods to kinematic problems.

Example 1. Two concentric spherical surfaces of radii a, b rotate with angular velocities ω_1, ω_2 about fixed diameters inclined to one another at an angle α. A sphere placed between them rolls in contact with both. Prove that the centre of the sphere describes a circle with angular velocity

$$\{a^2\omega_1{}^2 + 2ab\omega_1\omega_2 \cos\alpha + b^2\omega^2{}_2\}^{\frac{1}{2}}/(a+b) \qquad \text{(L.U.)}$$

Take a unit vector $\boldsymbol{e}$ along $OQGP$, as shown in Fig. 114. Let the line $OQGP$, regarded as a rigid rod, have angular velocity Ω. Then the velocity of G is $\dot{\boldsymbol{G}} = \Omega \times \frac{1}{2}(a+b)\boldsymbol{e}$, the velocities of the points of contact P, Q are $\dot{\boldsymbol{P}} = b\,\boldsymbol{\omega}_2 \times \boldsymbol{e}$, $\dot{\boldsymbol{Q}} = a\,\boldsymbol{\omega}_1 \times \boldsymbol{e}$. But $\dot{G} = \frac{1}{2}(\dot{\boldsymbol{P}} + \dot{\boldsymbol{Q}})$ and so

$$\boldsymbol{\Omega} \times \boldsymbol{e} = \left(\frac{a\,\boldsymbol{\omega}_1 + b\,\boldsymbol{\omega}_2}{a+b}\right) \times \boldsymbol{e}$$

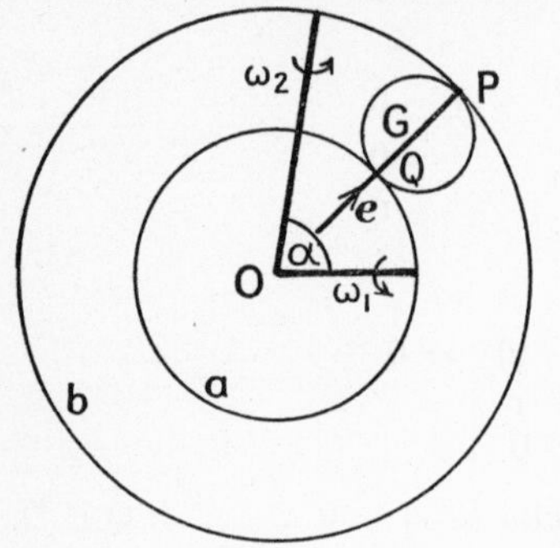

FIG. 114.

This shows that $OQGP$ moves with angular velocity

$$\boldsymbol{\Omega} = \frac{a\,\boldsymbol{\omega}_1 + b\,\boldsymbol{\omega}_2}{a+b}$$

and $|\boldsymbol{\Omega}| = \{a^2\omega_1{}^2 + b^2\omega_2{}^2 + 2ab\omega_1\omega_2 \cos\alpha\}^{\frac{1}{2}}/(a+b)$ Q.E.D.

In this problem the *herpolhode cone* of the (imaginary) rod $OQGP$ is this right circular cone described by $\boldsymbol{\Omega}$. The *polhode cone* is degenerate, being line $OQGP$ itself.

14.3 Euler's equations for the motion of a body about a fixed point

Take the point O which is fixed as origin and let $\boldsymbol{H}(O)$ be the angular momentum of the body, $\boldsymbol{\Gamma}(O)$ be the vector torque about O of the applied forces. Let $(\boldsymbol{i}, \boldsymbol{j}, \boldsymbol{k})$ be the principal axes of the body at O, and write

$$\mathscr{I}(O) = A\,\boldsymbol{ii} + B\,\boldsymbol{jj} + C\,\boldsymbol{kk} \quad . \quad . \quad . \quad (1)$$

Using the theory of rotating frames of reference, since $\boldsymbol{i}, \boldsymbol{j}, \boldsymbol{k}$ move with the body, we get

$$\frac{d}{dt}\boldsymbol{H}(O) = \frac{\partial}{\partial t}\boldsymbol{H}(O) + \boldsymbol{\omega} \times \boldsymbol{H}(O) = \boldsymbol{\Gamma}(O)$$

Since $\boldsymbol{H}(O) = \mathscr{I}(O).\boldsymbol{\omega}$ this gives

$$\mathscr{I}(O).\dot{\boldsymbol{\omega}} + \boldsymbol{\omega} \times \{\mathscr{I}(O).\boldsymbol{\omega}\} = \boldsymbol{\Gamma}(O) \quad . \quad . \quad (2)$$

Now (1) gives $\mathscr{I}(O).\boldsymbol{\omega} = A\omega_1\,\boldsymbol{i} + B\omega_2\,\boldsymbol{j} + C\omega_3\,\boldsymbol{k}$, and so (2) gives the three equations

$$\left.\begin{aligned} A\dot{\omega}_1 + (C - B)\omega_2\omega_3 &= L \\ B\dot{\omega}_2 + (A - C)\omega_3\omega_1 &= M \\ C\dot{\omega}_3 + (B - A)\omega_1\omega_2 &= N \end{aligned}\right\} \quad . \quad . \quad . \quad (3)$$

where $\boldsymbol{\Gamma}(O) = L\,\boldsymbol{i} + M\,\boldsymbol{j} + N\,\boldsymbol{k}$. These are called *Euler's equations*.*

Example 1. A body is free to move about a fixed point O of itself under no forces save the reaction at O. The angular velocity relative to principal axes at O has components ω_1, ω_2, ω_3 and the principal moments of inertia at O are A, B, C. If the centre of mass is on the

* L. Euler, Swiss mathematician, 1707–83.

axis of principal moment C at distance h from O, show that the reaction at O has components X, Y, Z, where $X = Mh\omega_1\omega_3 (C + B - A)/B$; $Y = Mh\omega_2\omega_3(C + A - B)/A$; $Z = -Mh(\omega_1^2 + \omega_2^2)$. If $\omega_1 = 0$ at $t = 0$ and $A = B$ ($> C$) show that ω_3 is constant and

$$\frac{X}{Y} = \tan\left\{\frac{(A - C)}{A}\omega_3 t\right\} \qquad \text{(L.U.)}$$

Write $\overline{OG} = \boldsymbol{r} = h\,\boldsymbol{k}$ and the reaction $\boldsymbol{R} = X\,\boldsymbol{i} + Y\,\boldsymbol{j} + Z\,\boldsymbol{k}$.

Then
$$M\frac{d^2\boldsymbol{r}}{dt^2} = \boldsymbol{R}$$

becomes
$$M\left(\frac{\partial}{\partial t} + \boldsymbol{\omega}\times\right)\left(\frac{\partial \boldsymbol{r}}{\partial t} + \boldsymbol{\omega}\times\boldsymbol{r}\right) = \boldsymbol{R} \qquad (4)$$

Since $\dfrac{\partial \boldsymbol{r}}{\partial t} = \boldsymbol{0}$, (4) becomes

$$Mh\{(\dot{\omega}_2 + \omega_1\omega_3)\boldsymbol{i} + (\omega_3\omega_2 - \dot{\omega}_1)\boldsymbol{j} - (\omega_1^2 + \omega_2^2)\boldsymbol{k}\} = \boldsymbol{R}$$

Substituting for $\dot{\omega}_1$, $\dot{\omega}_2$, $\dot{\omega}_3$ from (3) with $L = M = N = 0$ we get the required values for X, Y, Z.

With $A = B$ equations (3) now become

$$A\dot{\omega}_1 - (A - C)\omega_2\omega_3 = 0 \qquad (5)$$
$$A\dot{\omega}_2 + (A - C)\omega_3\omega_1 = 0 \qquad (6)$$
$$C\dot{\omega}_3 = 0 \qquad (7)$$

(7) gives ω_3 = constant, and (5) and (6) give

$$\omega_1\dot{\omega}_1 + \omega_2\dot{\omega}_2 = 0$$

Hence
$$\omega_1^2 + \omega_2^2 = \text{constant} = a^2 \quad \text{(say)}$$

Then (5) gives
$$\dot{\omega}_1 = \left(\frac{A - C}{A}\right)\omega_3\sqrt{a^2 - \omega_1^2}$$

so that
$$\omega_1 = a\sin\left(\frac{A - C}{A}\right)\omega_3 t$$
$$\omega_2 = a\cos\left(\frac{A - C}{A}\right)\omega_3 t$$

and
$$\frac{X}{Y} = \frac{\omega_1}{\omega_2} = \tan\left(\frac{A - C}{A}\right)\omega_3 t \qquad \text{Q.E.D.}$$

Example 2. A body moves about a point O under no forces, the principal moments of inertia at O being $3A$, $5A$ and $6A$. Initially the angular velocity of the body has components $\omega_1 = n$, $\omega_2 = 0$, $\omega_3 = n$ about the corresponding principal axes. Show that, at any later time, $\omega_2 = \dfrac{3n}{\sqrt{5}}\tanh\left(\dfrac{nt}{\sqrt{5}}\right)$, and that the body ultimately rotates about its mean axis. (L.U.)

Euler's equations give

$$3\dot{\omega}_1 + \omega_2\omega_3 = 0 \quad . \quad . \quad . \quad . \quad (8)$$

$$5\dot{\omega}_2 - 3\omega_3\omega_1 = 0 \quad . \quad . \quad . \quad . \quad (9)$$

$$3\dot{\omega}_3 + \omega_1\omega_2 = 0 \quad . \quad . \quad . \quad . \quad (10)$$

(8), (9) give $\quad 9\omega_1\dot{\omega}_1 + 5\omega_2\dot{\omega}_2 = 0$

so that $\quad 9\omega_1^2 + 5\omega_2^2 = \text{constant} = 9n^2 \quad . \quad . \quad . \quad (11)$

(8), (10) give $\quad \omega_1^2 - \omega_3^2 = \text{constant} = 0 \quad . \quad . \quad . \quad (12)$

Hence (9) gives

$$5\dot{\omega}_2 = 3\omega_1^2 = \tfrac{1}{3}(9n^2 - 5\omega_2^2)$$

Hence $$\int_0^{\omega_2} \frac{d\omega_2}{9n^2 - 5\omega^2} = \frac{t}{15}$$

and so $$\omega_2 = \frac{3n}{\sqrt{5}} \tanh\left(\frac{nt}{\sqrt{5}}\right) \qquad \text{Q.E.D.}$$

As $t \to \infty$, $\omega^2 \to \dfrac{9n^2}{5}$ and (11) and (12) show that ω_1 and ω_3 both tend to zero. The rotation is ultimately about the mean axis.

Q.E.D.

Example 3. A rigid body possesses an axis of symmetry OC and moves about O under a retarding couple $\lambda C\omega_3$ about OC; λ being a constant; A, A, C being the principal moments of inertia at O, and $(\omega_1, \omega_2, \omega_3)$ being the angular velocity components about the principal axes, the third axis being along OC. Initially the body is given an angular velocity ω about a line inclined at α to OC. Prove that ultimately the instantaneous axis will be perpendicular to OC and that the plane through it and OC will have turned through the angle

$$\left(\frac{A - C}{A\lambda}\right)\omega \cos \alpha. \qquad \text{(L.U.)}$$

At $t = 0$ we can take $\omega_1 = 0$, $\omega_2 = \omega \sin \alpha$, $\omega_3 = \omega \cos \alpha$ without loss of generality. Euler's equations become

$$A\dot{\omega}_1 + (C - A)\omega_2\omega_3 = 0 \quad . \quad . \quad . \quad (13)$$

$$A\dot{\omega}_2 + (A - C)\omega_1\omega_3 = 0 \quad . \quad . \quad . \quad (14)$$

$$\dot{\omega}_3 = -\lambda\omega_3 \quad . \quad . \quad (15)$$

(15) gives $\quad \omega_3 = (\omega \cos \alpha)e^{-\lambda t}$

Hence, as $t \to \infty$, $\omega_3 \to 0$ and $(\boldsymbol{\omega} . \boldsymbol{k}) \to 0$, $\boldsymbol{k}$ being along OC. Hence $\boldsymbol{\omega}$ becomes perpendicular to OC. (13) and (14) give

$$\omega_1{}^2 + \omega_2{}^2 = \text{constant} = \omega^2 \sin^2 \alpha$$

and then (13) gives

$$\dot{\omega}_1 = \left(\frac{A - C}{A}\right)\omega \cos \alpha . e^{-\lambda t}\sqrt{\omega^2 \sin^2 \alpha - \omega_1^2}$$

giving $\omega_1 = \omega \sin \alpha \sin [\phi(1 - e^{-\lambda t})]$

where $\phi = \left(\frac{A - C}{\lambda A}\right)\omega \cos \alpha.$

Hence $\omega_2 = \omega \sin \alpha \cos [\phi(1 - e^{-\lambda t})]$

Then $\boldsymbol{\omega}(0) = 0.\boldsymbol{i} + \omega \sin \alpha\, \boldsymbol{j} + \omega \cos \alpha\, \boldsymbol{k}$

$$\boldsymbol{\omega}(\infty) = \omega \sin \alpha \sin \phi\, \boldsymbol{i} + \omega \sin \alpha \cos \phi\, \boldsymbol{j} + 0.\boldsymbol{k}$$

The normal to the plane containing OC and $\boldsymbol{\omega}$ is in the direction of $\boldsymbol{k} \times \boldsymbol{\omega}$. Hence

$$\boldsymbol{k} \times \boldsymbol{\omega}(0) = -\omega \sin \alpha\, \boldsymbol{i}$$
$$\boldsymbol{k} \times \boldsymbol{\omega}(\infty) = -\omega \sin \alpha \cos \phi\, \boldsymbol{i} + \omega \sin \alpha \sin \phi\, \boldsymbol{j}$$

Hence $\{\boldsymbol{k} \times \boldsymbol{\omega}(0)\}.\{\boldsymbol{k} \times \boldsymbol{\omega}(\infty)\} = \omega^2 \sin^2 \alpha \cos \phi$

$$= (\omega \sin \alpha)(\omega \sin \alpha) \cos \theta$$

Hence the plane ultimately rotates through $\theta = \phi$. Q.E.D.

14.4 Poinsot's construction

We shall now examine in more detail the motion of a rigid body about a fixed point O *under no forces*. This arises whenever a body moves freely about its centre of mass, all the applied forces acting through the centre of mass.

The equation of motion is, once more,

$$\frac{d}{dt}\boldsymbol{H}(O) = \boldsymbol{0} \qquad (1)$$

and this is $\mathscr{J}(O).\dot{\boldsymbol{\omega}} + \boldsymbol{\omega} \times (\mathscr{J}(O).\boldsymbol{\omega}) = \boldsymbol{0}$ (2)

(1) gives $\boldsymbol{H}(O) = \mathscr{J}(O).\boldsymbol{\omega} = \text{constant vector}$ (3)

(2) gives $\boldsymbol{\omega}.\mathscr{J}(O).\dot{\boldsymbol{\omega}} = 0$

so that $\boldsymbol{\omega}.\mathscr{J}.\boldsymbol{\omega} = 2T$ (constant) (4)

The direction of $\boldsymbol{H}$ is called the *invariable line*, and any plane perpendicular to $\boldsymbol{H}$ is called an *invariable plane*. The locus of $\boldsymbol{H}$ in the body is called the *invariable cone*.

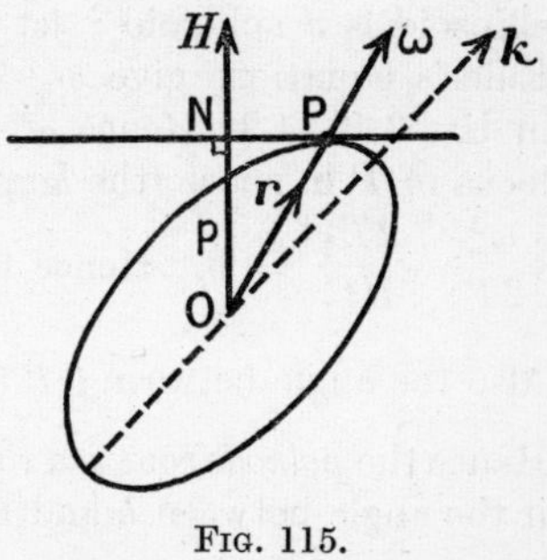

FIG. 115.

Now consider the momental ellipsoid at O (v. Fig. 115) and let P be the point where it is met by $\boldsymbol{\omega}$. Let N be the point of intersection of the invariable line and the tangent plane at P. We can see that ON is in fact perpendicular to this tangent plane, for the normal to the ellipsoid at P is parallel to $\mathscr{J}.\boldsymbol{r}$ (or $\mathscr{J}.\boldsymbol{\omega}$, since $\boldsymbol{r}$ is parallel to $\boldsymbol{\omega}$). Hence the normal at P is parallel to $\boldsymbol{H}$, the invariable line. Now the ellipsoid is $\boldsymbol{r}.\mathscr{J}.\boldsymbol{r} = 1$ and so, if $\boldsymbol{\omega} = \theta \boldsymbol{r}$, (4) gives $\theta^2 = 2T$.

Also $$p = \boldsymbol{r}.\{\text{unit vector along the normal at } P\}$$

$$= \frac{\boldsymbol{r}.(\mathcal{J}.\boldsymbol{r})}{|\mathcal{J}.\boldsymbol{r}|} = \frac{1}{|\mathcal{J}.\boldsymbol{r}|} = \frac{\theta}{|\boldsymbol{H}|}$$

so that $$p = \frac{\sqrt{2T}}{H} = \text{a constant}$$

Hence the tangent plane at P is a fixed plane, for all P. Hence *the motion of the body is equivalent to the rolling of the momental ellipsoid on the fixed tangent plane.* This is Poinsot's representation of the motion.* The rate of turn about the instantaneous axis OP is

$$\omega = \theta\,|\boldsymbol{r}| = (OP)\sqrt{2T}$$

The equation of the *polhode cone* is given by

$$\frac{(\mathcal{J}.\boldsymbol{r})^2}{(\boldsymbol{r}.\mathcal{J}.\boldsymbol{r})} = \frac{H^2}{2T}$$

which is $$2T(\mathcal{J}.\boldsymbol{r})^2 = H^2(\boldsymbol{r}.\mathcal{J}.\boldsymbol{r})$$

The Cartesian form, w.r.t. principal axes at O, is

$$2T\{A^2x^2 + B^2y^2 + C^2z^2\} = H^2(Ax^2 + By^2 + Cz^2)$$

The locus of P *in space* can be obtained by writing $NP = \rho$, whence

$$\rho^2 = r^2 - p^2 = \frac{\omega^2}{2T} - \frac{2T}{H^2} = x^2 + y^2$$

This a circle, centre N, radius $\left\{\dfrac{\omega^2}{2T} - \dfrac{2T}{H^2}\right\}^{\frac{1}{2}}$. By giving to ω its greatest and least values we obtain two concentric circles between which P always moves.

When the body possesses an axis of symmetry. In this case the ellipsoid is a spheroid : let $\boldsymbol{k}$ be the axis of symmetry (v. Fig. 115). Euler's equations give ω_3 = a constant, and $\omega_1{}^2 + \omega_2{}^2$ = constant as in Ex. 3 if 14.3. Hence $\omega^2 = \omega_1{}^2 + \omega_2{}^2 + \omega_3{}^2$ = constant, and so the locus of P in space (the *herpolhode curve*) is a circle of constant radius $\left\{\dfrac{\omega^2}{2T} - \dfrac{2T}{H^2}\right\}^{\frac{1}{2}} = \rho$. Hence the angle between OP and $\boldsymbol{H}$ is constant. Also the angle between OP and $\boldsymbol{k}$ is constant, viz. α where $\cos\alpha = \dfrac{\omega_3}{\omega}$. Hence the *polhode cone* is a right circular cone, axis $\boldsymbol{k}$, angle 2α. Finally, if the angle between $\boldsymbol{k}$ and $\boldsymbol{H}$ is β we have

$$H\cos\beta = \boldsymbol{H}.\boldsymbol{k} = C\omega_3 \quad . \quad . \quad . \quad (5)$$

There β = a constant ; the *axis of symmetry* $\boldsymbol{k}$ *describes a right circular*

* L. Poinsot, French mathematician, 1777–1859.

cone in space about the invariable line. Also, (5) gives $\cos\beta = \dfrac{C\omega_3}{H}$,

and since $\sin\beta = \dfrac{|\boldsymbol{H}\times\boldsymbol{k}|}{H}$, we get

$$\tan\beta = \frac{|\boldsymbol{H}\times\boldsymbol{k}|}{C\omega_3} \quad . \quad . \quad . \quad (6)$$

Similarly, α being the angle between $\boldsymbol{k}$ and $\boldsymbol{\omega}$ we have $\sin\alpha = \dfrac{|\boldsymbol{\omega}\times\boldsymbol{k}|}{\omega}$

and, as above, $\cos\alpha = \dfrac{\omega_3}{\omega}$. Hence

$$\tan\alpha = \frac{|\boldsymbol{\omega}\times\boldsymbol{k}|}{\omega_3} \quad . \quad . \quad . \quad . \quad (7)$$

Since $\boldsymbol{k}$ is an axis of symmetry $\boldsymbol{H}\times\boldsymbol{k} = A(\boldsymbol{\omega}\times\boldsymbol{k})$. Hence (6) and (7) give

$$\tan\beta = \frac{A}{C}\tan\alpha \quad . \quad . \quad . \quad . \quad (8)$$

Since the body has angular velocity $\boldsymbol{\omega}$ we have

$$\frac{d\boldsymbol{k}}{dt} = \boldsymbol{\omega}\times\boldsymbol{k}$$

so that

$$\boldsymbol{k}\times\frac{d\boldsymbol{k}}{dt} = \boldsymbol{\omega} - (\boldsymbol{k}.\boldsymbol{\omega})\boldsymbol{k}$$

Writing $\boldsymbol{\omega}.\boldsymbol{k} = n =$ spin about the axis of symmetry, we have

$$\boldsymbol{\omega} = n\,\boldsymbol{k} + \boldsymbol{k}\times\frac{d\boldsymbol{k}}{dt} \quad . \quad . \quad . \quad (9)$$

This is a general equation for a body possessing an axis of symmetry. In this case $n = \omega_3 =$ a constant. Hence (9) gives, on writing $\dfrac{d\boldsymbol{k}}{dt} = \Omega\,\boldsymbol{e}\times\boldsymbol{k}$, where $\boldsymbol{H} = H\,\boldsymbol{e}$,

$$\begin{aligned} \boldsymbol{\omega} &= n\,\boldsymbol{k} + \Omega\,\boldsymbol{e} - \Omega\cos\beta\,\boldsymbol{k} \\ &= (n - \Omega\cos\beta)\boldsymbol{k} + \Omega\,\boldsymbol{e} \end{aligned}$$

Hence

$$\begin{aligned} \omega^2 &= (n - \Omega\cos\beta)^2 + \Omega^2 + 2\Omega\cos\beta(n - \Omega\cos\beta) \\ &= n^2 + \Omega^2\sin^2\beta \quad . \quad . \quad . \quad . \quad . \quad . \quad . \quad (10) \end{aligned}$$

which gives the value of Ω, the angular velocity with which $\boldsymbol{k}$ rotates about $\boldsymbol{H}$, the invariable line.

14.5 Eulerian angles

The position of a rigid body, free to turn about a fixed point O of itself, can be defined by using Eulerian angles θ, ϕ, ψ. The angles θ, ϕ may be regarded as the usual spherical polar angles and ψ denotes a rotation about the radius vector $OP(\boldsymbol{e}_3)$.

Let $\boldsymbol{e}_3$ be a line fixed in the body and let $\boldsymbol{e}_1$, $\boldsymbol{e}_2$ complete the orthonormal triad, S, which rotates with the body. Let $\boldsymbol{i}$, $\boldsymbol{j}$, $\boldsymbol{k}$ be axes S_0 fixed in space. Now rotate S through θ about $\boldsymbol{m}$ and through ϕ about $\boldsymbol{k}$ so that $\boldsymbol{e}_2$ coincides with $\boldsymbol{m}$ and $\boldsymbol{e}_1$ coincides with $\boldsymbol{l}$ (v. Fig. 116). Then rotate S through ψ about $\boldsymbol{e}_3$ (v. Fig. 117) ; these angles define S completely w.r.t. S_0.

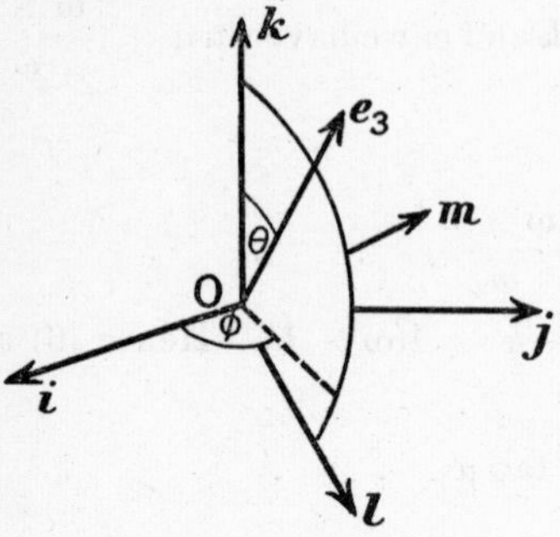

FIG. 116.

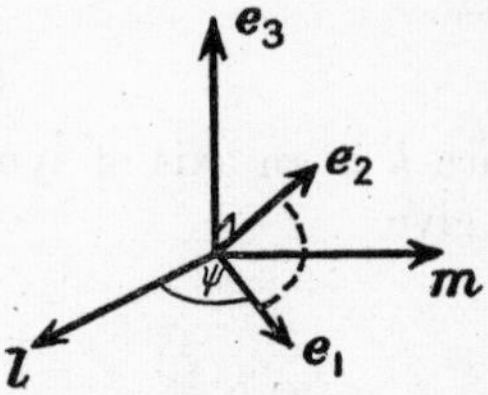

FIG. 117.

The angular velocity $\boldsymbol{\omega}$ of the body (i.e. of S) will be

$$\boldsymbol{\omega} = \dot{\theta}\boldsymbol{m} + \dot{\phi}\boldsymbol{k} + \dot{\psi}\boldsymbol{e}_3 \quad . \quad . \quad . \quad (1)$$

But
$$\boldsymbol{k} = \cos\theta\,\boldsymbol{e}_3 - \sin\theta\,\boldsymbol{l} \quad \text{(v. Fig. 116)}$$
$$\boldsymbol{l} = \cos\psi\,\boldsymbol{e}_1 - \sin\psi\,\boldsymbol{e}_2 \quad \text{(v. Fig. 117)}$$
and
$$\boldsymbol{m} = \sin\psi\,\boldsymbol{e}_1 + \cos\psi\,\boldsymbol{e}_2 \quad \text{(v. Fig. 117)}$$
Hence (1) gives
$$\begin{aligned}\boldsymbol{\omega} = {} & (\dot{\theta}\sin\psi - \dot{\phi}\sin\theta\cos\psi)\boldsymbol{e}_1 \\ & + (\dot{\theta}\cos\psi + \dot{\phi}\sin\theta\sin\psi)\boldsymbol{e}_2 \\ & + (\dot{\psi} + \dot{\phi}\cos\theta)\boldsymbol{e}_3 \quad . \quad . \quad . \quad (2)\end{aligned}$$

If $(\boldsymbol{e}_1, \boldsymbol{e}_2, \boldsymbol{e}_3)$ are chosen to be the principal axes of the body at O, (2) shows that the *kinetic energy* will be

$$T = \tfrac{1}{2}(A\omega_1^2 + B\omega_2^2 + C\omega_3^2)$$

giving

$$\begin{aligned}T = \tfrac{1}{2}\{ & (A\sin^2\psi + B\cos^2\psi)\dot{\theta}^2 + C\dot{\psi}^2 + C\cos^2\theta\,\dot{\phi}^2 \\ & + (A\sin^2\theta\cos^2\psi + B\sin^2\theta\sin^2\psi)\dot{\phi}^2 + 2C\dot{\psi}\dot{\phi}\cos\theta \\ & + 2(B - A)\sin\theta\cos\psi\sin\psi\,\dot{\theta}\dot{\phi}\} \quad . \quad . \quad . \quad (3)\end{aligned}$$

If $\boldsymbol{e}_3$ is also an axis of symmetry, $A = B$, and we get

$$T = \tfrac{1}{2}\{A(\dot{\theta}^2 + \sin^2\theta\,\dot{\phi}^2) + C(\dot{\psi} + \dot{\phi}\cos\theta)^2\} \quad . \quad (4)$$

Exercise XIV

1. OA, OB, OC are three edges of a cuboid and O', A', B', C' are the corners opposite to O, A, B, C. The cuboid is given angular velocities proportional to OA, OB, OC, BC, CA, AB about these edges, and forming right-handed screws with these directions. Prove that the pitch of the resultant screw motion is $\dfrac{3abc}{a^2 + b^2 + c^2}$, where a, b, c are the lengths OA, OB, OC. Find the equation of the instantaneous axis, using OA, OB, OC as axes. (L.U.)

2. The motion of a rigid body is defined by compounding an angular velocity ω_1 about a line OA and an angular velocity ω_2 about a line OB. State how to find the resultant angular velocity, and prove your result.

At a certain instant the motion of a rigid body is defined by the angular velocities ω_1 about the line $y = b$, $z = 0$; ω_2 about a line $z = c$, $x = 0$; ω_3 about the line $x = a$, $y = 0$, referred to rectangular cartesian coordinates. Prove that there is no point of the body whose velocity is zero unless

$$a\,\omega_2\omega_3 + b\,\omega_3\omega_1 + c\,\omega_1\omega_2 = 0$$

Prove that, if this condition is satisfied, then the body is instantaneously turning about a certain line which meets each of the three given lines.

[The sense of the angular velocities is taken to be that associated with a right-handed set of axes.] (L.U.)

3. Prove Euler's equations for the motion of a rigid body about a fixed point.

A lamina is free to move about a fixed point O of its plane and is set in motion by an impulse I perpendicular to its plane at the point $(x, y, 0)$ of the lamina referred to principal axes at O. Neglecting gravity, show that, in the subsequent motion, the component of the angular velocity parallel to its plane is constant and equal to

$$I\left(\frac{x^2}{B^2} + \frac{y^2}{A^2}\right)^{1/2}$$

where A, B, $A + B$ are the principal moments of inertia at O.

Prove also that, if the plane through the instantaneous axis perpendicular to the lamina makes an angle ϕ with the plane $y = 0$,

$$(A + B)\dot{\phi}^2 = (A - B)I^2\left(\frac{y^2}{A^2}\sin^2\phi - \frac{x^2}{B^2}\cos^2\phi\right) \qquad \text{(L.U.)}$$

4. Establish Euler's equations for the motion of a rigid body about a point. A rigid body moves under no forces about a point, its principal moments of inertia being the ratio of 6 : 5 : 2. Initially the body is rotating about a line in the plane of the axes of least and greatest inertia and inclined to them at 45°. Show that eventually it will rotate about the mean axis of inertia with $2/\sqrt{5}$ times the initial angular velocity. (M.T.)

5. A uniform lamina is free to move about a point O of itself and is set rotating with initial angular velocity ω about an axis inclined to its plane at an angle e and perpendicular to the p-axis of mean moment B at O. If $\cos 2\alpha = A/B$ where A, B, $A + B$ are the principal moments of inertia at O, show that the angular velocity at time t, about the axis of mean moment, is

$$\omega \cos e \tanh(\omega t \sin \alpha) \qquad \text{(L.U.)}$$

6. Write down, without proof, Euler's equations for the motion of a rigid body about a fixed point.

A plane lamina, under the action of no external forces, is set rotating with angular velocity Ω about an axis through its centre of mass G, whose angular co-ordinates are $\theta = \alpha$, $\phi = \beta$, referred to the principal axes at G. Prove that at time t the component angular velocities about these axes are

$$\omega_1 = \Omega \sin \alpha \cos \phi$$
$$\omega_2 = \Omega \sin z \sin \phi$$
$$\omega_3 = \Omega \left[\cos^2 \alpha - \frac{A - B}{A + B} \sin^2 \alpha \, (\sin^2 \beta - \sin^2 \phi) \right]^{\frac{1}{2}}$$

where A, B are the moments of inertia of the lamina about the principal axes in its plane. (L.U.)

7. A rigid body has one point O fixed, and there are no forces on the body other than the reaction at the fixed point. Establish the equations

$$A\dot{\omega}_1 - (B - C)\omega_2\omega_3 = 0$$
$$B\dot{\omega}_2 - (C - A)\omega_3\omega_1 = 0$$
$$C\dot{\omega}_3 - (A - B)\omega_1\omega_2 = 0$$

where the axes are fixed in the body and are principal axes of inertia at O, the moments of inertia about these axes are A, B, C, and ω_1, ω_2, ω_3 are components of angular velocity.

Consider in particular a uniform circular disc pivoted at its centre. The axis of rotation initially makes an angle α ($< \pi/2$) with the axis of symmetry. Prove that the motion can be represented by the rolling of a cone of angle α, fixed relative to the disc, on a cone fixed in space. Explain, and illustrate in a diagram, the relative positions of the cones, and prove that, whatever the value of α, the angle of the fixed cone cannot exceed $\sin^{-1} \frac{1}{3}$. (M.T.)

8. Two particles, each of mass m, are fixed at the ends of a diameter l of a uniform circular disc of mass $4m$ and radius a, which is free to rotate about its centre. The disc is set in motion with an angular velocity the components of which are $\Omega\sqrt{2}$ along l and Ω normal to the disc. If ω is the component of the angular velocity along the diameter perpendicular to l, show that at any subsequent time

$$\dot{\omega} = -\frac{1}{\sqrt{2}}(2\Omega^2 - \omega^2)$$

Deduce the components of the angular velocity along the principal axes of inertia at any subsequent time, and prove that the disc ultimately rotates with angular velocity $\Omega\sqrt{2}$ about the diameter perpendicular to l.

Find the ultimate direction of the axis of rotation in relation to the initial position of the disc. (M.T.)

9. Write down Euler's dynamical equations for the motion of a rigid body having one point fixed.

A rigid body has principal moments of inertia A, A, C at a point about which it moves under no forces except a resisting couple equal to k times the resultant angular velocity. If at time $t = 0$ the instantaneous axis makes angle α with the axis of symmetry, prove that at time t it makes angle ϕ with this axis, where

$$\tan\phi = \tan\alpha . \exp\{kt(C^{-1} - A^{-1})\}$$

Also show that the plane containing the instantaneous axis and the axis of symmetry has rotated about the latter through an angle

$$(C - A)\frac{C\omega\cos\alpha}{Ak}\left\{1 - \exp\left(-\frac{kt}{C}\right)\right\}$$

where ω is the magnitude of the initial angular velocity. (L.U.)

10. State and prove Euler's equations for the motion of a rigid body about a fixed point.

A plane lamina is pivoted at a point O and moves under the action of no forces other than the reaction at O. The principal axes in the plane of the lamina are Ox and Oy and the corresponding principal moments of inertia are A and B ($B > A$). Initially the lamina is rotating with angular velocity Ω about a line (not necessarily in the plane of the lamina) which makes a small angle with Ox. Show that, during the subsequent motion, the direction of the component of angular velocity in the plane of the lamina oscillates about Ox with period approximately

$$\frac{2\pi}{\Omega}\left(\frac{B + A}{B - A}\right)^{\frac{1}{2}} \qquad \text{(M.T.)}$$

11. A body is rotating about a fixed point O under no forces, OA is the axis of principal moment A and OH is the invariable line. Prove that the plane HOA rotates about OH with angular velocity

$$(2AT \operatorname{cosec}^2\phi - H^2\cot^2\phi)/AH$$

where ϕ is the angle HOA, T the kinetic energy and H the angular momentum. (L.U.)

12. A solid uniform cube is in motion about one of its corners O, which is fixed, and the constraint is smooth. If the resolutes of angular velocity of the cube along its three edges through O are ω_1, ω_2, ω_3 and gravity is neglected, prove that $\omega_1 + \omega_2 + \omega_3$ and $\omega_1\omega_2 + \omega_2\omega_3 + \omega_3\omega_1$ are each constant throughout the motion. (*L.U.*)

13. A uniform heavy square lamina, free to turn about its centre which is fixed, is set rotating with angular velocity Ω about an axis inclined at an angle of 45° to its plane. Show that, in the subsequent motion, the axis of figure of the lamina describes, with uniform angular velocity, a right circular cone whose axis is inclined at an angle $\tan^{-1}(\frac{1}{2})$ with the invariable line. Find the semi-angle of the cone and the uniform angular velocity with which it is described. (L.U.)

14. The momental ellipsoid at the centre of mass G of a rigid body is a sphere. Show that, if P is any other point of the body, then PG is a principal axis at P. Hence, or otherwise, find the principal moments of inertia of a uniform solid cube at a corner.

A uniform solid cube is free to turn about a corner O under no forces except the reaction at O. The cube is set rotating about an edge through O with angular velocity Ω. Show that the diagonal of the cube describes in space a cone of semi-vertical angle $\tan^{-1}(11/\sqrt{2})$. Find the angular velocity with which the diagonal describes the cone. (L.U.)

15. A body with an axis of symmetry moves under the action of no forces with a point O on the axis fixed. Prove that the instantaneous axis of rotation describes a circular cone in space and also a circular cone in the body.

Prove also that if the body is set rotating with angular velocity ω about an axis which makes an angle α with the axis of symmetry, then its axis of symmetry describes in space a cone of angle 2β, where $\tan\beta = \dfrac{A}{C}\tan\alpha$, C is the moment of inertia about the axis of symmetry and A is the moment of inertia about a perpendicular axis through O. (L.U.)

CHAPTER XV

GYROSCOPIC AND NON-HOLONOMIC PROBLEMS

15.1 The spinning top (vectorial treatment)

This is the problem of a rigid body possessing an axis of symmetry, $\boldsymbol{e}$, and moving about a point O of this axis in the constant gravitational field. Suppose $OG = h$, as in Fig. 118, and that $\boldsymbol{k}$ is a unit vector in the direction of the upward vertical ; take $\boldsymbol{e}^2 = 1$.

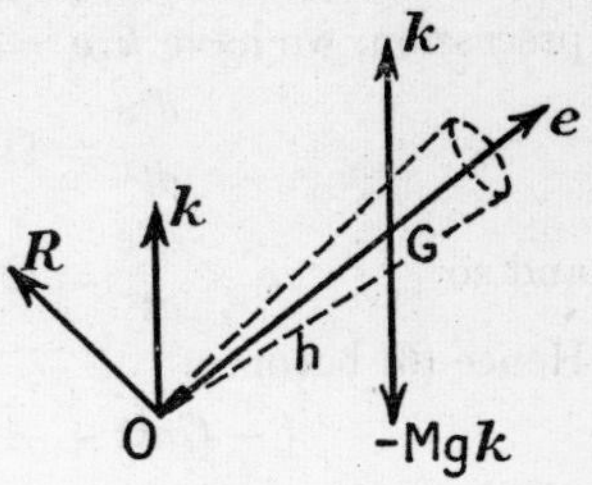

FIG. 118.

If the principal moments of inertia of the top at O are A, A, C ($\boldsymbol{e}$ is a principal axis at O), we can write $\mathscr{J}(O) = A(\boldsymbol{ll} + \boldsymbol{mm}) + C\ \boldsymbol{ee}$, where $(\boldsymbol{l}\ \boldsymbol{m}, \boldsymbol{e})$ is an orthonormal triad. Since $\mathscr{I} = \boldsymbol{ll} + \boldsymbol{mm} + \boldsymbol{ee}$ this is also

$$\mathscr{J}(O) = A\mathscr{I} + (C - A)\boldsymbol{ee} \quad . \quad . \quad (1)$$

Hence $$\boldsymbol{H}(O) = \mathscr{J}(O) . \boldsymbol{\omega} = A\,\boldsymbol{\omega} + (C - A)n\,\boldsymbol{e} \quad . \quad . \quad (2)$$

where $n = \boldsymbol{\omega} . \boldsymbol{e}$ = spin about the axis of symmetry.

But, as in 14.4(9), we have $\boldsymbol{\omega} = n\,\boldsymbol{e} + \boldsymbol{e} \times \dfrac{d\boldsymbol{e}}{dt}$ . . . . . (3)

(2) and (3) give $$\boldsymbol{H}(O) = Cn\,\boldsymbol{e} + A\,\boldsymbol{e} \times \frac{d\boldsymbol{e}}{dt} \quad . \quad . \quad . \quad . \quad (4)$$

Since $\dot{\boldsymbol{e}}$ is perpendicular to $\boldsymbol{e}$, (4) is almost obvious by inspection. Notice that we are not using the method of rotating frames of reference, at this stage.

The equation of motion $\dot{\boldsymbol{H}}(O) = \boldsymbol{\Gamma}(O)$ now becomes

$$C\frac{dn}{dt}\boldsymbol{e} + Cn\frac{d\boldsymbol{e}}{dt} + A\,\boldsymbol{e} \times \frac{d^2\boldsymbol{e}}{dt^2} = -\,Mgh\,\boldsymbol{e} \times \boldsymbol{k} \quad . \quad (5)$$

Multiplying (5) by $\boldsymbol{e}$. gives $\dfrac{dn}{dt} = 0$, or n = constant. This also follows from Euler's equations since $A = B$ and $N = 0$.

Hence $$Cn\frac{d\boldsymbol{e}}{dt} + A\,\boldsymbol{e} \times \frac{d^2\boldsymbol{e}}{dt^2} = -\,Mgh\,\boldsymbol{e} \times \boldsymbol{k} \quad . \quad . \quad (6)$$

The reaction $\boldsymbol{R}$ at O is given by

$$Mh\frac{d^2\boldsymbol{e}}{dt^2} = \boldsymbol{R} - Mg\,\boldsymbol{k} \quad . \quad . \quad . \quad . \quad (7)$$

The motion of $\boldsymbol{e}$ around the vertical $\boldsymbol{k}$ is called the *precession* of the top, whilst its motion in the plane of $\boldsymbol{e}$, $\boldsymbol{k}$ is called the *nutation* of the top. Equation (6) easily gives the condition for *steady precession.*

Thus, suppose that $\boldsymbol{e}$ moves round $\boldsymbol{k}$ with constant angular velocity Ω. Then

$$\frac{d\boldsymbol{e}}{dt} = \Omega\, \boldsymbol{k} \times \boldsymbol{e}$$

and
$$\frac{d^2\boldsymbol{e}}{dt^2} = \Omega^2\, \boldsymbol{k} \times (\boldsymbol{k} \times \boldsymbol{e}) = \Omega^2\{(\boldsymbol{k}.\boldsymbol{e})\boldsymbol{k} - \boldsymbol{e}\}$$

If the vector $\boldsymbol{e}$ is inclined at a constant angle α to $\boldsymbol{k}$ during the steady precession, we have $\boldsymbol{k}.\boldsymbol{e} = \cos\alpha$. Hence

$$\frac{d^2\boldsymbol{e}}{dt^2} = \Omega^2 \cos\alpha\, \boldsymbol{k} - \Omega^2\, \boldsymbol{e}$$

and so
$$\boldsymbol{e} \times \frac{d^2\boldsymbol{e}}{dt^2} = \Omega^2 \cos\alpha\, \boldsymbol{e} \times \boldsymbol{k}$$

Hence (6) becomes

$$\{-Cn\Omega + A\cos\alpha\, \Omega^2 + Mgh\}(\boldsymbol{e} \times \boldsymbol{k}) = \boldsymbol{0}$$

which implies
$$A\cos\alpha\,\Omega^2 - Cn\,\Omega + Mgh = 0 \quad . \quad . \quad . \quad (8)$$

There are therefore two real values of Ω provided

$$C^2n^2 > 4AMgh\cos\alpha \quad . \quad . \quad . \quad . \quad (9)$$

which is the condition for steady precession.

For general motion of the top, (6) gives the integrals of angular momentum and energy, as follows.

$$Cn(\dot{\boldsymbol{e}}.\boldsymbol{k}) + A(\boldsymbol{e} \times \ddot{\boldsymbol{e}}).\boldsymbol{k} = 0$$

so that
$$Cn(\boldsymbol{e}.\boldsymbol{k}) + A(\boldsymbol{e} \times \dot{\boldsymbol{e}}).\boldsymbol{k} = \text{constant}$$
$$= \boldsymbol{H}(O).\boldsymbol{k}. \quad . \quad . \quad (10)$$

Multiplying (6) in scalar product by $(\boldsymbol{e} \times \dot{\boldsymbol{e}})$ gives

$$A(\boldsymbol{e} \times \dot{\boldsymbol{e}}).(\boldsymbol{e} \times \ddot{\boldsymbol{e}}) = -Mgh(\boldsymbol{e} \times \dot{\boldsymbol{e}}).(\boldsymbol{e} \times \boldsymbol{k})$$
$$= -Mgh\, \dot{\boldsymbol{e}}.\boldsymbol{k}, \quad \text{since } \boldsymbol{e}\,.\,\dot{\boldsymbol{e}} = 0$$

This integrates to give

$$\tfrac{1}{2}A(\boldsymbol{e} \times \dot{\boldsymbol{e}})^2 + Mgh(\boldsymbol{e}.\boldsymbol{k}) = \text{constant} \quad . \quad . \quad (11)$$

which is the energy integral—the constant kinetic energy $\frac{1}{2}Cn^2$ being omitted from the lhs.

More detailed knowledge of the precession and nutation can now be obtained by introducing the two Eulerian angles θ, ϕ which define the position of $\boldsymbol{e}$. Although we shall discuss this analytically in the next section it is worth while to examine (10) and (11) in terms of θ and ϕ.

We can write
$$\boldsymbol{e}.\boldsymbol{k} = \cos\theta$$

and
$$\frac{d\boldsymbol{e}}{dt} = \boldsymbol{\omega} \times \boldsymbol{e}$$

where
$$\boldsymbol{\omega} = \dot{\phi}\,\boldsymbol{k} + \dot{\theta}\,\frac{\boldsymbol{k} \times \boldsymbol{e}}{|\,\boldsymbol{k} \times \boldsymbol{e}\,|}$$
$$= \dot{\phi}\,\boldsymbol{k} + \frac{\dot{\theta}}{\sin\theta}\,(\boldsymbol{k} \times \boldsymbol{e})$$

Hence
$$\frac{d\boldsymbol{e}}{dt} = \dot{\phi}\,\boldsymbol{k} \times \boldsymbol{e} + \frac{\dot{\theta}}{\sin\theta}\{-\,\boldsymbol{k} + \boldsymbol{e}\cos\theta\}$$

and
$$\boldsymbol{e} \times \frac{d\boldsymbol{e}}{dt} = \frac{\dot{\theta}}{\sin\theta}\,(\boldsymbol{k} \times \boldsymbol{e}) + \dot{\phi}(\boldsymbol{k} - \boldsymbol{e}\cos\theta)$$

Then (10) becomes
$$Cn\cos\theta + A\dot{\phi}\sin^2\theta = \text{constant} \qquad . \quad . \quad (12)$$
and (11) becomes
$$\tfrac{1}{2}A(\dot{\theta}^2 + \dot{\phi}^2\sin^2\theta) + Mgh\cos\theta = \text{constant} \qquad . \quad (13)$$

Example 1. The upper end of the axis of a top is compelled to describe a horizontal circle of radius c with uniform angular velocity ω. Prove that, if α is the inclination of the axis to the vertical when the motion is steady,
$$(A\sin\alpha + Mac)\omega^2 = (Cn\omega + Mga)\tan\alpha$$
where a is the distance of the centre of mass from the end of the axis, M the mass, C the moment of inertia about the axis of symmetry, A the moment of inertia about a perpendicular through the end of the axis, and n the spin about the axis of the top.

Prove that the periods of the small oscillations about the state of steady motion are $\dfrac{2\pi}{p}$, where p satisfies
$$\{A\sin\alpha(p^2 - \omega^2\sin^2\alpha) - M\omega^2ac\}\{Ap^2\sin\alpha - M\omega^2ac\}$$
$$= p^2\{A\omega\sin 2\alpha - Cn\sin\alpha\}^2 \quad \text{(L.U.)}$$

Fig. 119 shows steady precession. The velocity of O is
$$\boldsymbol{V} = c\,\frac{d\boldsymbol{i}}{dt} = c\omega\,\boldsymbol{k} \times \boldsymbol{i} \qquad . \quad (14)$$

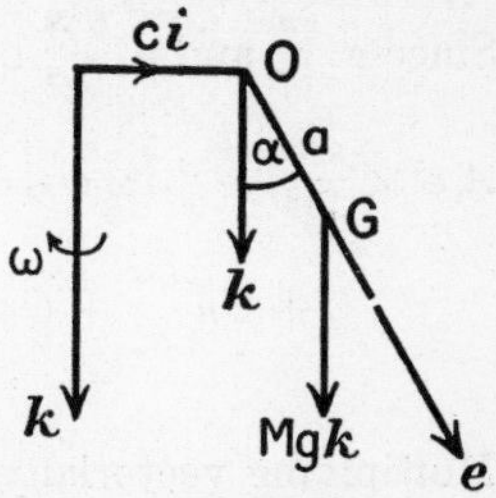

FIG. 119.

Also, by 9.2(3) and (4), we have, with $0 \equiv O'$,
$$\frac{d}{dt}\boldsymbol{H}(O') = \frac{d}{dt}\left\{Cn\,\boldsymbol{e} + A\,\boldsymbol{e} \times \frac{d\boldsymbol{e}}{dt}\right\}$$
$$+ Ma\,\boldsymbol{e} \times \frac{d\boldsymbol{V}}{dt} = \boldsymbol{\Gamma}(O')$$
$$= Mag\,\boldsymbol{e} \times \boldsymbol{k}$$

Hence n = constant, by multiplying by $\boldsymbol{e}$., and so we get
$$Ma\,\boldsymbol{e} \times \dot{\boldsymbol{V}} + Cn\,\dot{\boldsymbol{e}} + \boldsymbol{e} \times \ddot{\boldsymbol{e}} = Mag\,\boldsymbol{e} \times \boldsymbol{k} \qquad . \quad (15)$$

In *steady precession* we write $\dot{\boldsymbol{e}} = \omega\,\boldsymbol{k} \times \boldsymbol{e}$. Then (15) gives

$$-Ma\,\boldsymbol{e} \times (c\omega^2\,\boldsymbol{i}) + Cn\omega(\boldsymbol{k} \times \boldsymbol{e}) + A\,\boldsymbol{e} \times \{\omega^2(\boldsymbol{k}.\boldsymbol{e})\boldsymbol{k} - \omega^2\,\boldsymbol{e}\} = Mag\,(\boldsymbol{e} \times \boldsymbol{k})$$

where (14) has given $\dot{\boldsymbol{V}} = c\omega^2\{(\boldsymbol{k}.\boldsymbol{i})\boldsymbol{i} - \boldsymbol{i}\} = -c\omega^2\,\boldsymbol{i}$. We now have

$$Mac\omega^2\,(\boldsymbol{i} \times \boldsymbol{e}) + Cnw\,(\boldsymbol{k} \times \boldsymbol{e}) + A\omega^2 \cos\alpha\,(\boldsymbol{e} \times \boldsymbol{k}) = Mag\,(\boldsymbol{e} \times \boldsymbol{k})$$

Multiplying this by $(\boldsymbol{k} \times \boldsymbol{e}).$, we get

$$Mac\omega^2[-\cos\alpha \sin\alpha] + Cn\omega(1 - \cos^2\alpha) - [A\omega^2 \cos\alpha - Mag]\,(1 - \cos^2\alpha) = 0$$

i.e. $$(Cn\omega + Mag)\sin\alpha = (A \sin\alpha + Mac)\omega^2 \cos\alpha \quad . (16$$

Q.E.D

To discuss the *small oscillations* about this steady state we can proceed in the following vectorial manner.

Write $\boldsymbol{e} + \boldsymbol{x}$ for $\boldsymbol{e}$ in (15) with $|\,\boldsymbol{x}\,| \ll 1$, so that $\boldsymbol{e}.\boldsymbol{x} = 0$. Then we get

$$-Mac\omega^2(\boldsymbol{e} + \boldsymbol{x}) \times \boldsymbol{i} + Cn(\dot{\boldsymbol{e}} + \dot{\boldsymbol{x}}) + A(\boldsymbol{e} + \boldsymbol{x}) \times (\ddot{\boldsymbol{e}} + \ddot{\boldsymbol{x}}) = Mag\,(\boldsymbol{e} + \boldsymbol{x}) \times \boldsymbol{k}$$

Using (15), this reduces to

$$-Mac\omega^2\,\boldsymbol{x} \times \boldsymbol{i} + Cn\,\dot{\boldsymbol{x}} + A\,\boldsymbol{x} \times \ddot{\boldsymbol{e}} + A\,\boldsymbol{e} \times \ddot{\boldsymbol{x}} = Mag\,\boldsymbol{x} \times \boldsymbol{k}$$

But $\dot{\boldsymbol{e}} = \omega\,\boldsymbol{k} \times \boldsymbol{e}$, $\ddot{\boldsymbol{e}} = \omega^2 \cos\alpha\,\boldsymbol{k} - \omega^2\,\boldsymbol{e}$, and so

$$A\,\boldsymbol{e} \times \dot{\boldsymbol{x}} + Cn\,\dot{\boldsymbol{x}} + (A\omega^2 \cos\alpha - Mag)(\boldsymbol{x} \times \boldsymbol{k}) - Mac\omega^2(\boldsymbol{x} \times \boldsymbol{i}) - A\omega^2(\boldsymbol{x} \times \boldsymbol{e}) = \boldsymbol{0} \quad (17)$$

Now refer the motion of $\boldsymbol{x}$ to a frame of reference, rotating with $\boldsymbol{e}$ with angular velocity $\omega\,\boldsymbol{k}$—the steady state. Hence we write

$$\frac{\partial \boldsymbol{x}}{\partial t} + \omega\,\boldsymbol{k} \times \boldsymbol{x} \text{ for } \dot{\boldsymbol{x}}$$

and $$\frac{\partial^2 \boldsymbol{x}}{\partial t^2} + 2\omega\,\boldsymbol{k} \times \frac{\partial \boldsymbol{x}}{\partial t} + \omega^2\,\boldsymbol{k} \times (\boldsymbol{k} \times \boldsymbol{x}) \text{ for } \ddot{\boldsymbol{x}}$$

Since $\boldsymbol{e}.\dfrac{\partial \boldsymbol{x}}{\partial t}$ and $\boldsymbol{e}.\dfrac{\partial^2 \boldsymbol{x}}{\partial t^2}$ both vanish, (17) becomes

$$A\,\boldsymbol{e} \times \frac{\partial^2 \boldsymbol{x}}{\partial t^2} - 2A\omega \cos\alpha\,\frac{\partial \boldsymbol{x}}{\partial t} + A\omega^2(\boldsymbol{k}.\boldsymbol{x})(\boldsymbol{e} \times \boldsymbol{k}) - A\omega^2(\boldsymbol{e} \times \boldsymbol{x}) + Cn\,\frac{\partial \boldsymbol{x}}{\partial t} + Cn\omega(\boldsymbol{k} \times \boldsymbol{x}) + (A\omega^2 \cos\alpha - Mag)(\boldsymbol{x} \times \boldsymbol{k}) - Mac\omega^2(\boldsymbol{x} \times \boldsymbol{i}) - A\omega^2(\boldsymbol{x} \times \boldsymbol{e}) = \boldsymbol{0}$$

Multiplying vectorially by $\boldsymbol{e}$, we get

$$-A\,\frac{\partial^2 \boldsymbol{x}}{\partial t^2} - 2\omega A \cos\alpha\,\boldsymbol{e} \times \frac{\partial \boldsymbol{x}}{\partial t} + Cn\,\boldsymbol{e} \times \frac{\partial \boldsymbol{x}}{\partial t} - Cn\omega \cos\alpha\,\boldsymbol{x} + (A\omega^2 \cos^2\alpha - Mag \cos\alpha)\boldsymbol{x} - Mac\omega^2 \sin\alpha\,\boldsymbol{x} = -A\omega^2(\boldsymbol{k}.\boldsymbol{x})(\cos\alpha\,\boldsymbol{e} - \boldsymbol{k})$$

Using (16), this can be written

$$A \sin \alpha \frac{\partial^2 \boldsymbol{x}}{\partial t^2} + (A\omega \sin 2\alpha - Cn \sin \alpha)\boldsymbol{e} \times \frac{\partial \boldsymbol{x}}{\partial t} + Mac\omega^2 \boldsymbol{x}$$
$$- A\omega^2 \sin \alpha \cos \alpha\, (\boldsymbol{k}.\boldsymbol{x})\boldsymbol{e} + A\omega^2 \sin \alpha\, (\boldsymbol{k}.\boldsymbol{x})\boldsymbol{k} = \boldsymbol{0} \qquad (18)$$

Now take $(\boldsymbol{j}, \boldsymbol{e}, \boldsymbol{n})$ as an orthonormal triad, $\boldsymbol{n}$ being in the plane of $\boldsymbol{e}$ and $\boldsymbol{k}$ (v. Fig. 120). Hence we can write

$$\boldsymbol{x} = x\,\boldsymbol{n} + y\,\boldsymbol{j} \quad (x \neq |\,\boldsymbol{x}\,|)$$

and $$\boldsymbol{k} = -\sin \alpha\, \boldsymbol{n} + \cos \alpha\, \boldsymbol{e}$$

and (18) becomes

$$\{A \sin \alpha\, \ddot{x} - (A\omega \sin 2\alpha - Cn \sin \alpha)\dot{y} + Mac\omega^2 x + Ax\omega^2 \sin^3 \alpha\}\boldsymbol{n}$$
$$+ \{A \sin \alpha\, \ddot{y} + (A\omega \sin 2\alpha - Cn \sin \alpha)\dot{x} + Mac\omega^2 y\}\boldsymbol{j} = \boldsymbol{0} \qquad (19)$$

The possible frequencies are found by writing $x = P \cos (pt + \epsilon)$ and $y = Q \sin (pt + \epsilon)$; P, Q, ϵ, p constants. Substituting in (19) gives

$$\{-Ap^2 \sin \alpha + Mac\omega^2 + A\omega^2 \sin^3 \alpha\}P$$
$$- \{A\omega \sin 2\alpha - Cn \sin \alpha\}pQ = 0$$
$$- \{A\omega \sin 2\alpha - Cn \sin \alpha\}\, pP + \{-Ap^2 \sin \alpha + Mac\omega^2\}\, Q = 0$$

Eliminating P, Q gives the required expression. Q.E.D.

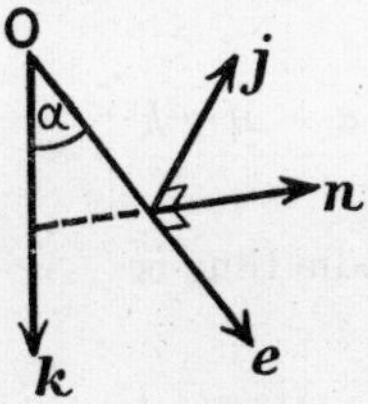

FIG. 120.

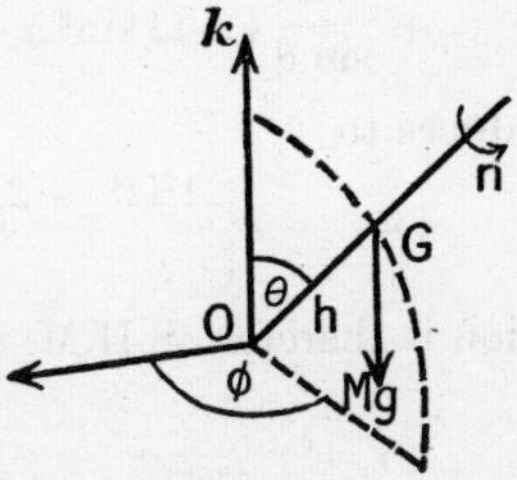

FIG. 121.

15.2 The spinning top (Lagrangian equations)

The position of the top can be defined by the Eulerian angles θ, ϕ, ψ of 14.5 (v. Fig. 121). By 14.5(4) we have the Lagrangian function

$$L = \tfrac{1}{2}A(\dot{\theta}^2 + \dot{\phi}^2 \sin^2 \alpha) + \tfrac{1}{2}C(\dot{\psi} + \dot{\phi} \cos \theta)^2 - Mgh \cos \theta \qquad (1)$$

We notice that ϕ, ψ are cyclic co-ordinates so that two of the Lagrangian equations are simply

$$\frac{\partial L}{\partial \dot{\psi}} = C(\dot{\psi} + \dot{\phi} \cos \theta) = Cn \text{ (constant)} \qquad (2)$$

and $$\frac{\partial L}{\partial \dot{\phi}} = A\dot{\phi} \sin^2 \theta + C \cos \theta\, (\dot{\psi} + \dot{\phi} \cos \theta) = \text{constant}$$

i.e. $$A\dot{\phi} \sin^2 \theta + Cn \cos \theta = Cn \cos \alpha \qquad (3)$$

if we suppose $\dot{\phi} = 0$ when $\theta = \alpha$. The third Lagrangian equation gives

$$A\ddot{\theta} - A\dot{\phi}^2 \sin \theta \cos \theta + C\, \dot{\phi} \sin \theta\, (\dot{\psi} + \dot{\phi} \cos \theta) - Mgh \sin \theta = 0 \qquad (4)$$

Equation (3) is the angular momentum equation 15.1(12) ; n is ω_3, the spin about the axis of symmetry, as in 15.1. The energy equation becomes (cf. 15.1(13))

$$A(\dot{\theta}^2 + \dot{\phi}^2 \sin^2 \theta) = 2Mgh\,(\cos \alpha - \cos \theta) \quad . \quad . \quad (5)$$

if we take initial conditions, $\dot{\theta} = \dot{\phi} = 0$, $\theta = \alpha$ at $t = 0$. *Steady precession* corresponds to $\theta = \alpha$, $\ddot{\theta} = \dot{\theta} = 0$, $\dot{\phi} = \Omega$ (const.). Hence (4) gives

$$A\Omega^2 \cos \alpha + Cn\Omega + Mgh = 0$$

as in 15.1. The two possible values for Ω become simple when n is very large, viz. $\Omega_1 = \dfrac{Cn}{A \cos \alpha}$, $\Omega_2 = \dfrac{Mgh}{Cn}$; one of these is large, the other small.

Stability of steady precession. This may be investigated by writing $\theta = \alpha + \epsilon$ (ϵ very small). Eliminating $\dot{\phi}$ between (3) and (4) gives, with $\dot{\phi} = \Omega$, $\theta = \alpha$ at $t = 0$,

$$A^2\ddot{\theta} - \frac{\cos \theta}{\sin^3 \theta}\{A\,\Omega \sin^2 \alpha + Cn \cos \alpha - Cn \cos \theta\}^2$$
$$+ \frac{Cn}{\sin \theta}\{A\,\Omega \sin^2 \alpha + Cn \cos \alpha - Cn \cos \theta\} = AMgh \sin \theta$$

which reduces to

$$\ddot{\epsilon} = -\,\epsilon\left\{\frac{A^2\Omega^4 - 2AMgh\,\Omega^2 \cos \alpha + M^2g^2h^2}{A^2\Omega^2}\right\}$$

The motion is therefore S.H.M. and the periodic time is

$$\tau = \frac{2\pi A\Omega}{\{A^2\Omega^4 - 2AMgh\,\Omega^2 \cos \alpha + M^2g^2h^2\}^{\frac{1}{2}}}$$

Nutation. This is the motion of the top expressed by the variation of θ alone. Taking the initial conditions as $\theta = \alpha$, $\dot{\theta} = \dot{\phi} = 0$, (3) and (5) give

$$A^2 \sin^2 \theta \,.\, \dot{\theta}^2 = A \sin^2 \theta \,.\, 2Mgh\,(\cos \alpha - \cos \theta) - C^2n^2\,(\cos \alpha - \cos \theta)^2 \quad (6)$$

Now define p by $C^2n^2 = 4AMghp$, then (6) becomes

$$A \sin^2 \theta \,.\, \dot{\theta}^2 = 2Mgh\,(\cos \alpha - \cos \theta)\{\sin^2 \theta - 2p\,(\cos \alpha - \cos \theta)\}$$
$$= -\,2Mgh\,(\cos \alpha - \cos \theta)\{\cos \theta - p + \sqrt{p^2 - 2p \cos \alpha + 1}\}$$
$$\times \{\cos \alpha - p - \sqrt{p^2 - 2p \cos \alpha + 1}\} \quad (7)$$

Hence $\dot{\theta}^2 = 0$ when $\theta = \alpha$ and (say) $\theta = \theta_1$, θ_2 where

$$\cos \theta_1 = p - \sqrt{p^2 - 2p \cos \alpha + 1}$$
$$\cos \theta_2 = p + \sqrt{p^2 - 2p \cos \alpha + 1}$$

But since $\cos \alpha < 1$ we have

$$p^2 - 2p \cos \alpha + 1 > (1 \sim p)^2$$

Hence $\cos\theta_1 < 1$ and $\cos\theta_2 > 1$, i.e. θ_1 is real and θ_2 is complex. Hence $\dot\theta^2$ vanishes when $\theta = \alpha$ and when $\theta = \theta_1$. Also

$$\begin{aligned} p^2 - 2p\cos\alpha + 1 &> p^2 - 2p\cos\alpha + \cos^2\alpha \\ &= (p - \cos\alpha)^2 \end{aligned}$$

so that $$\cos\theta_1 < p - (p - \cos\alpha) = \cos\alpha$$

Hence $\theta_1 > \alpha$ and (7) gives

$$A\sin^2\theta.\dot\theta^2 = (+\text{ve quantity})(\cos\alpha - \cos\theta)(\cos\theta - \cos\theta_1)$$

showing that $\dot\theta^2 \geqslant 0$ if, and only if,

$$\alpha \leqslant \theta \leqslant \theta_1$$

Hence the axis of the top moves between two right circular cones whose axes lie along the vertical and whose vertical angles are 2α and $2\theta_1$.

When n *is very large*, we get

$$\begin{aligned} \cos\theta_1 &= p\left\{1 - \left(1 - \frac{2\cos\alpha}{p} + \frac{1}{p^2}\right)^{\frac{1}{2}}\right\} \\ &= \cos\alpha - \frac{\sin^2\alpha}{2p} \quad (p \text{ very large}) \\ &= \cos(\alpha + \beta) \end{aligned}$$

if we take $$\beta = \frac{\sin\alpha}{2p} \quad \text{(very small)}$$

Example 1. A symmetrical top is set spinning about its axis when $\theta = \alpha$. Show that between the greatest approach to and recess from the vertical, the centre of mass describes an arc of length

$$h\tan^{-1}\left\{\frac{\sin\alpha}{p - \cos\alpha}\right\}$$

where $h = OG$ and $C^2n^2 = 4AMghp$.

The element of arc ds described by G in a time dt will be given by

$$ds^2 = h^2\,d\theta^2 + h^2\sin^2\theta\,d\phi^2$$

Hence in a time t_1, we have

$$s = h\int_0^{t_1}(\dot\theta^2 + \dot\phi^2\sin^2\theta)^{\frac{1}{2}}\,dt \quad . \quad . \quad . \quad (8)$$

But the energy equation gives

$$\dot\theta^2 + \dot\phi^2\sin^2\theta = \frac{2Mgh}{A}(\cos\alpha - \cos\theta)$$

and $t = t_1$ when $\theta = \theta_1$. Hence (8) becomes

$$s = h\sqrt{\frac{2Mgh}{A}}\int_\alpha^{\theta_1}\sqrt{\cos\alpha - \cos\theta}.\left(\frac{dt}{d\theta}\right).d\theta \quad . \quad (9)$$

But, from (7), we have

$$\dot{\theta}^2 = \left(\frac{2Mgh}{A}\right)\frac{(\cos\alpha - \cos\theta)}{\sin^2\theta}\{\sin^2\theta - 2p(\cos\alpha - \cos\theta)\}$$

so that (9) gives

$$\begin{aligned} s &= h\int_\alpha^{\theta_1}\frac{\sin\theta\, d\theta}{\{1 - 2p\cos\alpha - (\cos^2\theta - 2p\cos\theta)\}^{\frac{1}{2}}} \\ &= h\int_\alpha^{\theta_1}\frac{\sin\theta\, d\theta}{\{(p^2 - 2p\cos\alpha + 1) - (\cos\theta - p)^2\}^{\frac{1}{2}}} \\ &= h\left[\sin^{-1}\left\{\frac{\cos\theta - p}{\sqrt{p^2 - 2p\cos\alpha + 1}}\right\}\right]_{\theta_1}^{\alpha} \\ &= h.\frac{\pi}{2} + h\sin^{-1}\left\{\frac{\cos\alpha - p}{\sqrt{p^2 - 2p\cos\alpha + 1}}\right\} \\ &= h.\frac{\pi}{2} + h\tan^{-1}\left\{\frac{\cos\alpha - p}{\sin\alpha}\right\} \end{aligned}$$

$$s = h\tan^{-1}\left\{\frac{\sin\alpha}{p - \cos\alpha}\right\} \qquad \text{Q.E.D.}$$

Example 2. If hz measures the height of G above O, prove that, with the usual notation,

$$A^2\dot{z}^2 = (K - 2MghAz)(1 - z^2) - (H - Cnz)^2$$

where H, K are constants. Deduce that the motion of G varies between two horizontal planes.

If initially the axis is at rest with $z = \frac{1}{2}$ and $C^2n^2 = 4MghA$, show that thereafter $0 \leqslant z \leqslant \frac{1}{2}$ and that if, in addition, $4A = 3Mh^2$, the vertical component N of the reaction at O satisfies the inequalities

$$O \leqslant N \leqslant \tfrac{7}{3}Mg \qquad \text{(L.U.)}$$

Writing $z = \cos\theta$, (3) and (5) become, without specifying the initial conditions,

$$A\dot{\phi}(1 - z^2) + Cnz = H \quad . \quad . \quad (10)$$

$$\frac{A}{(1 - z^2)}.\dot{z}^2 + A\dot{\phi}^2(1 - z^2) + 2Mgzh = K/A \quad . \quad . \quad (11)$$

(10), (11) now give

$$A^2\dot{z}^2 = (K - 2MghAz)(1 - z^2) - (H - Cnz)^2 \quad . \quad (12)$$

Write $K = 2MghA.k$, $H = Cn.q$ and $C^2n^2 = 4AMgh.p$. Then (12) becomes

$$\begin{aligned} A^2\dot{z}^2 &= 2MghA\{(k - z)(1 - z^2) - 2p(q - z)^2\} \quad . \quad (13) \\ &\equiv 2MghA.f(z) \end{aligned}$$

Now if $\dot{z} = \dot{z}_0$ at some initial value $z = z_0$, we have $f(z)_0 > 0$. But $f(-1) < 0$ and $f(+1) < 0$. Hence the cubic $f(z)$ must have real roots between -1 and z_0 and between z_0 and $+1$; z_0 itself lies between -1 and $+1$ since it is some value of $\cos\theta$. Since $f(\infty)$ is $+$ve, $f(z)$ has a third real root between $+1$ and ∞, but this is irrelevant since $z = \cos\theta$. Hence (13) shows that, independently of the initial conditions

$$\dot{z}^2 \geqslant 0 \quad \text{if, and only if,} \quad z_1 \leqslant z \leqslant z_2$$

where $-1 < z_1$, $z_2 < +1$. The motion of G therefore takes place between two horizontal planes. Q.E.D.

Writing $\dot{z} = 0$ when $z = \frac{1}{2}$ and $p = 1$, $\dot{\phi}_0 = 0$, (10) and (11) give $q = \frac{1}{2}$ and $k = \frac{1}{2}$. Hence (13) gives

$$A\dot{z}^2 = 2Mgh.\tfrac{1}{2}.(1-2z)(2-z)z \quad . \quad . \quad (14)$$

Hence $\dot{z}^2 \geqslant 0$ for $0 \leqslant z \leqslant \frac{1}{2}$. Q.E.D.

The vertical reaction N, at O, is given by

$$Mh\ddot{z} = N - Mg \quad . \quad . \quad . \quad . \quad (15)$$

Writing $4A = 3Mh^2$, (14) gives

$$\frac{h}{2}\dot{z}^2 = \frac{2g}{3}z(1-2z)(2-z)$$

Hence

$$h\ddot{z} = \frac{4g}{3}(3z^2 - 5z + 1)$$

Then (15) gives

$$N = \frac{Mg}{3}(12z^2 - 20z + 7)$$

$$= \frac{Mg}{3}(2z-1)(6z-7)$$

Now $\dfrac{dN}{dz} = \frac{4}{3}Mg(6z-5) < 0$ when $z < 5/6$. Hence N is a decreasing function of z when $0 \leqslant z \leqslant \frac{1}{2}$. Hence, generally,

$$N(\tfrac{1}{2}) \leqslant N(z) \leqslant N(0)$$

or,

$$0 \leqslant N(z) \leqslant \tfrac{7}{3}Mg$$

Q.E.D.

Example 3. The Gyro-compass. Consider a heavy body possessing an axis of symmetry (such as a flywheel) which is made to rotate about its axis in a rigid frame, which is itself free to rotate only in a horizontal plane at a point P of the earth's surface (v. Fig. 122). We shall show that, because of the earth's rotation, the axis of such a body comes to rest in the local meridian of longitude as long as P is at rest relative to the earth. Such a device is, in essence, the gyro-

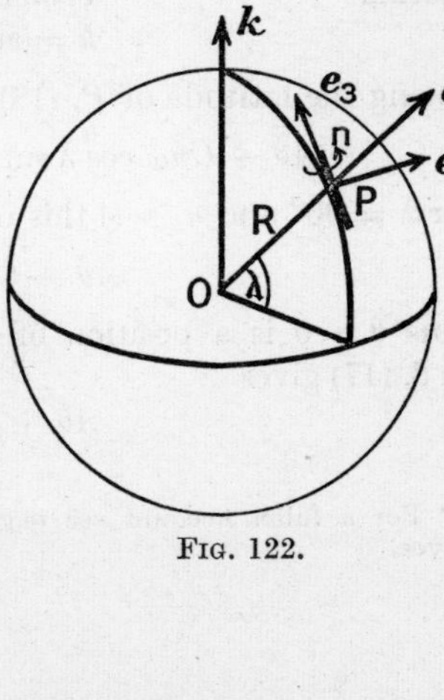

FIG. 122.

compass.* The rigid frame is floated in a bath of mercury and the wheel is driven electrically at a speed of the order of 20,000 revs./min. Any motion of the axis either out of the horizontal plane or out of its position of relative equilibrium in that plane is in fact oscillatory and these tendencies are counteracted by a damping device incorporated in the design.

We shall examine the motion of the axis in the horizontal plane only (v. Fig. 123).

Suppose the constant spin about the axis is n and let $\boldsymbol{e}$ be a unit vector along this axis. The moments of inertia of the body will be A, A, C (about $\boldsymbol{e}$) and let $\boldsymbol{\Omega}$ be its angular velocity, $\boldsymbol{\omega} = \omega\,\boldsymbol{k}$ the angular velocity of the earth. We can write

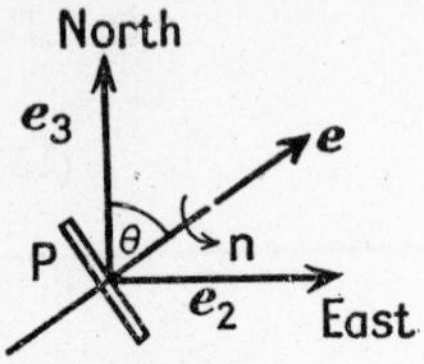

FIG. 123.

$$\underline{\boldsymbol{\Omega}} = n\,\boldsymbol{e} + \boldsymbol{e} \times \frac{d\boldsymbol{e}}{dt}$$

and so
$$\boldsymbol{H}(P) = \{A\mathscr{I} + (C - A)\boldsymbol{ee}\}.\boldsymbol{\Omega}$$
$$= Cn\,\boldsymbol{e} + A\,\boldsymbol{e} \times \frac{d\boldsymbol{e}}{dt}$$

If $\boldsymbol{\Gamma}$ = the external torque acting on the body, we have

$$\frac{d\boldsymbol{H}(P)}{dt} = \boldsymbol{\Gamma}$$

The supports are such that $\boldsymbol{\Gamma}.\boldsymbol{e}_1 = 0$, and so

$$\boldsymbol{e}_1.\frac{d\boldsymbol{H}(P)}{dt} = 0 \quad . \quad . \quad . \quad . \quad (16)$$

Now

$$\frac{d\boldsymbol{H}}{dt} = Cn\frac{d\boldsymbol{e}}{dt} + A\,\boldsymbol{e} \times \frac{d^2\boldsymbol{e}}{dt^2}$$
$$= Cn\left\{\frac{\partial \boldsymbol{e}}{\partial t} + \omega\,\boldsymbol{k} \times \boldsymbol{e}\right\} + A\,\boldsymbol{e} \times \left\{\frac{\partial^2 \boldsymbol{e}}{\partial t^2} + 2\omega\,\boldsymbol{k} \times \frac{\partial \boldsymbol{e}}{\partial t} + \omega^2\,\boldsymbol{k} \times (\boldsymbol{k} \times \boldsymbol{e})\right\}$$

Writing
$$\boldsymbol{e} = \sin\theta\,\boldsymbol{e}_2 + \cos\theta\,\boldsymbol{e}_3$$
$$\boldsymbol{k} = \sin\lambda\,\boldsymbol{e}_1 + \cos\lambda\,\boldsymbol{e}_3$$

λ being the latitude of P, (16) gives

$$A\ddot{\theta} + Cn\omega\cos\lambda\sin\theta - A\omega^2\cos^2\lambda\cos\theta\sin\theta = 0$$

For $\lambda \neq 90°$ and $n \gg \omega$ this reduces to

$$A\ddot{\theta} + Cn\omega\cos\lambda\sin\theta = 0 \quad . \quad . \quad . \quad (17)$$

Thus $\theta = 0$ is a position of relative equilibrium and, writing θ for $\sin\theta$, (17) gives

$$A\ddot{\theta} + (Cn\omega\cos\lambda)\theta = 0$$

* For a fuller account see (e.g.) R. F. Deimel, *Mechanics of the Gyroscope*, Dover.

Hence the oscillations about the meridian of longitude are of period

$$2\pi\sqrt{\frac{Cn\omega\cos\lambda}{A}}$$

When P has a velocity $\boldsymbol{v} = u_2\,\boldsymbol{e}_2 + u_3\,\boldsymbol{e}_3$ we can find the effect as follows :

1. The effect of the velocity u_2 (due East) is to alter the effective angular velocity of the earth. Thus u_2 is equivalent to writing

$$\boldsymbol{\omega} = \omega\,\boldsymbol{k} + y\,\boldsymbol{e}_3$$

where $y = \dfrac{u_2}{R}$, R being the radius of the earth ($\sim$ 4000 m.).

This gives $\qquad \boldsymbol{\omega} = \omega\sin\lambda\,\boldsymbol{e}_1 + (\omega\cos\lambda + y)\boldsymbol{e}_3$

so that $\omega\cos\lambda$ is replaced by $(\omega\cos\lambda + y)$. Equation (17) remains of the form $\ddot{\theta} + B\sin\theta = 0$ and so the position of relative equilibrium remains in the meridian of longitude.

2. The effect of the velocity u_3 (due North) is taken into account by writing

$$\boldsymbol{\omega} = \omega\,\boldsymbol{k} - x\,\boldsymbol{e}_2, \quad \text{where } x = \frac{u_3}{R} \ll \omega$$

and noting that $\dot{\lambda} = +\,x$.

With $\qquad \boldsymbol{\omega} = \omega\sin\lambda\,\boldsymbol{e}_1 - x\,\boldsymbol{e}_2 + \omega\cos\lambda\,\boldsymbol{e}_3$

we get
$$\frac{d\boldsymbol{e}}{dt} = (-\,xc - \omega s\cos\lambda)\boldsymbol{e}_1 + (c\dot{\theta} - \omega c\sin\lambda)\boldsymbol{e}_2 + (\omega s\sin\lambda - s\dot{\theta})\boldsymbol{e}_3$$

where $c = \cos\theta$, $s = \sin\theta$.

Also
$$\begin{aligned}\frac{d^2\boldsymbol{e}}{dt^2} = {} & (xs\dot{\theta} - \omega c\dot{\theta}\cos\lambda + \omega xs\sin\lambda)\boldsymbol{e}_1 \\ & + (c\ddot{\theta} - s\dot{\theta}^2 + \omega s\dot{\theta}\sin\lambda - \omega xc\cos\lambda)\boldsymbol{e}_2 \\ & + (\omega c\dot{\theta}\sin\lambda + \omega sx\cos\lambda + c\dot{\theta}^2 - s\ddot{\theta})\boldsymbol{e}_3 \\ & + (\omega\sin\lambda\,\boldsymbol{e}_1 - x\,\boldsymbol{e}_2 + \omega\cos\lambda\,\boldsymbol{e}_3) \times \frac{d\boldsymbol{e}}{dt}\end{aligned}$$

The coefficient of $\boldsymbol{e}_1$ in $\dfrac{d\boldsymbol{H}}{dt}$ now becomes

$$A\{-\,\ddot{\theta} + \omega x\cos\lambda\} - Cn\{\omega\cos\lambda\sin\theta + x\cos\theta\}$$

after neglecting terms in ω^2 and in x^2. If we also neglect the term $A\omega x\cos\lambda$ and write $\tan\alpha = \dfrac{x}{\omega\cos\lambda} = \sin\alpha$ (since α is small), (17) is replaced by

$$A\ddot{\theta} + Cn\omega\cos\lambda\sin(\theta + \alpha) = 0$$

This shows that the axis is in equilibrium at $\theta = -\,\alpha$, i.e. at α West of North. In the case of a ship moving with velocity u_3 due North the necessary small corrections (α) in the compass bearing must be allowed for in the navigation.

15.3 Some non-holonomic systems

We can see that a quite simple system, viz. the motion of a sphere rolling on a fixed rough horizontal plane, is in fact non-holonomic. If (x, y) are the co-ordinates of the centre of mass and (θ, ϕ, ψ) the Eulerian angles defining the rigid body relative to G, it is clear that the conditions of rolling are

$$\dot{x} - a\omega_2 = 0 = \dot{y} + a\omega_1$$

where we have taken the axes $\mathbf{e}_1$ and $\mathbf{e}_2$ of 14.5(2) as parallel to the x, y-axes respectively. These equations are

$$\dot{x} - a\dot{\theta} \cos \psi - a\dot{\phi} \sin \theta \sin \psi = 0$$
$$\dot{y} - a\dot{\theta} \sin \psi + a\dot{\phi} \sin \theta \cos \psi = 0$$

being non-integrable equations of constraint, as in 12.1(6).

Consider now a general non-holonomic system, defined by the independent co-ordinates $q_1, q_2, \ldots q_n$ and the non-integrable equations of constraint

$$a_{1i}\dot{q}_1 + a_{2i}\dot{q}_2 + \ldots + a_{ni}\dot{q}_n = 0 \quad (i = 1, 2, \ldots k) \qquad (1)$$

We may suppose that these kinematical constraints are equivalent to an additional set of generalised forces $Q'_1, Q'_2, \ldots Q'_n$. If the " ordinary " forces are $Q_1, Q_2, \ldots Q_n$ as in 12.1 the incremental work done in a completely arbitrary displacement (not now restricted by (1)) will be

$$\delta W = \sum_{r=1}^{n} (Q_r + Q_r') \, \delta q_r$$

and 12.1(9) are replaced by

$$\frac{d}{dt}\left(\frac{\partial T}{\partial \dot{q}_r}\right) - \frac{\partial T}{\partial q_r} = Q_r + Q'_r \quad (r = 1, 2, \ldots n) \qquad . \qquad (2)$$

But the $Q^1{}_r$ must be such that in a displacement compatible with the constraints (1), they do no work. Hence

$$Q_1' \, dq_1 + Q_2' \, dq_2 + \ldots + Q_n' \, dq_n = 0$$

for all values of the dq's satisfying the equations (1). Hence constants $\lambda_1, \lambda_2, \ldots \lambda_k$ exist such that

$$Q_r' = \lambda_1 a_{r1} + \lambda_2 a_{r2} + \ldots + \lambda_k a_{rk} \quad (r = 1, 2, \ldots n)$$

The Lagrangian equations of the system are now

$$\frac{d}{dt}\left(\frac{\partial T}{d\dot{q}_r}\right) - \frac{\partial T}{\partial q_r} = Q_r + \lambda_1 a_{r1} + \lambda_2 a_{r2} + \ldots + \lambda_k a_{rk} \qquad (3)$$
$$(r = 1, 2, \ldots n)$$

The sets (1) and (3) are now sufficient to find (theoretically) the quantities $q_1, q_2, \ldots q_n, \lambda_1, \lambda_2, \ldots \lambda_k$.

This theory amounts to introducing additional forces to make the system holonomic; the additional forces accounting for the non-holonomic constraints. In practice problems are often more easily solved by actually using these forces, in place of (3), and writing down the equations of motion for the separate rigid bodies of the system. Thus, in the problem of the sphere rolling and spinning on a rough plane, the Q_r' will be generated via the frictional forces acting at the point of contact.

In practice therefore we shall often find that direct vector methods are preferable for the solution of non-holonomic systems. We now give some examples.

Example 1. A solid sphere rolling and spinning on a rough horizontal plane table which is constrained to rotate about a fixed vertical axis with constant angular velocity Ω. To examine the motion of the centre of mass.

Take an origin O on the axis of rotation in a horizontal plane through G and let $\overline{OG} = \boldsymbol{r}$ (v. Fig. 124). Let A be the point of contact and let

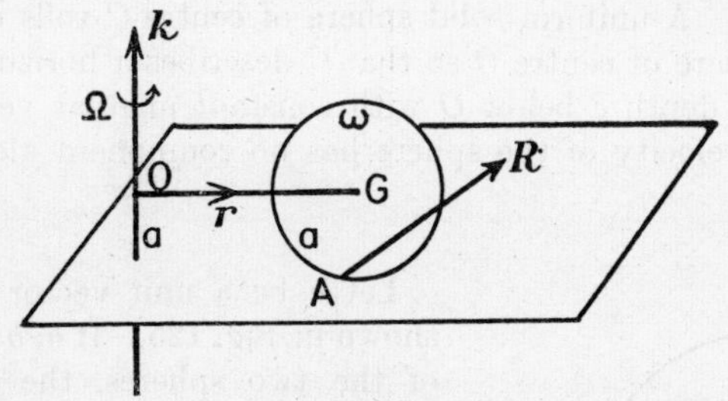

FIG. 124.

the reaction at A be $\boldsymbol{R}$ (this includes the friction). The equations of motion are

$$M\ddot{\boldsymbol{r}} = \boldsymbol{R} - Mg\,\boldsymbol{k} \quad . \quad . \quad . \quad (4)$$

$$\tfrac{2}{5}Ma^2\,\dot{\boldsymbol{\omega}} = -\,a\,\boldsymbol{k} \times \boldsymbol{R} \quad . \quad . \quad . \quad (5)$$

Velocity of A gives

$$\dot{\boldsymbol{r}} + \boldsymbol{\omega} \times (-\,a\,\boldsymbol{k}) = \Omega\,\boldsymbol{k} \times \boldsymbol{r} \quad . \quad . \quad . \quad (6)$$

(4) and (5) give

$$\frac{2a}{5}\,\dot{\boldsymbol{\omega}} = -\,\boldsymbol{k} \times (\ddot{\boldsymbol{r}} + g\,\boldsymbol{k}) = -\,\boldsymbol{k} \times \ddot{\boldsymbol{r}} \quad . \quad . \quad (7)$$

(6) gives $\qquad \Omega\,\boldsymbol{k} \times \dot{\boldsymbol{r}} = \ddot{\boldsymbol{r}} - a\,\dot{\boldsymbol{\omega}} \times \boldsymbol{k}$

and with (7) we get

$$\tfrac{2}{5}(\ddot{\boldsymbol{r}} - \Omega\,\boldsymbol{k} \times \dot{\boldsymbol{r}}) = \boldsymbol{k} \times (\boldsymbol{k} \times \ddot{\boldsymbol{r}})$$
$$= -\,\ddot{\boldsymbol{r}}$$

since $\boldsymbol{k}.\boldsymbol{r} = \boldsymbol{k}.\dot{\boldsymbol{r}} = \boldsymbol{k}.\ddot{\boldsymbol{r}} = 0$. Hence

$$7\ddot{\boldsymbol{r}} = 2\Omega\, \boldsymbol{k} \times \dot{\boldsymbol{r}}$$

giving

$$\dot{\boldsymbol{r}} = \left(\frac{2\Omega}{7}\right) \boldsymbol{k} \times (\boldsymbol{r} - \boldsymbol{r}_0) \quad . \quad . \quad (8)$$

$\boldsymbol{r}_0$ being an arbitrary constant vector. This proves that G describes a circle, centre $\boldsymbol{r}_0$, radius $|\boldsymbol{r} - \boldsymbol{r}_0|$, with uniform angular velocity $\frac{2\Omega}{7}$. We also notice that (7) gives

$$\dot{\boldsymbol{\omega}} = -\frac{5}{7}.\frac{\Omega}{a}.\{\boldsymbol{k} \times (\boldsymbol{k} \times \dot{\boldsymbol{r}})\} = \frac{5\Omega}{7a}\dot{\boldsymbol{r}}$$

Thus $\dot{\boldsymbol{\omega}}$ is parallel to the velocity of G, and also

$$|\dot{\boldsymbol{\omega}}| = \frac{5\Omega}{7a}.\frac{2\Omega}{7}|\boldsymbol{r} - \boldsymbol{r}_0|$$

$$= \frac{10\Omega^2 c}{49a}$$

c being the radius $|\boldsymbol{r} - \boldsymbol{r}_0|$ of the circle described by G.

Example 2. A uniform solid sphere of centre C rolls on the inside of a fixed sphere of centre O so that C describes a horizontal circle of radius c at a depth c below O with constant angular velocity Ω. If the angular velocity of the sphere has no component along OC show that $\Omega^2 = \frac{5g}{7c}$. (L.U.)

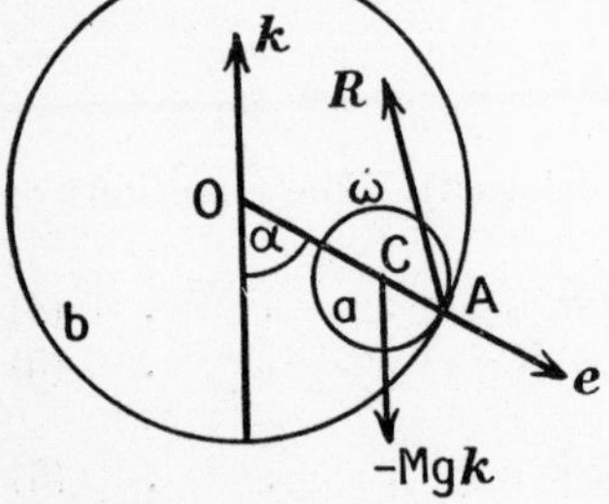

Fig. 125.

Let $\boldsymbol{e}$ be a unit vector along OC as shown in Fig. 125. If a, b are the radii of the two spheres, the equations of motion are

$$M(b - a)\ddot{\boldsymbol{e}} = \boldsymbol{R} - Mg\,\boldsymbol{k} \quad . \quad (9)$$

$$\tfrac{2}{5}Ma^2\,\dot{\boldsymbol{\omega}} = a\,\boldsymbol{e} \times \boldsymbol{R} \quad . \quad (10)$$

and for the velocity of A,

$$(b - a)\dot{\boldsymbol{e}} + \boldsymbol{\omega} \times a\,\boldsymbol{e} = \boldsymbol{0} \quad . \quad (11)$$

(9) and (10) give

$$\frac{2a}{5}\dot{\boldsymbol{\omega}} = \boldsymbol{e} \times \{g\,\boldsymbol{k} + (b - a)\ddot{\boldsymbol{e}}\} \quad (12)$$

(11) gives $\boldsymbol{\omega}.\dot{\boldsymbol{e}} = 0$ and (12) gives $\boldsymbol{e}.\dot{\boldsymbol{\omega}} = 0$. Hence $\frac{d}{dt}(\boldsymbol{\omega}.\boldsymbol{e}) = 0$ and so $\boldsymbol{\omega}.\boldsymbol{e} = \text{constant} = 0$ (given). Multiplying (11) vectorially by $\boldsymbol{e}$ and we get

$$(b - a)\boldsymbol{e} \times \dot{\boldsymbol{e}} = a\{(\boldsymbol{e}.\boldsymbol{\omega})\boldsymbol{e} - \boldsymbol{\omega}\} = -a\,\boldsymbol{\omega}$$

Then (12) gives

$$\frac{2a}{5}\left(\frac{b-a}{a}\right)\ddot{\boldsymbol{e}} \times \boldsymbol{e} = g\,\boldsymbol{e} \times \boldsymbol{k} + (b-a)\boldsymbol{e} \times \ddot{\boldsymbol{e}}$$

so that $\frac{7}{5}(b-a)(\boldsymbol{e} \times \ddot{\boldsymbol{e}}) = g(\boldsymbol{k} \times \boldsymbol{e})$ . . . . (13)

For steady precession about $\boldsymbol{k}$ we write $\dot{\boldsymbol{e}} = \Omega\,\boldsymbol{k} \times \boldsymbol{e}$, so that

$$\ddot{\boldsymbol{e}} = \Omega^2\{(\boldsymbol{k}.\boldsymbol{e})\boldsymbol{k} - \boldsymbol{e}\} = -\,\Omega^2\,(\cos\alpha\,\boldsymbol{k} + \boldsymbol{e})$$

Hence (13) gives

$$\{\tfrac{7}{5}(b-a)\Omega^2\cos\alpha - g\}(\boldsymbol{k} \times \boldsymbol{e}) = \boldsymbol{0}$$

Since $(b-a)\cos\alpha = c$ (given) this gives $\Omega^2 = \dfrac{5g}{7c}$. Q.E.D.

Example 3. A perfectly rough uniform sphere of radius a moves on the inner surface of a hollow circular cylinder which has internal radius b and is fixed with its axis horizontal. When the sphere is in contact with the lowest generator the velocity of its centre is V making an angle α with this generator and the sphere has a spin n_0 about the radius to the point of contact.

Prove that the sphere will come into contact with the highest generator if

$$7V^2\sin^2\alpha > 27(b-a)g$$

Show also that the spin about the radius to the point of contact, when that radius makes an angle θ with the downward vertical, is

$$n_0\cos\sqrt{\frac{2}{7}}.\theta - \sqrt{\frac{7}{2}}.\frac{V\cos\alpha}{a}\sin\sqrt{\frac{2}{7}}.\theta \qquad \text{(L.U.)}$$

Let $\boldsymbol{i}$ be a unit vector along the horizontal axis of the cylinder, $\boldsymbol{e}$ a unit vector along the radius to the point of contact. Let x measure the distance travelled along the axis in time t. Then

$$\overline{OC} = x\,\boldsymbol{i} + (b-a)\boldsymbol{e}$$

and the equations are

$$\ddot{x}\,\boldsymbol{i} + (b-a)\ddot{\boldsymbol{e}} = \frac{1}{M}\boldsymbol{R} - g\,\boldsymbol{k} \quad . \quad . \quad . \quad (14)$$

$$2a\,\dot{\boldsymbol{\omega}} = 5\boldsymbol{e} \times \boldsymbol{R} \quad . \quad . \quad . \quad . \quad (15)$$

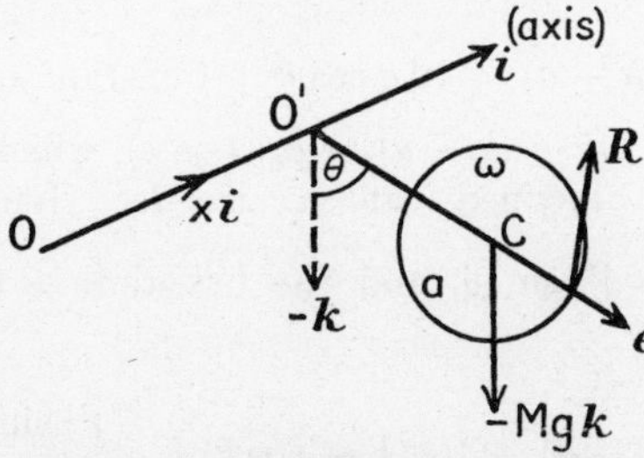

FIG. 126.

For the velocity of A,

$$\dot{x}\,\boldsymbol{i} + (b-a)\dot{\boldsymbol{e}} + a\,\boldsymbol{\omega} \times \boldsymbol{e} = \boldsymbol{0} \quad . \quad . \quad . \quad (16)$$

(14) and (15) give

$$2a\,\dot{\boldsymbol{\omega}} = 5\boldsymbol{e} \times \{g\,\boldsymbol{k} + \ddot{x}\,\boldsymbol{i} + (b-a)\ddot{\boldsymbol{e}}\} \quad . \quad . \quad (17)$$

(15) implies $\dot{\boldsymbol{\omega}}.\boldsymbol{e} = 0$, but (17) implies $\boldsymbol{\omega}.\dot{\boldsymbol{e}} \neq 0$. Hence $\boldsymbol{\omega}.\boldsymbol{e}$ is not constant ; we therefore write

$$\boldsymbol{\omega} = n\,\boldsymbol{e} + \boldsymbol{\Omega} \quad . \quad . \quad . \quad . \quad (18)$$

where $\boldsymbol{\Omega}.\boldsymbol{e} = 0$. Hence we get

$$\begin{aligned} \boldsymbol{e} \times (\boldsymbol{\omega} \times \boldsymbol{e}) &= \boldsymbol{\omega} - (\boldsymbol{e}.\boldsymbol{\omega})\boldsymbol{e} = n\,\boldsymbol{e} + \boldsymbol{\Omega} - n\,\boldsymbol{e} \\ &= \boldsymbol{\Omega} \quad . \quad . \quad . \quad . \quad (19) \end{aligned}$$

Multiplying (16) vectorially by $\boldsymbol{e}$ and using (19), we get

$$\dot{x}(\boldsymbol{e} \times \boldsymbol{i}) + (b-a)\boldsymbol{e} \times \dot{\boldsymbol{e}} + a\,\boldsymbol{\Omega} = \boldsymbol{0} \quad . \quad . \quad (20)$$

Using (18) in (17) and eliminating $\boldsymbol{\Omega}$ by (20), we get

$$\begin{aligned} 2a\dot{n}\,\boldsymbol{e} + 2an\,\dot{\boldsymbol{e}} - 2\frac{d}{dt}\{\dot{x}(\boldsymbol{e} \times \boldsymbol{i}) + (b-a)\boldsymbol{e} \times \dot{\boldsymbol{e}}\} \\ = 5\boldsymbol{e} \times \{g\,\boldsymbol{k} + \ddot{x}\,\boldsymbol{i} + (b-a)\ddot{\boldsymbol{e}}\} \quad (21) \end{aligned}$$

Since $\boldsymbol{e}$ rotates about $\boldsymbol{i}$ with angular velocity $-\dot{\theta}\,\boldsymbol{i}$, we can write

$$\dot{\boldsymbol{e}} = -\dot{\theta}\,\boldsymbol{i} \times \boldsymbol{e} \quad \text{and} \quad \ddot{\boldsymbol{e}} = -\dot{\theta}^2\,\boldsymbol{e} - \ddot{\theta}(\boldsymbol{i} \times \boldsymbol{e}) \quad (\boldsymbol{e}.\boldsymbol{i} = 0)$$

Hence $\quad \boldsymbol{e} \times \ddot{\boldsymbol{e}} = -\ddot{\theta}\,\boldsymbol{i} \quad \text{and} \quad \dot{\boldsymbol{e}} \times \boldsymbol{i} = -\dot{\theta}\,\boldsymbol{e}$

and (21) becomes

$$\begin{aligned} 2a\dot{n}\,\boldsymbol{e} + 2an(-\dot{\theta})(\boldsymbol{i} \times \boldsymbol{e}) + 2\ddot{x}(\boldsymbol{i} \times \boldsymbol{e}) + 2\dot{\theta}\dot{x}\,\boldsymbol{e} + 2\ddot{\theta}(b-a)\boldsymbol{i} \\ = 5g(\boldsymbol{e} \times \boldsymbol{k}) + 5\ddot{x}(\boldsymbol{e} \times \boldsymbol{i}) - 5\ddot{\theta}(b-a)\boldsymbol{i} \quad (22) \end{aligned}$$

But clearly $\boldsymbol{e} \times \boldsymbol{k} = -\sin\theta\,\boldsymbol{i}$ and so (22) is a relation between the linearly independent vectors (non-coplanar) $\boldsymbol{e}$, $\boldsymbol{i} \times \boldsymbol{e}$, $\boldsymbol{i}$. Equating the coefficients to zero gives

$$2a\dot{n} + 2\dot{\theta}\dot{x} = 0 \quad . \quad . \quad . \quad . \quad (23)$$

$$-2an\dot{\theta} + 7\ddot{x} = 0 \quad . \quad . \quad . \quad . \quad (24)$$

$$7\ddot{\theta}(b-a) + 5g\sin\theta = 0 \quad . \quad . \quad . \quad . \quad (25)$$

(25) implies that

$$7\dot{\theta}^2(b-a) - 10\,g\cos\theta + \text{Constant} = 0$$

When $\theta = 0$, $\dot{\boldsymbol{r}}_0 = \dot{x}_0\boldsymbol{i} + (b-a)(-\dot{\theta}_0)(\boldsymbol{i} \times \boldsymbol{e})$, which has modulus V and a direction inclined at α to $\boldsymbol{i}$. Hence $\dot{x}_0 = V\cos\alpha$ and $-(b-a)\dot{\theta}_0 = V\sin\alpha$ and the Constant $= 10g - \dfrac{7\,V^2\sin^2\alpha}{(b-a)}$.

Hence we get

$$7\dot{\theta}^2(b-a) + 10g(1-\cos\theta) = \frac{7\,V^2\sin^2\alpha}{b-a} \quad . \quad . \quad (26)$$

Now the sphere reaches the highest generator provided the normal reaction is positive at that point, i.e. $\boldsymbol{R}.(-\boldsymbol{e}) > 0$. But (14) gives

$$\begin{aligned} N &= \frac{1}{M}\boldsymbol{R}.\boldsymbol{e} = g\,\boldsymbol{k}.\boldsymbol{e} + (b-a)\boldsymbol{e}.\ddot{\boldsymbol{e}} \\ &= -g\cos\theta - (b-a)\{\dot{\theta}^2\,\boldsymbol{e} + \ddot{\theta}(\boldsymbol{i}\times\boldsymbol{e})\}.\boldsymbol{e} \\ &= -g\cos\theta - (b-a)\dot{\theta}^2 \\ &= -g\cos\theta - \frac{V^2\sin^2\alpha}{(b-a)} + \frac{10}{7}g(1-\cos\theta) \end{aligned}$$

Hence $N(\pi) < 0$ implies

$$\frac{V^2\sin^2\alpha}{(b-a)} > g + \frac{20}{7}g \qquad \text{Q.E.D.}$$

Now (23) and (24) give $2a^2n\dot{n} + 7\dot{x}\ddot{x} = 0$, so that

$$2a^2n^2 + 7\dot{x}^2 = \text{constant} = 2a^2{n_0}^2 + 7V^2\cos^2\alpha \qquad . \quad (27)$$

Hence (23) and (27) imply

$$a\dot{n} + \frac{\dot{\theta}}{\sqrt{7}}\{2a^2({n_0}^2 - n^2) + 7V^2\cos^2\alpha\}^{\frac{1}{2}} = 0$$

giving

$$\sqrt{\frac{7}{2}}\sin^{-1}\frac{n\sqrt{2}}{\sqrt{2{n_0}^2 + \dfrac{7V^2\cos^2\alpha}{a^2}}} = \beta - \theta, \quad \beta \text{ a constant}$$

Hence $$n\sqrt{2} = \sqrt{2n_0^2 + \frac{7V^2\cos^2\alpha}{a^2}}\sin\left(\beta - \sqrt{\frac{2}{7}}.\theta\right)$$

But $n = n_0$ when $\theta = 0$ and so

$$n\sqrt{2} = n_0\sqrt{2}\cos\sqrt{\frac{2}{7}}.\theta - \sqrt{7}.V\frac{\cos\alpha}{a}\sin\sqrt{\frac{2}{7}}.\theta$$

Q.E.D.

Example 4. A uniform sphere rolling and spinning inside a fixed vertical cylinder. To examine the motion.

Take a point O on the axis of the cylinder as origin (v. Fig. 127). Let $\boldsymbol{k}$ be a unit vector in the direction of the upward vertical, let $\boldsymbol{e}$ be a unit vector along $\overline{GA}$ where G is the centre of the sphere and A is the point of contact. If the height of G above O is z we have,

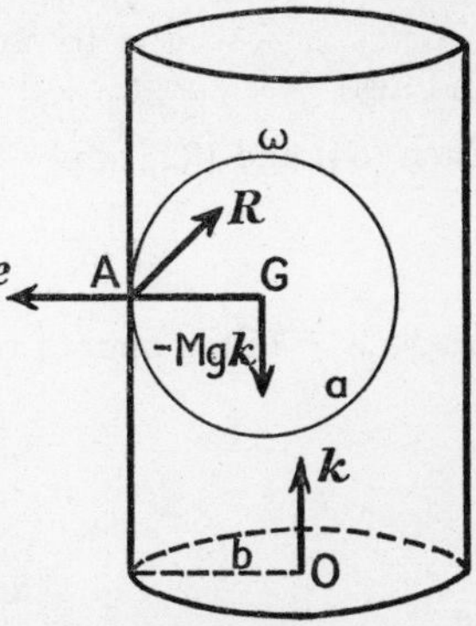

FIG. 127.

$$\overline{OG} = \boldsymbol{r} = z\,\boldsymbol{k} + (b-a)\boldsymbol{e}$$

so that $$\dot{\boldsymbol{r}} = \dot{z}\,\boldsymbol{k} + (b-a)\dot{\boldsymbol{e}}$$

Since A is at rest we have

$$\dot{z}\,\boldsymbol{k} + (b - a)\dot{\boldsymbol{e}} + \boldsymbol{\omega} \times a\,\boldsymbol{e} = \boldsymbol{0} \quad . \quad . \quad . \quad (28)$$

Also,

$$M\,\ddot{\boldsymbol{r}} = -\,Mg\,\boldsymbol{k} + \boldsymbol{R} \quad . \quad . \quad . \quad (29)$$

$$\tfrac{2}{5}Ma^2\,\dot{\boldsymbol{\omega}} = a\,\boldsymbol{e} \times \boldsymbol{R}. \quad . \quad . \quad . \quad (30)$$

Now (29) and (30) give

$$2a\,\dot{\boldsymbol{\omega}} = 5\boldsymbol{e} \times (\ddot{\boldsymbol{r}} + g\,\boldsymbol{k}) \quad . \quad . \quad . \quad (31)$$

G may be defined by *cylindrical polar co-ordinates* $(b - a,\ \theta,\ z)$ and we can then regard the vector $\boldsymbol{e}$ as rotating about $\boldsymbol{k}$ with angular velocity $\dot{\theta}$, i.e. we can write

$$\dot{\boldsymbol{e}} = \dot{\theta}(\boldsymbol{k} \times \boldsymbol{e})\ ;\ \ddot{\boldsymbol{e}} = \ddot{\theta}\,(\boldsymbol{k} \times \boldsymbol{e}) + \dot{\theta}(\boldsymbol{k} \times \dot{\boldsymbol{e}})$$
$$= \ddot{\theta}(\boldsymbol{k} \times \boldsymbol{e}) + \dot{\theta}^2\{(\boldsymbol{k}.\boldsymbol{e})\boldsymbol{k} - k^2\boldsymbol{e}\}$$
$$= \ddot{\theta}(\boldsymbol{k} \times \boldsymbol{e}) - \dot{\theta}^2\,\boldsymbol{e}, \quad \text{since } \boldsymbol{k}.\boldsymbol{e} = 0$$

Hence

$$\boldsymbol{e} \times \ddot{\boldsymbol{e}} = \ddot{\theta}\,\boldsymbol{e} \times (\boldsymbol{k} \times \boldsymbol{e}) = \ddot{\theta}\boldsymbol{k}$$

Since $\boldsymbol{e}$, $\boldsymbol{e} \times \boldsymbol{k}$, $\boldsymbol{k}$ are non-coplanar we can write

$$\boldsymbol{\omega} = \omega_1\,\boldsymbol{e} + \omega_2(\boldsymbol{e} \times \boldsymbol{k}) + \omega_3\,\boldsymbol{k}$$

so that

$$\dot{\boldsymbol{\omega}} = (\dot{\omega}_1 + \omega_2\dot{\theta})\boldsymbol{e} + (\dot{\omega}_2 - \omega_1\dot{\theta})(\boldsymbol{e} \times \boldsymbol{k}) + \dot{\omega}_3\,\boldsymbol{k}$$

Equation (28) gives

$$\dot{z}\,\boldsymbol{k} + (b - a)\dot{\theta}(\boldsymbol{k} \times \boldsymbol{e}) + a\omega_2\,\boldsymbol{k} - a\dot{\omega}_3(\boldsymbol{e} \times \boldsymbol{k}) = \boldsymbol{0}$$

so that

$$\dot{z} + a\omega_2 = 0 \quad . \quad . \quad . \quad . \quad (32)$$

$$(b - a)\dot{\theta} + a\omega_3 = 0 \quad . \quad . \quad . \quad . \quad (33)$$

Equation (31) gives

$$2a(\dot{\omega}_1 + \omega_2\dot{\theta})\boldsymbol{e} + 2a(\dot{\omega}_2 - \omega_1\dot{\theta})(\boldsymbol{e} \times \boldsymbol{k}) + 2a\dot{\omega}_3\,\boldsymbol{k}$$
$$= 5\ddot{z}(\boldsymbol{e} \times \boldsymbol{k}) + 5(b - a)\ddot{\theta}\,\boldsymbol{k} + 5g(\boldsymbol{e} \times \boldsymbol{k})$$

so that

$$\dot{\omega}_1 + \omega_2\dot{\theta} = 0 \quad . \quad . \quad . \quad (34)$$

$$2a(\dot{\omega}_2 - \omega_1\dot{\theta}) - 5(\ddot{z} + g) = 0 \quad . \quad . \quad . \quad (35)$$

$$2a\dot{\omega}_3 - 5(b - a)\ddot{\theta} = 0 \quad . \quad . \quad . \quad (36)$$

Now (33) and (36) imply

$$\ddot{\theta} = 0 \quad \text{and so} \quad \dot{\theta} = \Omega \quad \text{(a constant)}$$

and also

$$\dot{\omega}_3 = 0, \quad \text{so that} \quad \omega_3 = \text{constant}$$

Then (34) and (32) imply

$$\dot{z} = \frac{a}{\Omega}\dot{\omega}_1 \quad \text{and so} \quad \omega_1 = n + \frac{\Omega}{a}z$$

where n = initial spin of the sphere about $\boldsymbol{e}$. Equation (35) now gives

$$5\ddot{z} + 5g = -\frac{2a}{\Omega}\ddot{\omega}_1 - 2a\omega_1\Omega$$
$$= -\,2\ddot{z} - 2an\Omega - 2\Omega^2 z$$

i.e.

$$\ddot{z} + \frac{2\Omega^2}{7}\left\{z + \frac{an}{\Omega} + \frac{5g}{2\Omega^2}\right\} = 0$$

This is the equation of S.H.M., showing that the sphere oscillates vertically with periodic time $2\pi\sqrt{\dfrac{7}{2\Omega^2}}$ about the point

$$z = -\frac{1}{2\Omega^2}(2an\Omega + 5g)$$

Exercise XV

1. A symmetrical top of mass M, whose principal moments at the mass centre G are A, A, C, spins on a smooth horizontal plane. The end of the peg in contact with the plane is part of a sphere whose centre is at a distance h from G. The top is released with spin n about its axis of symmetry from a position in which that axis is stationary and inclined at an angle α to the vertical. Prove that if $2p \cos \alpha > 1$ the inclination of the axis oscillates between α and β, where $\cos \beta = p - \sqrt{(p^2 - 2p \cos \alpha + 1)}$, p standing for $n^2C^2/4MghA$.

Prove that, when the spin is large enough for $\beta - \alpha$ to be taken as a first order small quantity, the approximate rate of change of azimuth of symmetry after time t is given by

$$\frac{Mgh}{Cn}(1 - \cos Dt), \quad \text{where } D^2 = \frac{n^2C^2}{A(A + Mh^2 \sin^2 \alpha)} \qquad \text{(M.T.)}$$

2. A gyroscope, with principal moments of inertia A, A, C, is mounted so as to be able to rotate freely about its centre of mass. Initially it is spinning steadily about its axis with angular velocity n. An impulse J, perpendicular to the axis, is applied to the axis at a point at a distance a from the centre of mass. Prove that the axis subsequently describes a circular cone whose semi-vertical angle is $\tan^{-1}(Ja/Cn)$. Calculate the time taken for the axis of the gyroscope to describe the cone once. (M.T.)

3. An axially symmetric top of mass M is freely pivoted about a point O on its axis. Its centre of mass G is at a distance l from O and its principal moments of inertia at O are A, A and C. Initially the top is set in motion with its axis horizontal and with a small angular velocity n about its axis. Show that, when G is at its lowest point in the subsequent path, the axis of the top makes an angle approximately

$$\frac{Cn}{\sqrt{(2MglA)}}$$

with the downward vertical. (M.T.)

4. A uniform right circular cone of mass M is free to turn about its vertex which is fixed above a rough horizontal table on which is a sphere of radius a. The cone rolls on the sphere whose centre describes with angular velocity ω a circle of radius b whose centre is vertically below the vertex of the cone. Prove that in steady motion, the angular velocity Ω of the cone about its axis is

$$-\omega(a \sin \alpha \cos \beta \cos \gamma + b \cos \alpha \sin \gamma - b \sin^2 \beta)/(b + a \cos \beta) \sin \gamma$$

and that the condition for steady motion is

$$A\omega^2 \cos \alpha + C\Omega\omega = Mgh$$

where γ is the semi-vertical angle of the cone, α the inclination of its axis to the vertical, $\beta = \alpha - \gamma$ and C, A are the moments of inertia of the cone about its axis and a perpendicular axis through the vertex and h is the distance of the centre of gravity of the cone from its vertex. (L.U.)

5. A, A, C are the principal moments of inertia of a common top of mass M which is free to rotate about a fixed point O on its axis OZ, which is inclined at an angle θ to the vertical OH. The plane HOZ makes an angle ψ with a fixed vertical plane. The top is subject to a resisting couple $(-kA\omega_1, -kA\omega_2, -kC\omega_3)$. Obtain the first integrals of motion in the form

$$\omega_3 = ne^{-kt}, \quad A(1 - \xi^2)\frac{d\psi}{dt} = (H - Cn\xi)\, e^{-kt}$$

$$e^{2kt}\left(\frac{d\xi}{dt}\right)^2 = -\left(\frac{H - Cn\xi}{A}\right)^2 - \frac{2Mgh}{A}(1 - \xi^2)\int \frac{d\xi}{dt}\, e^{2kt}\, dt$$

where $\xi = \cos \theta$, $h = OG$ where G is the centre of mass, and H is constant. (L.U.)

6. Find the condition for steady precession of a spinning top and show that, in general, there are two possible angular velocities of precession.

A heavy uniform thin circular disc of radius a is mounted on a thin axle of negligible mass, capable of rotating freely about its lower end, which is freely jointed to the top of a fixed support at a distance $\frac{1}{2}a$ from the centre of the disc. Show that, if the disc is properly projected with axial spin $(2g/a)^{\frac{1}{2}}$, the axle will describe a cone of semi-vertical angle 60° about the vertical with angular velocity $(2g/a)^{\frac{1}{2}}$. (L.U.)

7. A light rigid isosceles triangular frame ABC of altitude h carries a flywheel of mass M on the base BC as axle, at the mid-point G of BC. Show that a steady motion is possible with the vertex A at rest on a perfectly rough table, AG at an angle θ with the upward vertical, and the plane ABC vertical (with C above B) and rotating with angular velocity Ω, provided

$$\Omega \cos \theta\{(A - Mh^2)\Omega \sin \theta - Cn\} = Mgh \sin \theta$$

where C, A are the moments of inertia of the flywheel along and perpendicular to BC, and n is the angular velocity of the flywheel about BC. (L.U.)

8. A top, symmetrical about its axis, is mounted so that it can turn freely about a point O on its axis. The mass of the top is M and its centre of mass G is at a distance h from O. The principal moments of inertia at O are A, A and C. The top is given a spin n about its axis when the axis is at rest and horizontal. Show that, if $4AMgh = C^2n^2\varepsilon$ where second order terms in ε are negligible, then at any subsequent time OG makes an angle θ with the downward vertical where

$$4A^2 \sin^2 \theta \, \dot{\theta}^2 = C^2 n^2 \cos \theta \, (\varepsilon - 2 \cos \theta)(2 + \varepsilon \cos \theta)$$

Find the greatest value of the precessional velocity of G in the subsequent motion. (L.U.)

9. A uniform solid sphere rolls without slipping inside a stationary inverted cone of semi-angle $\pi/4$ with its axis vertical. If the centre of the sphere describes a horizontal circle of radius c with angular velocity $(5g/9c)^{\frac{1}{2}}$, prove that the sphere will have no component angular velocity about the vertical.

Show that the coefficient of friction between sphere and cone is not less than 2/7. (L.U.)

10. A uniform sphere of radius a rolls on a rough plane which rotates with spin Ω about a fixed axis making an angle α with the upward vertical. Find the differential equations giving the co-ordinates x, y of the centre C of the sphere in the plane π parallel to the rotating plane at a distance a, the x-axis being horizontal, and the y-axis up the line of greatest slope through a point on the axis of rotation of the plane.

Show that the locus of C in a plane coincident with π, but moving with speed $(5g/2\Omega) \sin \alpha$ parallel to the x-axis, is a circle described with angular velocity $(2/7)\Omega$. (L.U.)

11. A uniform heavy sphere is rolling with velocity V along the highest generator of a fixed rough horizontal circular cylinder and without spin about its vertical diameter when it receives a slight disturbance in a direction at right angles to its motion. Show that so long as the sphere remains in contact with the cylinder the component of the velocity of its centre parallel to the axis of the cylinder is $V \cos \sqrt{\frac{2}{7}}\theta$, where θ is the angle between the vertical plane through the axis of the cylinder and the plane that contains both the axis and the centre of the sphere. Show further that contact between the sphere and the cylinder ceases when $\theta = \cos^{-1} \frac{10}{17}$. (M.T.)

12. A uniform solid sphere, of mass M and radius a, rolls without slipping on the outside of a rough circular cylinder of radius $(c - a)$ which is fixed with its axis horizontal. If θ denotes the angle that the half-plane through the axis of the cylinder and the centre of the sphere makes with the upward vertical, and u denotes the component of velocity of the centre of the sphere in the direction of the axis of the cylinder, establish the equations

$$\ddot{\theta} = \frac{5}{7}\frac{g}{c} \sin \theta, \quad \frac{d^2u}{d\theta^2} + \frac{2}{7}u = 0$$

Consider the particular problem in which initially $\theta = \alpha \, (< \pi/2)$, $\dot{\theta} = u = 0$, and the spin of the sphere about the diameter through the point of contact with the cylinder is Ω. Find how u varies with θ during this motion. (M.T.)

13. A sphere of radius a rotates about a fixed vertical diameter with constant angular velocity $\sqrt{(35\,g/a)}$. A solid uniform sphere, also of radius a, is placed on its highest point and gently displaced from rest. Prove that, while the free sphere is rolling on the other one, the angle θ between the line of centres and the vertical satisfies the equation

$$\dot{\theta}^2 = (5g/7a)\tan^2\frac{\theta}{2}\cos\theta \qquad \text{(L.U.)}$$

14. A uniform circular disc of radius a moves on a smooth horizontal plane with its centre of mass G at rest, the axis normal to the disc at G making a constant angle α with the vertical through G, about which it precesses uniformly at a rate Ω. Find an equation giving the spin n of the disc about its axis.

If the same disc now rolls on a rough horizontal plane, with G moving in a circle of centre O and radius λa, with its axis at the same constant angle α with the vertical and precessing about the vertical through O at the same uniform rate Ω, show that the spin of the disc about its axis is $n/3$, and that λ is $n/(3\Omega)$. (L.U.)

15. A heavy uniform solid right circular cone of mass M, slant edge l, and angle 2α at the vertex O is smoothly pivoted about O, which is fixed above a rough horizontal plane so that the cone rolls on the plane with the topmost generator always horizontal and the axis rotates about the vertical through O at a constant rate Ω. Show that the reaction R between the cone and plane is vertical and is given by

$$R = \tfrac{3}{8}Mg(1 + \sec 2\alpha) - \frac{3}{80}Ml\Omega^2(3\tan 2\alpha + \sin 2\alpha) \qquad \text{(L.U.)}$$

16. A uniform solid sphere of radius a rolls on the outside of a fixed rough cylinder of the same radius whose axis is horizontal. Initially the sphere stands on top of the cylinder and spins about its vertical axis with angular velocity Ω. When the normal at the point of contact makes an angle θ with the vertical, show that $7a\dot{\theta}^2 = 5g(1 - \cos\theta)$. Show also that the angular velocity of the sphere about the normal is then $\Omega\cos n\theta$, where $7n^2 = 2$. (L.U.)

CHAPTER XVI

SMALL OSCILLATIONS

16.1 A conservative system with one degree of freedom

Consider a dynamical system defined by the single co-ordinate q, and suppose that $q = q_0$ defines a position of equilibrium. We shall take the kinetic energy T to be of the form $T = \frac{1}{2}f(q)\dot{q}^2$, and the potential energy will be $V(q)$. The form of T ensures that the integral of energy exists (v. 12.4).

Now we consider the possibility of small oscillations about the position of equilibrium $q = q_0$; by "small oscillations" we mean motion in which, for small initial values of $| q - q_0 |$ and $\dot{q}$, the subsequent values remain bounded and of the same order as the initial values.

Writing $\xi = q - q_0$, $\dot{\xi} = \dot{q}$, and expanding by Taylor's theorem, we get

$$f(q) = f(q_0) + O(\xi)$$

and $$V(q) = V(q_0) + \xi V'(q_0) + \tfrac{1}{2}\xi^2 V''(q_0) + O(\xi^3)$$

But in equilibrium $$V'(q_0) = 0$$

(v. 3.3(3)) and since $V(q_0)$ is a constant we can write

$$V(q) = \tfrac{1}{2}\xi^2 V''(q_0) + O(\xi^3)$$

The energy integral to the second order in ξ, $\dot{\xi}$ becomes

$$\tfrac{1}{2}f(q_0)\dot{\xi}^2 + \tfrac{1}{2}\xi^2 V''(q_0) = \text{constant}$$

giving $$\ddot{\xi} + \frac{V''(q_0)}{f(q_0)}\cdot\xi = 0 \quad . \quad . \quad . \quad . \quad (1)$$

(1) is the equation of S.H.M. provided $\dfrac{V''(q_0)}{f(q_0)} > 0$. But $f(q_0)$ must be positive since T is positive. Hence (1) is S.H.M. provided $V''(q_0) > 0$. We therefore deduce "*the position of equilibrium $q = q_0$ is a stable position when $V(q)$ is a minimum at $q = q_0$, and is unstable when $V(q_0)$ is a maximum.*"

The period of the small oscillations about the position of stable equilibrium, $q = q_0$, is

$$\tau = 2\pi\sqrt{\frac{f(q_0)}{V''(q_0)}} \quad . \quad . \quad . \quad . \quad (2)$$

Example 1. Four equal uniform rods, each of mass m and length $2a$ are smoothly jointed to form a rhombus $ABCD$, which is hung from a fixed point A. A and C are connected by a light elastic string of natural length a and modulus $2mg$. Show that the energy equation, for that motion of the system in which C remains vertically below A, is given by

$$a(1 + 3\sin^2\theta)\dot{\theta}^2 - 6g\cos\theta(1 - \cos\theta) = \text{constant},$$

where $\angle BAD = 2\theta$ and $\cos\alpha > \frac{1}{4}$. Show that the length of the equivalent simple pendulum, for small oscillations about the position $\theta = \dfrac{\pi}{3}$, is $\dfrac{13a}{18}$. (L.U.)

The co-ordinates G_1 and G_2 (v. Fig. 128) are

$$G_1 = a(\cos\theta, \sin\theta);$$
$$G_2 = a(3\cos\theta, \sin\theta)$$

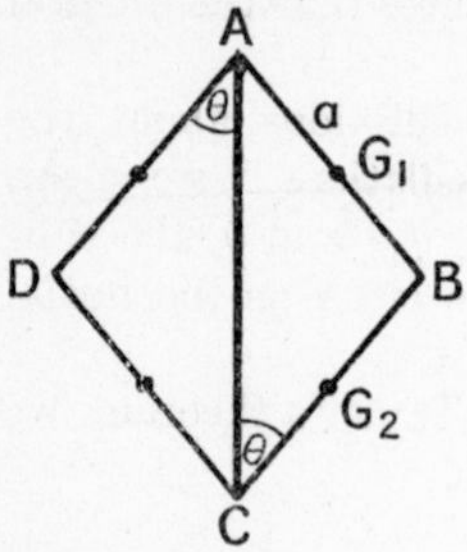

FIG. 128.

Hence the total kinetic energy will be

$$T = \tfrac{1}{2}ma^2\{2\dot{\theta}^2 + 2(9\sin^2\theta.\dot{\theta}^2 + \cos^2\theta.\dot{\theta}^2)\} + \tfrac{4}{2}.m\frac{a^2}{3}.\dot{\theta}^2$$

i.e. $T = \frac{1}{2}ma^2\{1 + 3\sin^2\theta\}.\frac{16}{3}.\dot{\theta}^2$. (3)

The potential energy will be

$$V = -2mga\{\cos\theta + 3\cos\theta\} + \tfrac{1}{2}.\frac{\lambda}{a}.(4a\cos\theta - a)^2$$

where $\lambda = 2mg$.

Hence $V = mga.16\cos\theta(\cos\theta - 1) + \text{constant}$ . . . (4)

Now $V'(\theta) = 16mga.(\sin\theta - \sin 2\theta) = 0$ when $\theta = \pi/3$

Hence $\theta = \pi/3$ is a position of equilibrium. Also

$$V''(\theta) = 16mga(\cos\theta - 2\cos 2\theta)$$

giving $V''(\pi/3) = 16mga.\frac{3}{2}$ . . . . . (5)

Now (3) and (4) give the energy equation

$$a(1 + 3\sin^2\theta)\dot{\theta}^2 - 6g\cos\theta(1 - \cos\theta) = \text{constant}$$

Q.E.D.

Also (3) gives

$$f(q) = f(\theta) = \tfrac{16}{3}ma^2(1 + 3\sin^2\theta)$$

so that $f(\pi/3) = \frac{16}{3}ma^2.\frac{13}{4}$

Hence, with (5), (2) gives

$$\tau = 2\pi\left\{\frac{13a}{18g}\right\}^{\frac{1}{2}}$$

Q.E.D.

16.2 A system with n degrees of freedom

Let the system be defined by the independent co-ordinates $q_1, q_2, \ldots q_n$, with $T = \frac{1}{2}g_{rs}\dot{q}_r\dot{q}_s$ ($r, s = 1, 2, \ldots n$), v. 12.2(6), and

$V = V(q_1, q_2, \ldots q_n)$. Without loss of generality we may suppose that a position of equilibrium corresponds to $q_r = 0$, all r. Hence, by 3.3(3),

$$0 = \frac{\partial V}{\partial q_1} = \frac{\partial V}{\partial q_2} = \ldots = \frac{\partial V}{\partial q_n} \quad \text{at } q_r = 0, \text{ all } r \quad . \quad (1)$$

We may therefore replace T and V, for small $q_r, \dot{q}_r$, by the expressions

$$T = \tfrac{1}{2}a_{rs}\dot{q}_r\dot{q}_s \quad (r, s = 1, 2, \ldots n) \quad . \quad . \quad (2)$$

$$V = b_{rs}q_rq_s \quad (r, s = 1, 2, \ldots n) \quad . \quad . \quad (3)$$

where $\qquad a_{rs} = g_{rs}(0, 0, \ldots 0) = (\text{constant})_{rs}$

and where the b_{rs} are independent of the q's also, involving second derivatives $\dfrac{\partial^2 V}{\partial q_i\, \partial q_j}$ at $q_1 = q_2 = \ldots = q_n = 0$. Expressions (2) and (3) are *quadratic forms* in the $\dot{q}$'s and the q's respectively and if we write the generalised vector $\boldsymbol{q}$ for the row or column matrix $(q_1, q_2, \ldots q_n)$ and $\mathscr{A}$ for the matrix (a_{rs}), $\frac{1}{2}\mathscr{B}$ for the matrix (b_{rs}), we have, for (2) and (3),

$$T = \tfrac{1}{2}(\dot{\boldsymbol{q}}.\mathscr{A}.\dot{\boldsymbol{q}}) \quad . \quad . \quad . \quad . \quad (4)$$

$$V = \tfrac{1}{2}(\boldsymbol{q}.\mathscr{B}.\boldsymbol{q}) \quad . \quad . \quad . \quad . \quad (5)$$

the products denoted by . being matrix multiplication "row into column." Now it is possible to find a real linear transformation from the q's to (say) a set $\xi_1, \xi_2, \xi_3, \ldots \xi_n$ such that both T and V become "sums of squares." They are then said to be reduced to *canonical form*. Such a transformation will be expressed by finding a *transformation matrix* $\mathscr{S}$ so that, e.g.

$$\begin{pmatrix} q_1 \\ q_2 \\ \cdot \\ \cdot \\ \cdot \\ q_n \end{pmatrix} = \mathscr{S} \begin{pmatrix} \xi_1 \\ \xi_2 \\ \cdot \\ \cdot \\ \cdot \\ \xi_n \end{pmatrix}$$

which can be written $\qquad \boldsymbol{q} = \mathscr{S}.\boldsymbol{\xi}$

If $\mathscr{S}'$ denotes the transpose of $\mathscr{S}$, (4) and (5) will become

$$T = \tfrac{1}{2}\{\dot{\boldsymbol{\xi}}.\mathscr{S}'\mathscr{A}\mathscr{S}.\dot{\boldsymbol{\xi}}\}. \quad . \quad . \quad . \quad (6)$$

$$V = \tfrac{1}{2}\{\boldsymbol{\xi}.\mathscr{S}'\mathscr{B}\mathscr{S}.\boldsymbol{\xi}\}. \quad . \quad . \quad . \quad (7)$$

where $\mathscr{S}'\mathscr{A}\mathscr{S}$ and $\mathscr{S}'\mathscr{B}\mathscr{S}$ are *diagonal* matrices. This reduction is always possible by virtue of the fact that T is a *positive definite form* (i.e. $T > 0$ when $\boldsymbol{q} \neq \boldsymbol{0}$) and because of the following theorem.

Theorem I. *Two quadratic forms* $\boldsymbol{q}.\mathscr{A}.\boldsymbol{q}$ *and* $\boldsymbol{q}.\mathscr{B}.\boldsymbol{q}$ *can be simultaneously reduced to canonical form provided either (i) the roots* (λ) *of* det $(\mathscr{A} - \lambda B) = 0$ *are distinct, or (ii) one of the two forms is positive definite,*

In the first instance, let the roots be $\lambda_1, \lambda_2, \ldots \lambda_n$. These are called the *eigenvalues of the pencil* $\mathscr{A} - \lambda\mathscr{B}$ (cf. 13.1). Let the corresponding eigenvectors (column/row matrices of order $n \times 1$ or $1 \times n$) be denoted by $\boldsymbol{i}_1, \boldsymbol{i}_2, \ldots \boldsymbol{i}_n$. Then

$$(\mathscr{A} - \lambda_\alpha\mathscr{B})\boldsymbol{i}_\alpha = \boldsymbol{0} \quad (\alpha = 1, 2, \ldots n)$$

Suppose these $\boldsymbol{i}_\alpha$ have been found ; then write $\mathscr{S} = (\boldsymbol{i}_1, \boldsymbol{i}_2, \ldots \boldsymbol{i}_n)$, where $\boldsymbol{i}_r$ is the rth column of $\mathscr{S}$. The matrices $\mathscr{A}$ and $\mathscr{B}$ become $\mathscr{A}^0 = \mathscr{S}'\mathscr{A}\mathscr{S}$ and $\mathscr{B}^0 = \mathscr{S}'\mathscr{B}\mathscr{S}$ and these are clearly diagonal matrices, since (e.g.) $\mathscr{S}'\mathscr{A}\mathscr{S}$ involves the product $\boldsymbol{i}_r.\mathscr{A}.\boldsymbol{i}_s$ for the element in the rth row and sth column ($\mathscr{S}'$ is formed by placing $\boldsymbol{i}_r$ in the rth row), and so

$$a^0_{rs} = \boldsymbol{i}_r.\mathscr{A}.\boldsymbol{i}_s = \lambda_s\boldsymbol{i}_r.\mathscr{B}\boldsymbol{i}_s = \lambda_s b^0_{rs}$$

whilst $$a^0_{rs} = (\boldsymbol{i}_r.\mathscr{A}).\boldsymbol{i}_s = \lambda_r\boldsymbol{i}_r.\mathscr{B}.\boldsymbol{i}_s = \lambda_r b^0_{rs}$$

since $\mathscr{A}$ and $\mathscr{B}$ are symmetric and $\boldsymbol{i}.\mathscr{A} = \mathscr{A}.\boldsymbol{i}$. Hence $\lambda_r \neq \lambda_s$ implies $a_{rs} = b_{rs} = 0$ $(r \neq s)$. This proves (i) of the theorem.

In the second instance (ii), assume the reduction is possible for matrices of order $(n-1) \times (n-1)$, and that $\boldsymbol{q}.\mathscr{A}.\boldsymbol{q}$ is positive definite. Let λ be any root of det $(\mathscr{A} - \mathscr{B}\lambda) = 0$, and let $\boldsymbol{i}_1$ be an eigenvector so that

$$\mathscr{A}\,\boldsymbol{i}_1 = \lambda\mathscr{B}\,\boldsymbol{i}_1$$

Now let $\boldsymbol{i}_2, \boldsymbol{i}_3, \ldots \boldsymbol{i}_n$ be any $(n-1)$ linearly independent vectors which satisfy the equation (in $\boldsymbol{i}$), $\boldsymbol{i}_1.\mathscr{A}.\boldsymbol{i} = 0$. Since $\boldsymbol{i}$ possesses n components this equation is a single equation in n variables : therefore we can always find $(n-1)$ linearly independent solutions. Then the vectors $\boldsymbol{i}_1, \boldsymbol{i}_2, \ldots \boldsymbol{i}_n$ will also be linearly independent provided $\boldsymbol{i}_1.\mathscr{A}.\boldsymbol{i}_1 \neq 0$, for otherwise $\boldsymbol{i}_1$ would be orthogonal to n vectors $\mathscr{A}.\boldsymbol{i}_s$, whereas it cannot be orthogonal to more than $(n-1)$ vectors—and these are $\mathscr{A}.\boldsymbol{i}_s$, $s = 2, 3, \ldots n$). But $\boldsymbol{i}_1.\mathscr{A}.\boldsymbol{i}_1 \neq 0$ since $\boldsymbol{q}.\mathscr{A}.\boldsymbol{q}$ is positive definite. Now the elements $\boldsymbol{i}_1.\mathscr{A}.\boldsymbol{i}_s = 0 = \boldsymbol{i}_1.\mathscr{B}\boldsymbol{i}_s$ $(s > 1)$ in the transformed matrices $\mathscr{S}'\mathscr{A}\mathscr{S}$ and $\mathscr{S}'\mathscr{B}\mathscr{S}$. Hence $\mathscr{S} = (\boldsymbol{i}_1, \boldsymbol{i}_2, \ldots \boldsymbol{i}_n)$ has reduced all the elements in the first row and the first column, other than that on the leading diagonal, to zero. Hence if the reduction is possible for matrices of order $(n-1)^2$, it is possible for matrices of order n^2. The theorem is therefore established by the principle of induction.

Having obtained a transformation matrix $\mathscr{S}$ which reduces $\mathscr{A}$ and $\mathscr{B}$ of (4) and (5) to diagonal form, a further trivial change of variable will make T take the form $\frac{1}{2}(\xi_1{}^2 + \ldots + \xi_n{}^2)$. Now for any eigenvalue λ and its corresponding eigenvector $\boldsymbol{i}$ we shall have $\boldsymbol{i}.\mathscr{A}.\boldsymbol{i} = \lambda\boldsymbol{i}.\mathscr{B}.\boldsymbol{i}$ and so, in this case, V will become

$$\tfrac{1}{2}\{\lambda_1^{-1}\xi^2{}_1 + \lambda_2^{-1}\xi^2{}_2 + \ldots + \lambda_n^{-1}\xi^2{}_n\}$$

When, in addition to T being positive definite, V is also positive definite (so that the position of equilibrium corresponds to a minimum value for V) we see that

$$\lambda = \frac{\boldsymbol{i} . \mathscr{A} . \boldsymbol{i}}{\boldsymbol{i} . \mathscr{B} . \boldsymbol{i}} > 0$$

Take therefore the case when (i) T and V are positive definite quadratic forms, (ii) $\mathscr{S}$ is found to transform T and V into

$$T = \tfrac{1}{2}(\dot{\xi}_1^{\,2} + \dot{\xi}_1^{\,2} + \dots + \dot{\xi}^2) \quad . \quad . \quad . \quad (8)$$

$$V = \tfrac{1}{2}(\lambda_1^{-1}\xi_1^{\,2} + \lambda_2^{-1}\xi_2^{\,2} + \dots + \lambda_n^{-1}\xi_n^{\,2}) \quad . \quad (9)$$

i.e. with $\boldsymbol{q} = S\boldsymbol{\xi}$. Then the Lagrangian equations become

$$\frac{d}{dt}\left(\frac{\partial T}{\partial \dot{\xi}_r}\right) + \frac{\partial V}{\partial \xi_r} = 0 \quad (r = 1, 2, \dots n)$$

giving $$\ddot{\xi}_r + \lambda_r^{-1}\xi_r = 0 \quad (r = 1, 2, \dots n)$$

with $\lambda_r > 0$ (all r).

This is the equation of S.H.M. of period $2\pi\sqrt{\lambda_r}$, showing that motion about a position of minimum V is bounded— the position is therefore one of stable equilibrium.

The co-ordinates ξ_r are called *normal co-ordinates* ; the motion in which ξ_m varies and ξ_r does not $(r \neq m)$ is called the *mth normal mode* of oscillation. In such a mode we have $q_r \propto \xi_m$ $(r = ,1\ 2, \dots n)$ and so all the co-ordinates move with the same period $2\pi\sqrt{\lambda_m}$.

Example 1. A smooth circular wire of radius a and mass $8m$ moves in a vertical plane, being suspended by an inextensible string of length a attached to a fixed point of the wire. The wire carries a bead of mass m free to slide on the wire. Prove that the equivalent simple pendulums of the three normal modes of oscillation about the stable position of equilibrium of the system are of lengths $\frac{8a}{9}, \frac{8a}{3}, \frac{a}{3}$.

(L.U.)

Fig. 129 shows a general position : stable equilibrium corresponds to $\theta = \phi = \psi = 0$. The co-ordinates of C and P are

$$C = \{a\,(\cos\theta + \cos\phi),\ a\,(\sin\theta + \sin\phi)\}$$

$$P = \{a\,(\cos\theta + \cos\phi + \cos\psi),\ a\,(\sin\theta + \sin\phi + \sin\psi)\}$$

with velocities, at $\theta = \phi = \psi = 0$,

$$\dot{\boldsymbol{C}} = \{0,\ a(\dot\theta + \dot\phi)\}\ ; \quad \dot{\boldsymbol{P}} = \{0,\ a(\dot\theta + \dot\phi + \dot\psi)\}$$

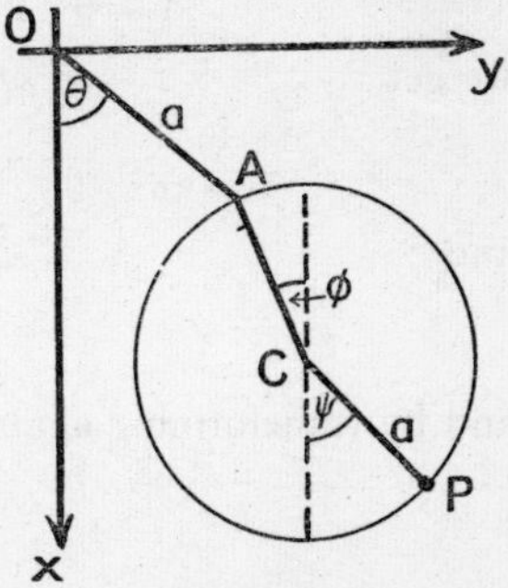

FIG. 129.

These give

$$\frac{2T}{ma^2} = 9\dot\theta^2 + 17\dot\phi^2 + \dot\psi^2 + 18\dot\theta\dot\phi + 2\dot\phi\dot\psi + 2\dot\theta\dot\psi \quad . \quad (10)$$

and $$\frac{2V}{ma^2} = \frac{g}{a}(9\theta^2 + 9\phi^2 + \psi^2) \quad . \quad . \quad . \quad . \quad . \quad (11)$$

Here we can write

$$\mathscr{A} = \begin{pmatrix} 9 & 9 & 1 \\ 9 & 17 & 1 \\ 1 & 1 & 1 \end{pmatrix}, \quad \mathscr{B} = \begin{pmatrix} 9 & 0 & 0 \\ 0 & 9 & 0 \\ 0 & 0 & 1 \end{pmatrix}$$

with $\boldsymbol{q} = (\theta \quad \phi \quad \psi)$. The eigenvalues λ are roots of

$$\det(\mathscr{A} - \lambda\mathscr{B}) = \begin{vmatrix} 9(1-\lambda) & 9 & 1 \\ 9 & (17-9\lambda) & 1 \\ 1 & 1 & (1-\lambda) \end{vmatrix} = 0$$

giving $$81\lambda^3 - 315\lambda^2 + 288\lambda - 64 = 0$$

i.e. $$(3\lambda - 1)(9\lambda - 8)(3\lambda - 8) = 0$$

Hence the periods are

$$2\pi\sqrt{\frac{a\lambda_r}{g}} \quad (r = 1, 2, 3)$$

giving simple pendulums of lengths $\frac{8a}{9}, \frac{8a}{3}, \frac{a}{3}$. Q.E.D.

The components of the vectors $\boldsymbol{i}_\alpha$ may be written $l : m : n$ whence (e.g.)

$$l : m : n = \begin{vmatrix} (17-9\lambda) & 1 \\ 1 & (1-\lambda) \end{vmatrix} : -\begin{vmatrix} 9 & 1 \\ 1 & (1-\lambda) \end{vmatrix} : \begin{vmatrix} 9 & (17-9\lambda) \\ 9 & 1 \end{vmatrix}$$

(i) When $9\lambda = 8$, $l_1 : m_1 : n_1 = 0 : 1 : -9$ (using an alternative set of minors)

(ii) When $9\lambda = 24$, $l_2 : m_2 : n_2 = 2 : 3 : 3$

(iii) When $9\lambda = 3$, $l_3 : m_3 : n_3 = 5 : -3 : -3$

Writing

$$\mathscr{S} = \begin{pmatrix} 0 & 2 & 5 \\ 1 & 3 & -3 \\ -9 & 3 & -3 \end{pmatrix}, \quad \mathscr{S}' = \begin{pmatrix} 0 & 1 & -9 \\ 2 & 3 & 3 \\ 5 & -3 & -3 \end{pmatrix}$$

we get $$\mathscr{S}'\mathscr{A}\mathscr{S} = \begin{pmatrix} 80 & 0 & 0 \\ 0 & 288 & 0 \\ 0 & 0 & 105 \end{pmatrix}$$

and $$\mathscr{S}'\mathscr{B}\mathscr{S} = \begin{pmatrix} 90 & 0 & 0 \\ 0 & 108 & 0 \\ 0 & 0 & 315 \end{pmatrix}$$

and by transforming again via

$$\mathscr{P} = \begin{pmatrix} 80^{-\frac{1}{2}} & 0 & 0 \\ 0 & 288^{-\frac{1}{2}} & 0 \\ 0 & 0 & 105^{-\frac{1}{2}} \end{pmatrix}$$

we get $$\frac{2T}{ma^2} = \xi_1^2 + \xi_2^2 + \xi_3^2$$

and
$$\frac{2V}{ma^2} = \left(\frac{g}{a}\right)\{(\tfrac{9}{8})\xi_1^2 + (\tfrac{3}{8})\xi_2^2 + (\tfrac{3}{1})\xi_3^2\}$$

The normal co-ordinates are such that

$$\begin{pmatrix}\theta\\ \phi\\ \psi\end{pmatrix} = \mathscr{S}\mathscr{P}\begin{pmatrix}\xi_1\\ \xi_2\\ \xi_3\end{pmatrix} = \mathscr{S}\begin{pmatrix}k_1\xi_1\\ k_2\xi_2\\ k_3\xi_3\end{pmatrix} \quad \text{(say)}$$

i.e.
$$\begin{aligned}\theta &= 2k_2\xi_2 + 5k_3\xi_3\\ \phi &= k_1\xi_1 + 3k_2\xi_2 - 3k_3\xi_3\\ \psi &= -9k_1\xi_1 + 3k_2\xi_2 - 3k_3\xi_3\end{aligned}$$

Hence we can solve for the ξ's in terms of the q's.

Exercise XVI

1. A bead A of mass m slides on a smooth horizontal rail, and a particle B of mass m is attached to the bead by a light string of length $2a$. The system moves in the vertical plane through the rail, and the string remains taut. The horizontal displacement of the mid-point G of AB at time t is denoted by x, and the inclination of AB to the downward vertical by θ. Prove that, during the motion, $\dot{x}$ and

$$a\dot{\theta}^2(1 + \sin^2\theta) - 2g\cos\theta$$

remain constant.

If the system is released from rest with the string inclined at a small angle to the vertical, find the period of the small oscillations.

2. If the potential energy and kinetic energy of a conservative system having one degree of freedom (co-ordinate θ) are expressible in the form $F(\theta)$ and $G(\theta)\dot{\theta}^2$ respectively, show that (i) the positions of stable equilibrium satisfy, in general, the conditions $F'(\theta) = 0$, $F''(\theta) < 0$, (ii) if $\theta = \alpha$ is such a position, the period of small oscillations about this position is

$$2\pi\sqrt{\frac{2G(\alpha)}{F''(\alpha)}}$$

A smooth semi-circular wire is fixed in a vertical plane with its diameter vertical. A bead of weight w slides on the wire and is connected to the topmost point of the wire by a light spring of modulus $2w$ and natural length equal to the diameter of the wire. A constant horizontal force of magnitude $2w$ in the plane of the wire and outwards from the diameter acts on the bead. Show that there is a position of stable equilibrium in which the spring makes an angle of 30 degrees with the vertical.

Determine the period of small oscillations about this position. (L.U.)

3. A uniform solid right circular cone of height h, vertical angle 2α, and radius of gyration k about an axis through its centre of inertia at right angles to its axis of figure, rests with its vertex downwards between two rough parallel rails at a distance $2c$ apart in a horizontal plane. Prove that, if the equilibrium is stable, the period of the small oscillations about it is

$$\pi\sqrt{[\{16k^2 \sin^2 \alpha + (3h \sin \alpha - 4c \cos \alpha)^2\}/g \sin \alpha \cos \alpha\, (4c - 3h \tan \alpha)]}$$

(C.)

4. A uniform heavy circular hoop of radius $3a$ hangs in equilibrium over a rough horizontal cylindrical peg of radius a, the plane of the hoop being normal to the axis of the peg. A heavy particle is suspended from the bottom point of the hoop by a light string of length $2a$. The system is then slightly disturbed in such a way that the subsequent motion is entirely in a plane normal to the axis of the peg. Show that if the masses of hoop and particle are equal, the periods of the normal modes of the system are in the ratio $\sqrt{12} : 1$. Indicate their forms by sketches. (M.T.)

5. A body with a vertical axis of symmetry is suspended by a light spiral spring from a fixed support. The downward force F and the torque L (about the axis) that must be applied in order to lower the body through a distance x and to turn it through an angle θ are given by

$$F = ax + b\theta$$
$$L = b'x + c\theta$$

where a, b, b', c are constants. Show that the forces exerted by the spring on the body are conservative if and only if $b = b'$. Find an expression for the potential energy when this condition is satisfied.

Prove that there are two normal modes of vibration of the system in which the body describes a screw motion $x = k\theta$. If the mass of the body is M, its moment of inertia about the axis is I, and IMb^2 is small compared with $(Ia - Mc)^2$, show that for one of these vibrations the period is approximately $2\pi\sqrt{(M/a)}$ and k is approximately equal to $(Ia - Mc)/(Mb)$, while for the other the period is approximately $2\pi\sqrt{(I/c)}$ and k is approximately equal to $-(Ib)/(Ia - Mc)$. (M.T.)

6. A particle of mass m is fixed to a uniform circular ring of mass m and radius a. The ring is hung over a small smooth peg and oscillates in a vertical plane about the configuration of stable equilibrium. Using as co-ordinates the angles θ, ϕ between the vertical and the radii through the peg and the particle respectively, prove that the principal periods are $\dfrac{2\pi}{p}$, where $3ap^2 = (3 \pm \sqrt{3})g$. Determine the ratio of θ to ϕ in each of the corresponding normal modes. (M.T.)

7. A uniform rod AB $(2a, 8m)$ can turn freely about a fixed horizontal axis through its mid-point O. A string of length a is fastened to B and to a particle of mass m. If the system is slightly disturbed from its position of stable equilibrium, find the normal modes (for motion in a vertical plane). When the system oscillates in the normal mode of longer period, prove that the line of the string always passes through a fixed point at a height $2a$ above O, and find the corresponding point for the mode of shorter period. (L.U.)

8. A smooth wire, of mass m, in the shape of a circle of centre O and radius a, is freely pivoted at a point A of its circumference to a fixed support, and can rotate in its own plane under gravity. A bead of mass m slides freely on the wire. If B is the other end of the diameter through A, find the kinetic and potential energies of the system in terms of θ, the angle between AB and the downward vertical, and ϕ, the angle between OB and the radius drawn from O to the bead.

Apply Lagrange's equations to write down the equations of motion of the system, and for θ, ϕ small simplify these equations by retaining only terms of the first order in θ, ϕ and their time derivatives.

Show that, if the simplified equations are satisfied by $\theta = A \cos pt$, $\phi = B \cos pt$, where A, B are constants, then

$$2p^4 - 5p^2n^2 + 2n^4 = 0$$

$n^2 = g/3$. (M.T.)

9. A uniform rod of mass m and length l turns freely in a vertical plane about a fixed axis through one end O. A light elastic string of modulus mg and natural length $\frac{1}{4}l$ has one end attached to the mid-point of the rod and the other to a fixed point A at distance $\frac{1}{2}l$ vertically above O. If θ is the angle made by the rod with the upward vertical OA, show that the equation of motion of the rod is

$$2l\ddot{\theta} = 3g(1 - 2\sin\tfrac{1}{2}\theta)\cos\tfrac{1}{2}\theta$$

Show also that the period of small oscillations about the position of equilibrium $\theta = \frac{1}{3}\pi$ is the same as that of a simple pendulum of length $8l/9$. (L.U.)

10. The end points A_1, A_2 of a uniform rod A_1A_2, which is at rest on a smooth horizontal table, are joined to two fixed points O_1, O_2 on the table by light strings O_2A_2, O_2A_2; the points O_1, O_2 are at a distance $4a$ apart, the rod is of mass m and length $2a$, each string is of length a, and the tension in each string is P. The system is disturbed, and the rod executes small transverse oscillations in contact with the table. Find the kinetic and potential energies of the system, and deduce that the normal periods are $2\pi/n_1$, $2\pi/n_2$ where

$$amn_1^2 = 2P, \quad amn_2^2 = 6P$$

Find the position of the rod at time t if the motion is started by applying a small transverse impulse I to the end A_1 of the rod. (L.U.)

11. A bead of mass m is threaded on a smooth uniform circular wire of mass M and radius a; one point O of the circumference of the wire is fixed and the wire can rotate freely about O in a fixed vertical plane. If the system is slightly disturbed from its configuration of stable equilibrium, show that the periods of the normal vibrations are $2\pi/p_1$ and $2\pi/p_2$, where

$$2ap_1^2 = g, \quad Map_2^2 = (M + m)g \qquad \text{(L.U.)}$$

12. A uniform disc of radius b and mass m is attached by symmetrically placed equal elastic strings, of stretched and unstretched lengths l and a respectively and of modulus λ, to three points which lie at the vertices of an equilateral triangle on a smooth horizontal plane. Prove that the normal periods of vibration in this plane are $2\pi/p$, where

$$p^2 = \frac{3\lambda}{ma}\left(1 - \frac{a}{2l}\right) \quad \text{and} \quad p^2 = \frac{6\lambda}{mb}\left(1 - \frac{a}{l}\right)\left(1 + \frac{b}{l}\right). \qquad \text{(L.U.)}$$

13. The kinetic energy T and the potential energy V of a conservative system, oscillating about a position of stable equilibrium given by $x = 0$, $y = 0$, $z = 0$, are expressed in the forms

$$T = \tfrac{1}{2}m(\dot{x}^2 + \dot{y}^2 + \dot{z}^2)$$
$$V = M\omega^2(yz + zx + xy)$$

Find the periods of the normal small oscillations.

Obtain a set of normal co-ordinates, and, by means of them, express T and V as sums of squares. (L.U.)

14. The kinetic and potential energies of a system of three degrees of freedom are given by

$$2T = \dot{x}^2 + \dot{y}^2 + \dot{z}^2$$
$$2V = n^2(x^2 + y^2 + z^2) + n^2 \tan^2 \alpha\{z^2 + 2\varepsilon z(x + y)\}$$

where n, α, ε are constants. Show that, if ε^3 can be neglected, the co-ordinates ξ, η, ζ given by

$$x + y = 2(\xi + \varepsilon\zeta), \quad x - y = 2\eta, \quad z = \zeta - 2\varepsilon\xi$$

are normal co-ordinates for small oscillations of the system, the normal time periods being

$$T(1 + \varepsilon^2 \tan^2 \alpha), \quad T, \quad T \cos \alpha(1 - \varepsilon^2 \sin^2 \alpha)$$

respectively, where $T = 2\pi/n$.

If initially $x = \varepsilon a$, $y = z = 0$ and the system is at rest, find x, y, z explicitly in terms of t, neglecting ε^3, and show that the motion in the x, y co-ordinates can be regarded as simple harmonic oscillations, with slowly varying simple harmonic amplitudes of period $(2T \cot^2 \alpha)/\varepsilon^2$. (L.U.)

15. Explain what is meant by a normal mode of small oscillations of a system of n degrees of freedom.

A uniform rod AB, of mass $3m$ and length $2a$, swings freely about a smooth horizontal axis through A. One end of an elastic string BC, of natural length a, is attached to the rod at B and carries a particle of mass m at the end C. When the system hangs freely at rest the length of the string is $3a$. If the system performs small oscillations in a vertical plane through AB, the rod and the string making angles θ and ϕ with the downward vertical, and the length of the string is $3a + x$, show that x, $2\theta - \phi$, and $5\theta + 6\phi$ are normal co-ordinates of the system, and that the lengths of the corresponding equivalent simple pendulums are $2a$, $3a/5$ and $4a$. (L.U.)

16. A uniform rod AB, of mass $2m$ and length $2a$, swings freely about a smooth horizontal axis through the end A. One end of a light elastic string is attached to the end B of the rod, and carries a particle of mass m at its other end. When the system is in stable equilibrium, the string is of length $4a/3$, its extension being ε. If the system performs small oscillations in a vertical plane through AB, the rod and the string making angles θ and ϕ respectively with the downward vertical, and the length of the string being $x + 4a/3$, show that

$$x, \quad \phi + 2\theta, \quad 2\phi - 3\theta$$

are normal co-ordinates for the system, and that the lengths of the corresponding equivalent simple pendulums are ε, $8a/3$ and $a/3$. (L.U.)

M4